CAD/CAM
Concepts and Applications

Chennakesava R. Alavala

B.E., M.E. (Mech.), M.Tech (CAD/CAM),
Ph.D. (Mech.), Ph.D. (CAD/CAM),
M.ISTE., M.IIF., M.IIW., M.ISME., M.IE., M.IIPE., C.Engg.

Professor
Department of Mechanical Engineering
Jawaharlal Nehru Technological University
Hyderabad

PHI Learning Private Limited

Delhi-110092
2013

₹ 395.00

CAD/CAM: CONCEPTS AND APPLICATIONS
Chennakesava R. Alavala

ISBN-978-81-203-3340-6

The export rights of this book are vested solely with the publisher.

Fifth Printing ... ... **November, 2013**

Published by Asoke K. Ghosh, PHI Learning Private Limited, Rimjhim House, 111, Patparganj Industrial Estate, Delhi-110092 and Printed by Mudrak, 30-A, Patparganj, Delhi-110091.

To
Sasi and Santhosh

Contents

v

7. Surface Modelling

13. Manual Part Programming

26. Computer-integrated Manufacturing

Preface

The use of computers for various activities in the industry gave new dimensions to design and manufacturing to meet the challenges of global competition. The field of computer-aided design and computer-aided manufacturing (CAD/CAM) has widened the scope of traditional design and manufacturing. In order to be competitive in the global economy, it is imperative that all the manufacturing industries adopt CAD/CAM. Thus, we need to train the manpower on CAD/CAM technology for the necessity of present day industries. Understanding the need of the industry the CAD/CAM has been introduced into the curricula of all Indian universities.

This book is intended to provide a comprehensive coverage of the technical topics related to CAD/CAM. The topics include interactive computer graphics, CAD, finite element analysis (FEA), numerical control (NC), computer numerical control (CNC), direct numerical control (DNC), adaptive control systems (ACS), group technology (GT), flexible manufacturing systems (FMS), computer-aided process planning (CAPP), computer-aided production planning and control (CAPPC), computer-aided quality control (CAQC), concurrent engineering (CE) and robotics.

The book is intended for the undergraduate students of engineering and professionals, who are interested in the CAD/CAM technology and its applications to design and manufacturing. This book consists of 26 chapters. Each chapter starts with objectives and is followed by question bank which are intended for the preparation of university examinations and multiple-choice questions for the competitive exams. All the topics are explained with illustrative examples. Some case studies are also included in the textbook. Extensive and carefully selected references are an invaluable resource for further study of CAD/CAM.

Chapter 1 introduces the definitions of CAD and CAM, types of manufacturing industries, product life cycle and applications of CAD/CAM. Chapter 2 covers the CAD/CAM hardware. Chapter 3 provides software modules and graphics standards. Chapter 4 presents interactive computer graphics.

Geometric modelling, wireframe modelling, surface modelling and solid modelling are explained in detail in Chapters 5, 6, 7 and 8. Computer-aided drafting and finite element analysis are discussed in Chapters 9 and 10, respectively. Numerical controls and computer numerical control are introduced in Chapters 11 and 12, respectively. Manual, turning and computer-aided programming are covered in Chapters 13, 14 and 15.

Direct numerical controls and adaptive control systems are demonstrated with applications in Chapters 16 and 17. Group technology, computer-aided process planning, computer-aided planning of resources for manufacturing and computer-aided quality control are discussed with case studies in Chapters 18, 19, 20 and 21. Industrial robots and their applications are reviewed in Chapter 22.

The latest topics on flexible manufacturing systems, cellular manufacturing, lean manufacturing and computer integrated manufacturing are presented in Chapters 23, 24, 25 and 26.

Chennakesava R. Alavala

Acknowledgements

I am grateful to the undergraduate and postgraduate students, and research scholars at Jawaharlal Nehru Technological University, Hyderabad, who worked with me and contributed to a large volume of information presented in this book. I wish to express my deep sense of gratitude to my colleagues who have significantly contributed to my ideas in CAD/CAM during their long association at Jawaharlal Nehru Technological University, Hyderabad. I also acknowledge my family members who constantly cooperated withme while writing this book. I am thankful to all the students who have learned this subject from me, for the questions and comments during the process of learning CAD/CAM subject. I thank the editorial and production teams of Prentice-Hall of India who encouraged, edited and reviewed this book.

A large number of companies and organizations have liberally provided information and illustrations for utilization in this book. I am thankful to all those authors and contributors mentioned in the reference list and the following organizations and companies:

ANSYS Inc., USA; Autodesk Inc., USA; Bridgeport Machines, Textron Inc., USA; Central Institute of Tool Design, Hyderabad, India; Cincinnati, Milacron, USA; EXAPT, Germany; Georg Fischer FMS, Switzerland; Haas Automation Inc., California; IBM; Leningrad Institute, USSR; Metal Institute Classification System, The Netherlands; METAVIS, India; Mitsubishi Electric Corporation, Tokyo; Optiz, University of Aachen, West Germany; Servomechanism Laboratory, MIT, USA; Toyota Motor Company, Tailchi ohno; United Computer Corp., Carson, California; UPMC-CARAT, Tokyo Seinmitsu; Weber NC System, Wisconsia and Yamazaki Mazak Corp., Japan.

I invite the readers of this book for their valuable feedback which may help in updating this book to the great extent.

Chennakesava R. Alavala

Chapter 1

Fundamentals of CAD/CAM

After reading this chapter, the reader will be able to understand the following concepts:

- ➲ Role of computers in manufacturing
- ➲ CAD
- ➲ CAM
- ➲ Product lifecycle
- ➲ Various types of manufacturing industries
- ➲ Types of production
- ➲ Types of plant layout
- ➲ Types of automation
- ➲ Applications of CAD/CAM

1.1 INTRODUCTION

CAD/CAM means computer-aided design, and computer-aided manufacturing. It is the technology concerned with the application of digital computers to perform certain functions in design and manufacturing. This technology is moving in the direction of greater integration and interaction of design and manufacturing. Ultimately, this technology will be directed toward one goal: the fully automated factory of the future.

In engineering practice, CAD/CAM has been utilised in different ways by different people as shown in Figure 1.1.

1

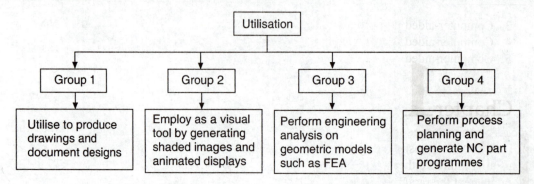

Fig. 1.1   Utilisation of CAD/CAM process by different people.

1.2   ROLE OF COMPUTERS IN INDUSTRIAL MANUFACTURING

Products have characteristics that describe their performance relative to customer requirements or expectations. Characteristics such as the power loss of a home water heater, or the breaking strength of bridge beams, or profile of a rocket nozzle, are all examples of product characteristics that are of concern to customers at one time or another. The quality of a product is measured in terms of these characteristics.

Quality is related to the loss to society caused by a product during its lifecycle. A truly high quality product will have a minimal loss to society as it goes through its lifecycle. If a product does not perform as expected, the customer senses some loss. After a product is shipped, the manufacturer can do nothing to the product. Before shipment, the manufacturer can use expensive or inexpensive process or materials, etc; but once shipped, the commitment is made for a certain product expense during the remainder of its life.

It is becoming increasingly important for manufacturers to initiate steps for manufacturing quality products. There is therefore, a need to optimise the design of a product, the means and techniques to achieve production improvement, cost reduction, fulfilment of scheduled delivery times, and flexibility (to facilitate variety, quality and quantity of product) of the manufacturing system.

It has become imperative for the manufacturer to take advantage of the powerful multi-functional capabilities of computers in industrial manufacturing. Hence, the use of computers in the manufacturing industries has become a reality. The role of computers in industrial manufacturing is broadly classified into the following three groups:

1. Pre-processing support applications of the manufacturing system
2. Monitoring and control of the manufacturing process
3. Post-processing support applications of the manufacturing system

The first category involves all the support functions that computers can provide to facilitate the efficient, and economical manufacturing of a product:

1. Computer-aided design and drafting
2. Finite element analysis

3. Computer-aided part programming
4. Computer-aided process planning
5. Computer-aided scheduling
6. Computer-aided tool design
7. Computer-aided material requirement planning

The computer indirectly supports the manufacturing process to provide part programming, process planning, time standards for manufacturing operations, production scheduling, forecasting and inventory, and instructions and information as shown in Figure 1.2. In this system, human beings are required either to enter the input to the computer or to interpret the computer output and implement the required action.

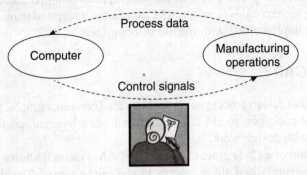

Fig. 1.2 Pre-processing support applications of the manufacturing system.

The second category includes applications wherein computers are directly interfaced with manufacturing. The computer is connected directly to the manufacturing process for the purpose of monitoring or controlling the process as shown in Figure 1.3. Monitoring involves a direct interface of the computer with the manufacturing process for the purpose of observing the process and collecting data from the process (Figure 1.3(a)). The manufacturing process is controlled by the operator but not by the computer. Controlling the computer implies not only monitoring the manufacturing process but also controlling the process based on the observations (Figure 1.3(b)). The computer issues command signals to the manufacturing process on the basis of control algorithms contained in its software.

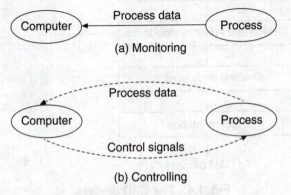

Fig. 1.3 Computer interfacing.

The third category consists of all the support functions that enable computers to deliver quality product to the customers. These include:

1. Computer-aided assembly
2. Computer-aided inspection and quality control
3. Computer-aided cost analysis
4. Computer-aided packing and labelling
5. Computer-aided analysis of market feedbacks
6. Computer-aided billing

The use of computers in industrial manufacturing signifies a methodological approach to be implemented in the entire process of product development and manufacture. This requires a whole lot of enabling technologies (CAD, CAM, computer-integrated manufacturing, Business functions, etc.) to be implemented with the aid of computers.

1.3   WHAT IS CAD?

CAD may be defined as a design process using sophisticated computer graphics techniques, backed by computer software packages, to aid in the analytical, development, costing, and ergonomic problems associated with design work.

The implementation of a CAD process on a CAD/CAM system is shown in Figure 1.4. Once a conceptual design is materialised, the geometric model can be started. The choice of a geometric

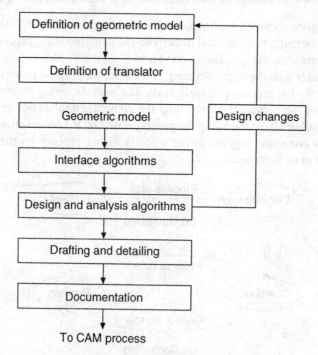

Fig. 1.4   The CAD process.

model depends on the type of analysis to be performed. A valid geometric model is created by the CAD system through its definition translator that converts the designer input into the proper database format. Interface algorithms are provided by the system to extract the required data from the model database to perform engineering analysis. In the case of finite element analysis, these algorithms form the finite element modelling of the system. Design testing and evaluation may necessitate changing the geometric model before finalising it. When the final design is achieved, the drafting and detailing of the models starts, followed by documentation and production of final drawings.

1.4   WHAT IS CAM?

CAM may be defined as the use of computer systems to plan, manage, and control the operations of a manufacturing plant through either direct or indirect computer interface with the production resources of the plant.

The implementation of the CAM process on the CAD/CAM system is shown in Figure 1.5. The geometric model generated during the CAD process forms the basis for the CAM process. Various activities in CAM may require different types of information of the CAD process. Interface algorithms are used to extract such information from the CAD database. NC programme, along with ordering tools and fixtures, result from process planning. Once the parts are manufactured, computer-aided quality control software is used to inspect the parts. This is achieved by superposing an image of the real part with a master image stored in its model database. After passing inspection, all the parts are assembled by robots to result in the final product.

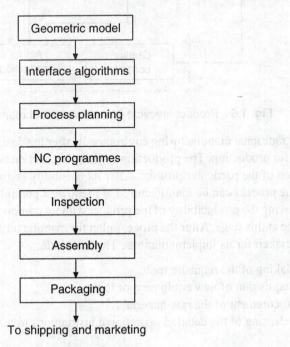

Fig. 1.5   The CAM process.

1.5 PRODUCT LIFECYCLE

A manufactured product has a life. The demand for a product does not last long. The lifecycle is driven by customers and markets, which demand the product. The product cycle begins with a concept, an idea for a product. This concept is cultivated, refined, analysed, improved upon and translated into a plan for the product through the design engineering process. The conventional product lifecycle is shown in Figure 1.6.

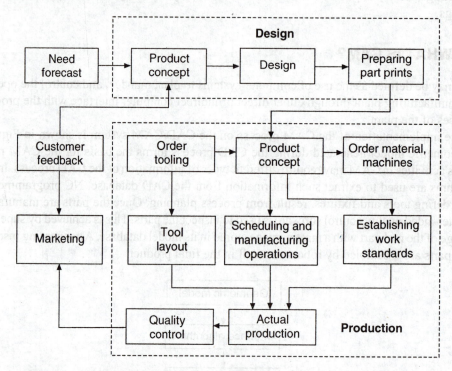

Fig. 1.6 Product lifecycle in a conventional manufacturing environment.

In a traditional manufacturing environment, after the design of the product, the part prints are released for production. The production engineering section would first consider the feasibility of production of the particular product. After its feasibility is ascertained, process planning is done so that the product can be manufactured at the lowest possible cost. Any redesign that is needed for improving the producibility of the product without comprising on its functionality would have to be done at this stage. After the process plan for manufacturing is decided, the necessary actions are undertaken for its implementations. These include:

- Making of the requisite tools
- Acquisition of new equipment or tools
- Procurement of the raw materials
- Releasing of the detailed operational instructions to the shop floor, etc.

The product lifecycle in a computer-aided manufacturing environment is shown in Figure 1.7. The product begins with a need which is identified on the basis of the customers' and market's demands. The product goes through two main processes from inception to a finished product: which are:

- The design process, and
- The manufacturing process.

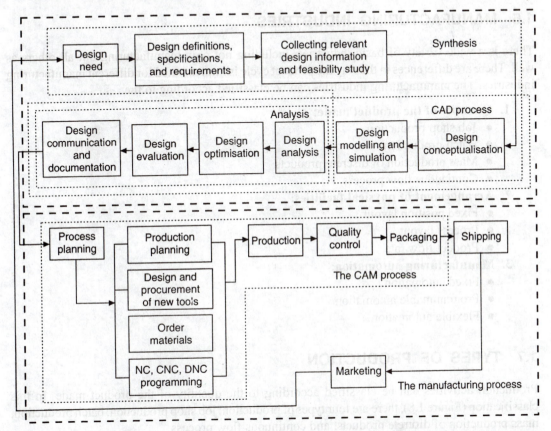

Fig. 1.7 The product lifecycle in a computer-aided manufacturing environment.

The philosophy, functionality, and uniqueness of the product are all determined during synthesis. Most of the information generated during synthesis is qualitative and consequently difficult to capture in a computer system. The information establishes the relationship among the various product parts. The end goal of the synthesis is a conceptual design of the prospective product.

The analysis begins with an attempt to put the conceptual design in the context of the abstracted engineering sciences to evaluate the performance of the expected product. This constitutes design modelling and simulation. The quality of the results and decisions involved in the activities to follow such as design analysis, optimisation, and evaluation is directly related to and limited by the quality of the chosen design model. A computer environment wherein various design alternatives can be investigated is ideal for making better design decisions in shorter periods of time.

Once the major elements of the design have been analysed and their nominal dimensions determined, the design evaluation phase starts. Prototypes can be built in a laboratory or a computer to test the design. The designer can also generate bills of materials, specify tolerances, and perform cost analyses. The last phase of the analysis is design communication and documentation, which involves preparation of drawings, reports and presentations. Drawings are utilised to produce blueprints to be passed to the manufacturing process.

1.6 MANUFACTURING INDUSTRIES

There is a wide variety of basic industries, including not only manufacturing but all others as well. There are differences in the way the product cycle is implemented for different manufacturing industries. The manufacturing industries can be classified according to the:

1. **Quantity of the product made:**
   - Job shop production
   - Batch production
   - Mass production of discrete products
   - Continuous flow process
2. **Arrangement of physical facilities:**
   - Fixed position layout
   - Process layout
   - Product flow rate
3. **Manufacturing automation:**
   - Fixed automation
   - Programmable automation
   - Flexible automation.

1.7 TYPES OF PRODUCTION

Production activities can be classified according to the quantity of the product made. In this classification (Figure 1.8), there are four types of production: job shop production, batch production, mass production of discrete products, and continuous flow process.

1.7.1 Job Shop Production

This category involves a low volume of production. The manufacturing lot sizes in this case are very small, preferably one of a kind. There is a great variety in the type of work. The manufacturing equipment must be flexible and general purpose to facilitate this variety of work. Examples of products manufactured in a job shop are machine tools, space vehicles, aircraft, and prototypes of future products.

1.7.2 Batch Production

Batch production refers to the manufacturing of products in medium lots. The lots may be produced only once and may be manufactured at regular intervals. The purpose of batch production is often to satisfy continuous customer demand for an item. The production equipment must be general purpose but designed for higher rates of production. Batch production industries include machine shops, casting foundries, plastic moulding factories and press working shops.

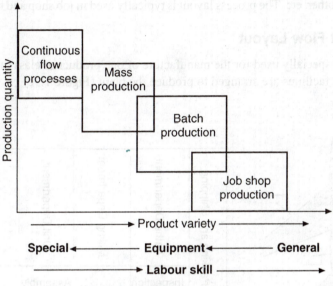

Fig. 1.8 Types of production.

1.7.3 Mass Production

This category involves a very high volume of production. The equipment in this case is completely dedicated to the manufacture of a particular product, and there are very high demand rates for the product. Examples of this production include automobiles, household appliances, etc.

1.7.4 Continuous Flow Production

This category involves continuous dedicated bulk manufacturing of large amounts of a product. Examples of these products include continuous chemical plants and oil refineries.

1.8 TYPES OF PLANT LAYOUT

Plant layout comprises the arrangement of physical facilities in a manufacturing plant. There are three types of plant layouts (shown in Figure 1.9): fixed position layout, process layout and product flow layout.

1.8.1 Fixed Position Layout

In this type of layout, the term 'fixed position' refers to the product. The product remains at one location because of its size and weight, and the equipment and machinery used in its manufacturing are brought to it. Examples this type of product are aircraft assembly (Figure 1.9a) and ship building.

1.8.2   Process Layout

In a process layout (Figure 1.9b), the production machines are arranged into groups according to the type of manufacturing process used. For instance, the lathes are in one department, drill machines are in another, etc. The process layout is typically used in job shop and batch production.

1.8.3   Product Flow Layout

If a plant layout is specially used for the manufacture of one product or class of product in large volumes, the plant facilities are arranged to produce the plant (Figure 1.9c).

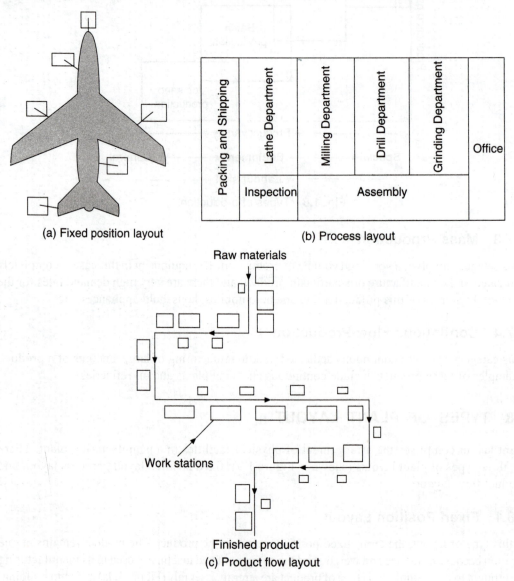

(a) Fixed position layout

(b) Process layout

(c) Product flow layout

Fig. 1.9   Types of plant layouts.

1.9 TYPES OF AUTOMATION

Automation is a technology concerned with the application of mechanical, electrical, electronic and computer-based systems to operate and control production. An automated system should be highly flexible to survive several product lifecycles. Automation systems (Figure 1.10) can be classified into three basic types: fixed automation, programmable automation and flexible automation.

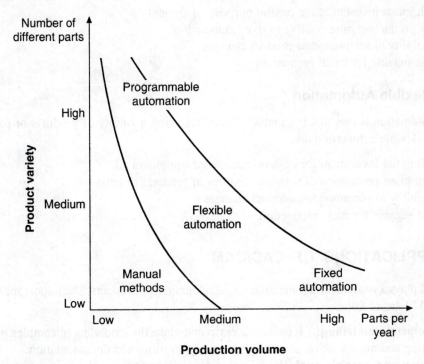

Fig. 1.10 Types of automation.

1.9.1 Fixed Automation

This signifies a system in which the sequence of processing operations is fixed by the equipment configuration. The operations in the sequence are usually simple. It is the integration and configuration of many such operations into one piece of equipment that makes the system complex. The typical features of fixed automation are:

- High initial investment for custom-engineered equipment
- High production rates
- Relative inflexibility in accommodation of product changes

The examples of fixed automation include mechanised assembly lines like conveyors and machining transfer lines.

1.9.2   Programmable Automation

In programmable automation, the production machinery is designed with the capability to change the sequence of operation to accommodate different products. The operation sequence is controlled by a programme, which consists of a set of coded instructions so that the system can read and interpret them. New programmes can be prepared and entered into the equipment to produce new products. The typical features of programmable automation are:

- High initial investment for general purpose equipment
- Low production rates relative to fixed automation
- Flexibility to accommodate product changes
- Most suitable for batch production

1.9.3   Flexible Automation

Flexible automation is one that is capable of manufacturing a variety of products or parts. The features of flexible automation are:

- High initial investment for custom-engineered equipment
- Continuous production of variable mixtures of products or parts
- Flexibility to accommodate product changes
- Most suitable for mass production

1.10   APPLICATIONS OF CAD/CAM

CAD/CAM plays a vital role in the manufacturing of qualitative products. The import applications of CAD/CAM are as follows:

1. **Geometric modelling:**   It enables users to undertake the modelling of complex products, editing and manipulation of existing geometry, drafting and documentation.
2. **Design engineering analysis:**   Engineering analysis takes the form of stress-strain analysis, heat transfer analysis, dynamic analysis, optimisation of product size and shape, etc. Finite element analysis is available on most CAD/CAM systems to aid design engineering analysis.
3. **Design evaluation and review:**   CAD/CAM features help in evaluating and reviewing the product design as follows:
   - Automatic dimensioning of routines, which determine the precise distance measures between surfaces on the geometry.
   - Inference checking routines, which identify whether two objects occupy the same space or not, this is especially helpful in the design of assemblies.
   - Kinetic routines, which test the operation of mechanical linkages using the animation capability of CAD/CAM systems.
4. **Manufacturing database:**   When documentation (i.e., dimensions, material specifications, bill of materials, etc.) is created for the product design, much of the required database to manufacture the product is also created.

5. **Computer-aided process planning (CAPP):** The process planning procedure is highly dependent on the experience and judgment of the planner. Accordingly, there are differences among the operation sequences developed by the various planners. CAPP facilitates production planning that is rational, consistent, and perhaps even optimal.

6. **Interactive graphics NC part programming:** G- and M-codes can be developed directly from the geometry modelling of the product.

7. **Finely tuned production planning:** Computerised systems have been developed for forecasting, production planning, development of the master schedule, purchasing, etc.

8. **Material requirements planning (MRP):** It involves determining when to order raw materials and components for assembled products.

9. **Shop floor control:** It involves a direct connection between the computer and the manufacturing process for the purpose of monitoring the operation.

10. **Computer-aided inspection and quality control:** Computer-aided inspection and testing help in improving the product quality.

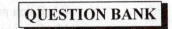

QUESTION BANK

A. Descriptive Questions

1. What is CAD?
2. What is CAM?
3. Explain the product lifecycle in conventional and computer-aided manufacturing environments.
4. Classify the manufacturing industries on the basis of the type of production, plant layout and automation.
5. Explain the various categories of production.
6. Explain the various categories of plant layouts.
7. Explain the various categories of automation.
8. What are the various applications of CAD/CAM?

B. Multiple Choice Questions

1. The use of computer software packages to aid in the analytical, development, costing and ergonomic problems associated with product design is known as:
   (a) CAD   (b) CAM   (c) CAPP   (d) FEM

2. The final stage in the implementation of a CAD system is:
   (a) Geometric modelling   (b) Drafting and detailing
   (c) Documentation   (d) Design changes

3. The use of computer systems to plan, manage and control the operations of a manufacturing plant through either direct or indirect computer interface with the production resources is known as:
   (a) CAD   (b) CAM   (c) CAPP   (d) GT

4. In the computer direct interface, the manufacturing process is controlled by the:
   (a) Operator
   (b) Computer
   (c) Manager
   (d) Communication system

5. The end goal of the synthesis sub-process is:
   (a) Final drawing
   (b) Final design
   (c) Conceptual design
   (d) Final shape

6. The different phases that a product undergoes from the conceptualisation of the product until the end-product reaches the customer is known as:
   (a) Design cycle
   (b) Manufacturing cycle
   (c) Product cycle
   (d) None of the above

7. Job shop production involves:
   (a) Low volume of production
   (b) High volume of production
   (c) Medium volume of production
   (d) Use of transfer lines

8. Aircrafts are manufactured by:
   (a) Mass production
   (b) Batch production
   (c) Job shop production
   (d) Continuous flow production

9. Ship building is done in:
   (a) Process layout
   (b) Product layout
   (c) Fixed position layout
   (d) All of the above

10. Fixed automation is characterised by:
    (a) High production rates
    (b) Low production rates
    (c) High quality products
    (d) Low quality products

11. Programmable automation is suitable for:
    (a) Mass production
    (b) Batch production
    (c) Continuous flow production
    (d) Job shop production

Chapter 2

CAD/CAM Hardware

After reading this chapter, the reader will be able to understand the following concepts:

- ➲ Mainframe-based systems
- ➲ Minicomputer-based systems
- ➲ Workstation-based systems
- ➲ Input devices: keyboard, mouse, lightpen, joystick, digitiser, data glove, trackball, and thumbwheels
- ➲ Output devices: random scan, raster scan, direct view storage tube display, vector refresh display, raster refresh display, liquid crystal display, plasma display, impact dot matrix printer, ink jet printer, laser printer, flatbed-moving arm plotter, flatbed-moving head plotter, drum plotter and pinch roller plotter
- ➲ Hardware integration and networking

2.1 INTRODUCTION

A complete CAD/CAM system consists of hardware and software components. The hardware includes digital computer and its peripherals. A digital computer is a machine that can solve problems for people by carrying out instructions given to it. Its speed and storage capacity have facilitated the rapid growth of the CAD/CAM industry. In order to understand CAD/CAM, it is essential to be familiar with the concepts and technology of the digital computer. This chapter presents a brief review of the latest developments in computers.

2.2 BASIC COMPUTER ARCHITECTURE

The basic computer architecture of a typical computing system is shown in Figure 2.1. The modern digital computer is an electronic machine that can perform mathematical, logical computations and data processing instructions in accordance with a pre-determined programme of instructions. There are four basic components of simple digital computer as shown in Figure 2.1.

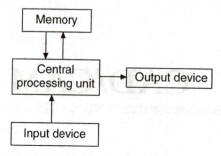

Fig. 2.1   The basic computer architecture.

The central processing unit (CPU) is the brain of the computer. Its function is to execute programs stored in the main memory by fetching their instructions, examining them, and then executing them one after another. The CPU is composed of two sub-sections: a control unit and an arithmetic and logical unit. The control unit is responsible for fetching instructions from the main memory and determining their type. The control unit also coordinates the operations of other components. It controls the input and output of information between the computer and the outside world through the input and output devices. The arithmetic and logical unit performs operations such as addition and Boolean AND, needed to carry out the instructions. The input devices are keyboard, mouse, etc. while the output devices are printer, plotter, etc.

2.3 CENTRAL PROCESSING UNIT (CPU)

The central processing unit (CPU) regulates the operation of all system components and performs the arithmetic and logical operations on the data. The CPU consists of several distinct parts. The organisation of a simple computer with one CPU and two I/O devices is shown in Figure 2.2.

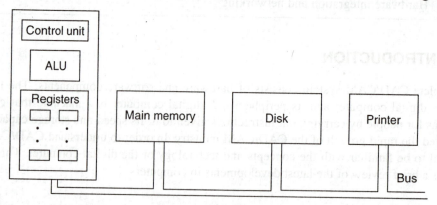

Fig. 2.2   The organisation of a simple computer with one CPU and two I/O devices.

The control unit coordinates the various operations specified by the program instructions. The CPU also contains a small, high-speed memory used to store temporary results and certain control information. This memory consists of a number of registers, each of which has a certain function. The most important register is the ***program counter*** (PC), which points to the next instruction to be executed. Also important is the ***instruction register*** (IR), which holds the instruction currently being executed. ***Accumulator*** is a temporary storage register used during an arithmetic or logical operation. For example, while adding two numbers, the accumulator is used to store the first number while the second number is fetched. ***Status register*** is used to indicate the internal condition of the CPU. The ***arithmetic and logical unit*** (ALU) provides the circuitry required to perform the various calculations and manipulations of data.

The CPU executes each instruction in a series of small steps:

1. Fetch the next instruction from memory into the instruction register.
2. Change the program counter to point to the following instruction.
3. Determine the type of instruction just fetched.
4. If the instruction uses data in memory, determine where they are.
5. Fetch the data, if any, into internal CPU registers.
6. Execute the instruction.
7. Store the results in the proper place.
8. Go to step 1 to begin executing the following instruction.

The organization of CPU is shown in Figure 2.3. The registers feed into two ALU input registers, labelled A and B. These registers hold the ALU input while the ALU is computing. The ALU itself performs addition, subtraction, and other simple operations on its inputs, yielding a result in the output register. This output register can be stored back into a register, and from there, back into memory, if desired. In the example, addition is illustrated.

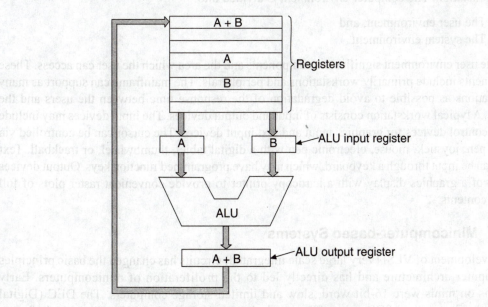

Fig. 2.3 Illustration of CPU organisation.

Instruction can be divided into three categories: register–memory, register–register and memory–memory. Register–memory instructions allow memory words to be fetched into registers, where they can be used as ALU inputs in subsequent instructions. A typical register–register instruction fetches two operands from the registers, brings them to the ALU input registers, performs some operation on them, and stores the result back in a register. A memory-memory instruction fetches its operands from memory into the ALU input registers, performs its operation, and then the result back into memory. The operation of the data path is the heart of most CPUs. To a considerable extent, it defines what the machine can do.

2.4   CLASSIFICATION OF HARDWARE CONFIGURATIONS

The classification hardware configuration is as follows:

(a) Mainframe-based systems
(b) Minicomputer-based systems
(c) Microcomputer-based systems
(d) Workstation-based systems

2.4.1   Mainframe-based Systems

Mainframe-based CAD/CAM systems are used in large organisations for handling massive amounts of data and a multitude of concurrent activities of remote separate software applications. Mainframes often host hundreds of remote workstations operating and communicating over a vast network (sometimes covering thousands of kilometres and crossing international boundaries).

Figure 2.4 shows a schematic of the mainframe-based CAD system components and details of a workstation. The computer environment is divided into:

• The user environment, and
• The system environment

The user environment signifies the components and the area which the user can access. These components include primarily workstations and peripherals. The mainframe can support as many workstations as possible to avoid degradation of the response time between the users and the system. A typical workstation consists of input and output devices. The input devices may include cursor control devices for graphics input and text input devices. The cursor can be controlled via a light pen, joystick, mouse, electronic pen with a digital tablet, thumbwheel, or trackball. Text input can be input through a keyboard, which may have programmed function keys. Output devices consist of a graphics display with a hardcopy printer to provide convenient raster plots of full screen contents.

2.4.2   Minicomputer-based Systems

The development of VLSI (very large scale integrated) circuits has changed the basic principles of computer architecture and has directly led to the proliferation of minicomputers. Early versions on minis were 16-bit word, slow and limited-storage computers. The DEC (Digital Equipment Corporation) PDP series offers a typical example. In the late 1970s, the arrival of super

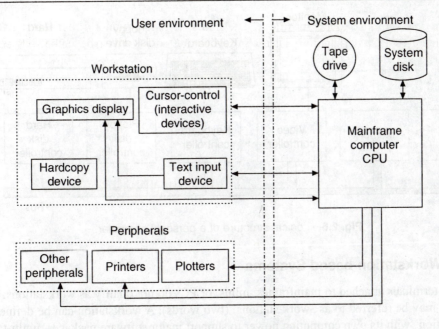

Fig. 2.4 Mainframe-based CAD system.

minicomputers, such as the VAX 11/780, with 32-bit word and virtual memory operating systems, boosted CAD/CAM applications and facilitated decentralisation from mainframes. Minicomputers have enabled the rapid growth of the CAD/CAM industry. The 32-bit minicomputer is capable of handling complex geometric software and large quantities of data. The schematic of minicomputer is shown in Figure 2.5.

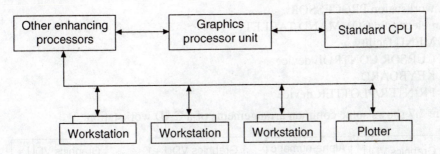

Fig. 2.5 Schematic of a minicomputer.

2.4.3 Microcomputer-based Systems

The advent of the IBM Personal Computer (PC) provided the first significant impetus for CAD on micros. Two main factors are responsible for the popularity and fast emergence of micro-based CAD systems. First, the speed, size, and accuracy problems are being reduced. Microcomputers of a 32-bit word length are available with enough memory size, disk storage, and speed for CAD/CAM applications. Second, various application programs have matured and cover most, if not all, user needs.

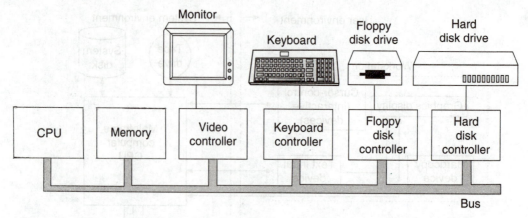

Fig. 2.6 Logical structure of a personal computer.

2.4.4 Workstation-based Systems

Graphics terminals attached to mainframes, minis, or PCs do not qualify as workstations. These terminals may be referred to as 'work stations' (two words). A workstation can be defined as a 'work station' with its own computing power to support major software packages, multi-tasking capabilities demanded by increased usage and complex tasks, and networking potential with other computing environments. The workstation concept seems to form the basis of the present generation of CAD/CAM systems.

The basic elements of a CAD workstation are:

- A graphics screen called the VISUAL DISPLAY UNIT (VDU)
- An ALPHA-NUMERIC DISPLAY (word and number screen)
- A workstation PROCESSOR
- An electronic COMMAND TABLET
- A MENU facility
- A CURSOR CONTROL device
- A KEYBOARD
- A PRINTER/PLOTTER device

Figure 2.7 shows some common arrangements of a CAD workstation.

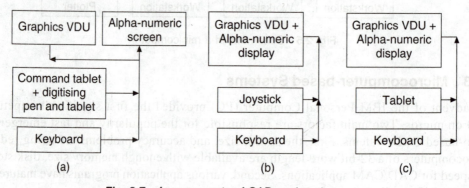

Fig. 2.7 Arrangements of CAD workstations.

2.5 MEMORY

The memory is that part of the computer wherein programs and data are stored. When selecting a memory chip for use in the digital computer, a designer normally has a wide selection from which to choose. Following is a list of features that are commonly examined during selection of a specific memory chip:

1. Capacity and organisation
2. Timing characteristics
3. Power consumption and bus loading
4. Physical dimensions and packaging
5. Cost
6. Reliability
7. Availability

The capacity of a memory chip is generally measured in terms of the number of bits or bytes it contains. As most chips contain more than a few thousand bits, the memory capacity is expressed in kilobytes (KB) or megabytes (MB) or gigabytes (GB). Timing characteristics are AC characteristics. Power consumption and bus loading are also known as DC characteristics.

The memory which is integral to the computer is called 'main' or 'primary memory'. The main memory is divided into three categories:

1. Main data storage or solid-state memory
2. Control storage comprising micro-programs to assist the CPU circuitry in performing its functions
3. Local storage (high-speed working registers).

Semiconductor memories are used for storing information. The various types of semiconductor memory units available are as follows:

1. Read only memory (ROM)
2. Programmable ROM (PROM)
3. Random access memory (RAM)
4. Erasable PROM (EPROM)
5. Electrically erasable and PROM (EEPROM)
6. Flash memory

Read only memory (ROM) can only be read but cannot be written on. Most of the system software is generally provided in the form of ROM. A user-programmable ROM, also known as PROM, or one-time *programmable ROM*, can be programmed by the user just once. After being programmed, the PROM behaves just like the ROM.

Non-volatile memories are very useful in situations where we would not like the information to be destroyed when the power to the memory is removed. Disks and tapes are also non-volatile memories. However, these are too slow to serve as primary memories in a digital computer system. Read only memories that are erasable, have been the most popular non-volatile semiconductor memories amongst designers. This is because data stored in these chips can be easily and inexpensively altered. Chips that permit data to be erased by exposure to ultraviolet light and can be reprogrammed are known as *EPROMs*.

The inconvenience and other technical problems associated with the removal of the EPROM from its normal circuit of operation are taken care of in *Electrically erasable and programmable ROMs*, more popularly known as EEPROMs. The EEPROM can be erased, and programmed, while under normal operation. This makes the EEPROM ideal for applications wherein some parametric data needs to be changed over a period of time.

Random access memory (RAM) is essentially a read and write memory. The information can be read as well as written into the memory. Presently RAM chips are available with lithium battery permanently embedded in the casing of the RAM chip. The information present in the RAM chip is retained even when the external power supply is cut off. RAM chips are available in two varieties:

- Static RAMs, and
- Dynamic RAMs

A *static RAM chip* (*SRAM*) is characterised by the fact that once a bit of information is written into a cell, the cell retains this information until it is overwritten or electrical power is taken off the chip. The cell itself is a flip-flop and may consist of four to six transistors.

A *dynamic RAM chip* (*DRAM*) has a much smaller cell than a static RAM. One bit of information is stored as the charge on a capacitor. Typically, a dynamic RAM can store about four times as much information as a static RAM in the same area due to the smaller cell structure. Since the information is stored as charge on a capacitor, the dynamic RAM needs to be refreshed once every few milliseconds in order to retain the stored information. This refreshing necessitates extra circuitry and makes the interfacing of dynamic RAMs to the computer more complex than the interfacing of static RAMs. Most personal computers use dynamic RAMs as primary memories.

Dynamic RAMs are further classified as:

1. Fast page mode dynamic RAM (FPM DRAM)
2. Extended data out dynamic RAM (EDO DRAM)
3. Synchronous dynamic RAM (SDRAM)

FPM DRAM allows replicated memory access with minimum waiting time for the next instruction. EDO DRAM provides increased performance by outputting data at the same time that it is searching for new information. SDRAM is a fast, high-bandwidth memory designed to work best with systems using high performance PC chipsets and processors. This technology synchronises itself with the system clock that controls the CPU, thereby eliminating time delays and increasing processor efficiency.

2.5.1 Bits

The basic unit of memory is the binary digit, called a 'bit'. A bit may contain a 0 and a 1. It is the simplest possible unit.

The binary number system requires only two values to be distinguished. Consequently, it is the most reliable method for encoding digital information. Some computers, such as the large IBM mainframes, have decimal as well as binary arithmetic. This trick is accomplished by using four bits to store one decimal digit. Four bits provide 16 combinations, used for the 10 digits 0 through 9, with six combinations not used. The number 1944 is shown below encoded in decimal and in pure binary, using 16 bits in each example:

Decimal: 0001 1001 0100 0100
Binary: 0000011110011000

Sixteen bits in the decimal format can store the numbers from 0 to 9999, giving only 10,000 combinations, whereas a 16-bit pure binary number can store 65,536 different combinations. For this purpose, people say that binary is more efficient.

2.5.2 Memory Addresses

Memories consist of a number of *cells* (or *locations*) each of which can store a piece of information. Each cell has a number, called its ***address***, by which programs can refer to it. If a memory has n cells, they will have addresses 0 to ($n-1$). All cells in a memory contain the same number of bits. If a cell consists of k bits, it can hold any one of 2^k different bit combinations. Figure 2.8 shows three different organisations for 96-bit memory.

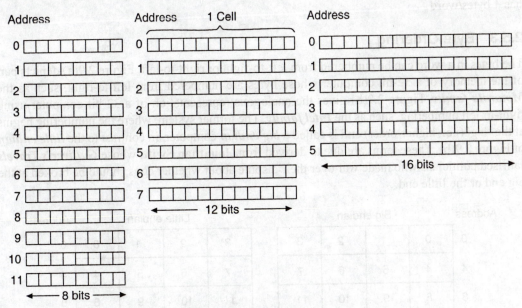

Fig. 2.8   Three ways of organising a 96-bit memory.

Computers that use the binary number system (including octal and hexadecimal notation for binary numbers) also express memory addresses as binary numbers. If an address has m bits, the maximum number of cells directly addressable is 2^m. For example, an address used to reference the memory of Figure 2.8 would need at least 4 bits in order to express all the numbers from 0 to 11. The number of bits in the address is related to the maximum number of directly addressable cells in the memory and is independent of the number of bits per cell. A memory with 2^{12} cells of 8 bits each and a memory with 2^{12} cells of 60 bits each would need 12-bit addresses.

The number of bits per cell for some computers that have been sold commercially are as follows:

Burroughs B1700	: 1 bit per cell
IBM PC	: 8 bits per cell
DEC PDP-8	: 12 bits per cell
IBM 1130	: 16 bits per cell
DEC PDP-15	: 18 bits per cell
XDS 940	: 24 bits per cell
Electrologica X8	: 27 bits per cell
XDS Sigma 9	: 32 bits per cell
Honeywell 6180	: 36 bits per cell
CDC 3600	: 48 bits per cell

The significance of the cell is that it is the smallest addressable unit. In recent years, most computer manufacturers have standardised an 8-bit cell, which is called a *byte*. Bytes are grouped into *words*. A computer with a 16-bit word has 2 bytes/word, whereas a computer with a 32-bit word has 4 bytes/word.

2.5.3   Byte Ordering

The bytes in a word can be numbered from left-to-right or right-to-left. Figure 2.9(a) depicts part of the memory of a 32-bit computer whose bytes are numbered from left-to-right, such as the *Motorola family*. Figure 2.9(b) gives the analogous representation of a 32-bit computer using right-to-left numbering, such as the *Intel family*. The former system, where the numbering begins at the 'big' (i.e., higher-order) end is called a *big endian* computer, in contrast to the *little endian* of Figure 2.9(b). These terms are due to derived from **Jonathan Swift**, whose *Gulliver's Travels* satirised politicians who made war over their dispute about whether eggs should be broken at the big end or the little end.

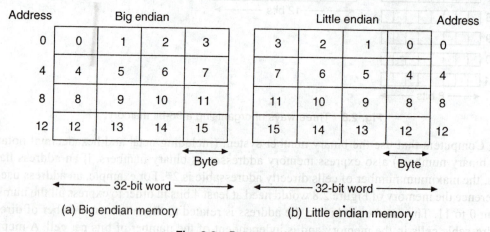

Fig. 2.9   Byte ordering.

2.5.4   Error Correcting Codes

Computer memories can occasionally make errors due to voltage spikes on the power line or other causes. In order to guard against errors, most memories use error-detecting or error-correcting codes. When these codes are used, extra bits are added to each memory word in a special way. When a word is read out of memory, the extra bits are checked to see if an error has occurred.

In order to understand how errors can be handled, it is necessary to look closely at what an error really is. Suppose that a memory word consists of m data bits to which we will add r redundant, or check bits. Let the total length be n (i.e., $n = m + r$). An n-bit unit containing m data and r check bits is often referred to as an n-bit ***codeword***.

Given any two codewords, say, 10001001 and 10110001, it is possible to determine how many corresponding bits differ. In this case, three bits differ. In order to determine how many bits differ, just compute the bit-wise Boolean EXCLUSIVE OR of the two codewords, and count the number of one bits in the result. The number of bit positions in which two codewords differ is called the *Hamming* distance. Its significance is that if two codewords are at a Hamming distance d apart, it will require d single-bit errors to convert one into the other. For example, the codewords 11110001 and 00110000 are at a Hamming distance three apart because it takes three single-bit errors to convert one into the other.

With an m-bit memory word, all 2^m bit patterns are legal, but due to the way the check bits are computed, only 2^m of the 2^n codewords are valid. If a memory read turns up an invalid codeword, the computer knows that a memory error has occurred. Given the algorithm for computing the check bits, it is possible to construct a complete list of the legal codewords, and from this list to find the two codewords whose Hamming distance is the minimum. This distance is the Hamming distance of the complete code.

The error-detecting and error-correcting properties of a code depend on its Hamming distance. In order to detect d single-bit errors, you need a distance $d + 1$ code because with such a code there is no way that d single-bit errors can change a valid codeword into another valid codeword. Similarly, to correct d single-bit errors, you need a distance $2d + 1$ code because that way the legal codewords would be so far apart that even with d changes, the original codeword is still closer than any other codeword, so it can be uniquely determined.

As a simple example of an error-detecting code, consider a code in which a single parity bit is appended to the data. The parity bit is chosen so that the number of one bits in the codeword is even (or odd). Such a code has a distance 2, since any single-bit error produces a codeword with the wrong parity. It can be used to detect single errors. Whenever a word containing the wrong parity is read from memory, an error condition is signified and special action is taken. The program cannot continue, but at least no incorrect results are computed.

As a simple example of an error-correcting code, consider a code with only four valid codewords:

$$0000000000, \quad 0000011111, \quad 1111100000, \quad \text{and } 1111111111$$

This code has a distance 5, which means that it can correct double errors. If the codeword 0000000111 arrives, the receiver knows that the original must have been 0000011111 (if there was no more than a double error). If, however, a triple error changes 0000000000 into 0000000111, the error will not be corrected properly.

2.6 STORAGE DEVICES

Since every word in the main memory must be directly accessible in a very short time, the main memory is relatively expensive. Consequently, most computers have slower, cheaper, and usually much larger secondary memories as well. Secondary memories are used to hold sets of data far larger than what the main memory can hold. The storage devices can be classified as follows:

1. Magnetic tapes
2. Magnetic disks
3. Winchester disks
4. Floppy disks
5. CD ROM
6. DVD

2.6.1 Magnetic Tapes

Historically a magnetic tape was the first kind of storage device. A computer tape drive is analogous to a home tape recorder: a 2400-ft long tape is wound from the feed reel past a recording head to the take-up reel. By varying the current in the recording head, the computer can write information on the tape in the form of little magnetised spots.

Figure 2.10 shows how information is organised on a magnetic tape. On a computer with 8-bit bytes, each frame contains one byte, plus an extra, redundant bit, railed a parity bit, to improve reliability. The typical recording density 1600 frames (bytes) per inch (denoted as 1600 bpi), which means that a frame takes up less than 1/1000 of an inch. Other common densities are 800 bpi and 6250 bpi. After a tape drive has finished writing a physical record (a sequence of frames), it leaves a gap on the tape while slowing down. If the program writes short physical records on the tape, most of the space will be wasted in the gaps. By writing physical records that are much longer than the gap, one can keep tape utilisation high.

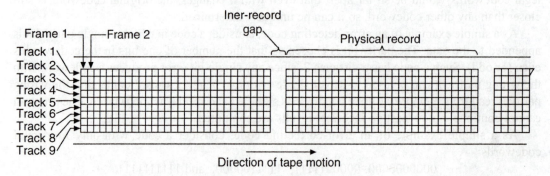

Fig. 2.10 Data on a magnetic tape is recorded as a sequence of rectangular bit matrices.

Magnetic tapes are sequential access devices. If the tape is positioned at the beginning, to read physical record n, it is first necessary to read the physical records 1 through $(n-1)$, one at a time. If the information desired is near the end of the tape, the program will have to read almost the entire tape, which may take several minutes. Forcing a CPU that can execute millions of instructions per second to wait 200 seconds while a tape is advanced is wasteful. Tapes are most appropriate when the data must be accessed sequentially.

2.6.2 Magnetic Disks

A disk is a piece of metal, ranging from about 5 to 10 inches in diameter, to which a magnetisable coating has been applied at the factory, generally on both sides (see Figure 2.11). Information is recorded on a number of concentric circles, called 'tracks'. Disks are typically between 40 and a few hundred tracks per surface. Each disk drive has a movable head that can be moved closer to, or farther from, the centre. The head is wide enough to read or write information from exactly one track. A disk drive often has several disks stacked vertically about an inch apart. In such a configuration, the arm will have one head next to each surface, all of which move in and out together. The radial position of the heads (distance from the spindle) is called the cylinder. A disk drive with n platters will have $2n$ heads and, hence $2n$ tracks per cylinder.

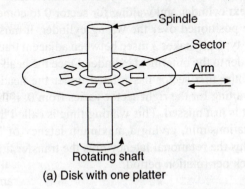

(a) Disk with one platter

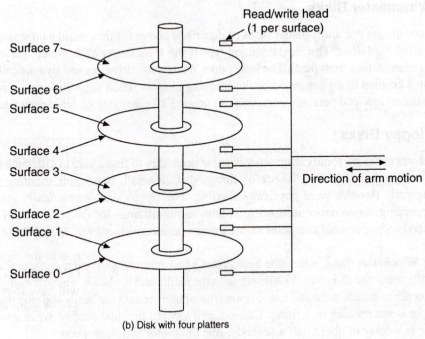

(b) Disk with four platters

Fig. 2.11 Magnetic disks.

Tracks are divided into sectors, normally between 10 and 100 sectors per track. A sector consists of a certain number of bytes, usually 512.

In order to specify a transfer, the program must provide the following information: the cylinder and head, which together specify a unique track, the sector number where the information starts, the number of words to be transmitted, the main memory address where the information comes from or goes to, and whether information is to be read from the disk into memory or written from memory to the disk.

Disk transfers always start at the beginning of a sector, never in the middle. If a multi-sector transfer crosses a track boundary within a cylinder (e.g., from surface 0 to surface 1 at the same arm position), no time is lost because switching from one head to another is done electronically. However, if the transfer crosses a cylinder boundary, one rotation time may be lost while re-positioning the heads to the next cylinder and waiting for sector 0 to come around.

If the head happens to be positioned over the wrong cylinder, it must first be moved. This motion is called a seek. A seek typically takes 3 msec between adjacent tracks and 20 to 100 msec to go from the innermost cylinder to the outermost cylinder. Once the head is positioned properly, the controller must wait until the first sector has rotated under the head before beginning the transfer. The time wasted in waiting for the right sector varies from 0, if the program is lucky, to the complete rotation time if it is just missed. This waiting time is called the 'rotational latency'. Most disks rotate at 3600 rotations/min, giving a maximum latency of 16.67 msec. The total access time is the seek time plus the rotational latency plus the transfer time. The information is transferred at a rate of one track per rotation period.

2.6.3   Winchester Disks

Nearly all computers use multi-platter disks as described above for their main data storage. These are often called *hard disks*. The most common type is the ***Winchester disk***, which is a sealed unit (to avoid contamination from dust). The heads on a Winchester drive are aerodynamically shaped and float on a cushion of air generated by the spinning platters. Their capacities range from about 20 megabytes on low-end personal computers to around 10 gigabytes on large mainframes.

2.6.4   Floppy Disks

With the advent of the personal computer, it became necessary to find a way to distribute software. The solution was found in the diskette or floppy disk, a small, removable medium so-called because the early floppies were physically flexible. The floppy disk was actually invented by IBM for recording maintenance information about its mainframes for the service staff, but was quickly seized on by personal computer manufacturers as a convenient way to distribute software for sale.

Unlike Winchester disks, where the heads float a few microns above the surface, floppy disk heads actually touch the diskettes. As a result, both the media and the heads wear out comparatively quickly. In order to reduce wear and tear, personal computers retract the heads and stop the rotation when a drive is not reading or writing. Consequently, when the next read or write command is given, there is a delay of about half a second while the motor acquires speed.

Nowadays, two sizes are commonly used, 5.25 inch and 3.5 inch. Each of these has a low-density and a high-density version. The 3.5 inch diskettes come in a rigid jacket for protection, so they are not really 'floppy'. Since the 3.5 inch disks store more data and are better protected, they will eventually replace the 5.25 inch ones. The most important parameters of all four types are given in Table 2.1.

Table 2.1 Comparison of four common diskette types

Size (inches)	5.25	5.25	3.5	3.5
Capacity (bytes)	360K	1.2M	720K	1.44M
Tracks	40	80	80	80
Sectors/track	9	15	9	18
Heads	2	2	2	2
Rotations/min	300	360	300	300
Date rate (kbps)	250	500	250	500
Type	Flexible	Flexible	Rigid	Rigid

2.6.5 CD ROM

In recent years, optical disks have become available. They have much higher recording densities than conventional magnetic disks. Optical disks were originally developed for recording television programs, but they can be put to more aesthetic use as computer storage devices. Television has a bandwidth of 6 MHz, so a one-hour disk has a theoretical capacity of about 10 gigabits. Practical systems achieve about half of that. (**Bandwidth** is an electrical engineering term and refers to the information-carrying capacity of a wire or other channel. A bandwidth of 1 Hertz (Hz) is typically, but not always, good for transmitting one bit per second).

Due to their potentially enormous capacity, optical disks have been the subject of a great deal of research and have gone through an incredibly rapid evolution. The first generation was invented by the Dutch electronics conglomerate, Philips, and further developed in collaboration with Sony. These disks are based on the same technology used in Compact Disc audio players and are called *CD ROMs* (*Compact Disc Read Only Memory*).

A CD ROM is prepared by using a high-power laser to burn one-micron $(10^{-6}$ of a metre) holes in a master disk. From this master, a mould is made. This mould is used to stamp out copies on plastic disks in the same way that phonograph records are made. A thin layer of aluminium is then deposited on the surface, followed by a transparent plastic layer for protection. CD ROMs are read by devices similar to CD audio players, by having a detector measure the energy reflected off the surface when a low-power laser is aimed at the surface. The holes, called *pits*, and the unburned areas between the pits, called *lands*, have different reflectivity, making it possible to distinguish between pits and lands.

This technology has some important consequences. Since the CD ROMs are stamped rather than recorded like conventional floppy disks, fully automated machinery can mass produce them at a very low price.

Despite this enormous potential, CD ROMs are not writable, which limits their utility as computer storage devices. The desire to have a writable medium led to the next phase, the WORM (Write Once Read Many) optical disk. This device allows users to write information on optical disks themselves. However, once a pit has been burned into the surface, it cannot be erased. Such disks are good for making data archives, accounting audit trails, and other information that is (semi-) permanent. They are not well suited for making and erasing temporary scratch files. However, given the large capacity of these disks, a slash-and-burn style of just appending temporary files until the disk is full and then throwing it away is conceivable. Presently, commercial CD ROMs can store 650 MB of information on a 5.25 inch removable optical disk. The laser beam used on a CDROM player has a wavelength of 780 nanometers.

It is clear that the existence of write-once disks has a major impact on the way software is written. Not being able to modify files tends to suggest a different kind of file system, in which a file is really a sequence of immutable versions, none of which can be changed, and each of which replaces the previous one. This model is quite different from the usual update-in-place model used on magnetic disks.

The third phase of optical disk evolution is erasable optical media. These use magneto-optical technology. The plastic disk is coated with alloys of metals so exotic, such as terbium and gadolinium, that few people have ever even heard of them. These metals have the interesting property that at low temperatures they are insensitive to magnetic fields, but at high temperatures, their molecular structure aligns itself with any magnetic field present.

In order to use this property to record information, the drive's heads contain a laser and a magnet. A laser fires an ultra-short light burst at the metal, raising its temperature instantaneously, but not pitting the surface. At the same time, the magnet is issuing a field in one of two directions. When the laser pulse is over, the metal has been magnetised in one of two possible directions, representing 0 or 1. This information can be read back in the same way as with a CD ROM, using a much weaker laser. The disk can also be erased and overwritten in the same way that it was written in the first place.

Writable optical disks are not likely to replace conventional Winchester disks for some time, probably many years, if ever, for two reasons. First, their seek times are of an order of magnitude which is slower than those of Winchester disks. Second, their data rates are also of an order of magnitude that is slower. Together, the overall performance of magnetic disks is simply much better. While optical disks will no doubt improve in time, magnetic disks will probably improve just as fast to stay ahead. Nevertheless, for applications wherein a large amount of removable storage is critical, optical disks have a bright future ahead of them.

2.6.6 DVD

Digital video disk (DVD) is read by an infrared laser focused through a protective plastic layer onto the disc reflective layer. The transparent layer is 1.2 mm thick on a CD ROM, but only 0.6 mm on a DVD ROM. The beam reflects off pits burned into the reflective layer by the recording laser and is passed through optics to the pick-up. The laser beam used on DVD ROM players has a wavelength of 650 nanometres. Disks come in capacities of 4.7, 8.5, 9.4 and 17 GB.

2.7 INPUT DEVICES

The user of a CAD/CAM system spends a lot of time sitting at a workstation communicating and interacting with the computer to develop a particular engineering design. A number of input devices are available. These devices are used to input the two possible types of information: text and graphics. Text input devices are the alphanumeric (character-oriented) keyboards. There are three classes of graphics input devices: locating devices, digitisers, and image-input devices.

The locating devices provide a position or location on the screen. These include light pens, mice, digitising tablets and styluses, joysticks, trackballs, thumbwheels, touchscreens, and touchpads. The keyboard arrow keys are inadequate for most graphics applications. Locating devices typically operate by controlling the position of a cursor on the screen. Thus, they are also referred to as cursor-control devices.

Digitisers are considered as electronic drafting boards. A digitiser consists of a large synthesised electronic board with a movable stylus called the 'cursor'. It is a two dimensional input device with high resolution and accuracy. The typical sizes are 36×48 and 48×72 inches. The available resolution and accuracy are up to 0.001 and 0.003 inch respectively. Digitisers can be divided into three kinds relative to the mode of operation of the cursor. They are free-cursor, constrained-cursor, and motor-cursor digitisers. In the first kind, the cursor is attached to the end of a flexible chord, while in the second, it slides along a gantry that traverses the entire digitising board area, and in the third kind, the cursor motion is accomplished by motors driven by an operator-controlled joystick. Each kind has its advantages and disadvantages. The first kind provides greater ease of moving the cursor. The cursor is restricted in the second kind but the digitiser can be used in an upright position. Motorised digitisers are expensive but combine the best features of the first two.

Image input devices are video frame grabbers and scanners. Electronic imaging is an area of relevance to image processing. This area may become significant to the CAD/CAM field if robot vision systems have to be driven by CAD/CAM databases. Video digitisers constitute another area where digitisers are connected to a video source, whether it is a video camera or a recorder. They can utilise standard NTSC (National Television System Committee) composite input or colour input with separate RGB (red, green, blue) inputs. The resolution of video digitisers is determined by that of the original source. Image scanners constitute another form of image input devices. They are used to convert flat paper drawings or plots into digital bit-map form. They range in size and have been applied to help in the conversion of existing engineering blue prints into a CAD database.

There are four parameters to measure the performance of graphics input devices. These are resolution, accuracy, repeatability and linearity. The resolution of a device is defined as the smallest distance that the device requires to recognise two adjacent points as spatially separate or addressable. Accuracy is defined as the error in the measurement of actual data by the input device. Repeatability measures the ability of the device to return to a given position. For example, if the same point is digitised many times, how close are the coordinates of the resulting point? Linearity measures the response of a device to the user's hand movements.

2.7.1 Keyboard

The keyboard (Figure 2.12) is the most basic input medium for all computers. The layout of keys on a keyboard generally consists of the traditional typewriter keys together with some special keys, which are used for controlling the execution of the program or the screen display. The presence of a higher number of keys would facilitate the interaction. How does the keyboard communicate with the CAD/CAM software or the main application program? How is the software interrupted to receive the keyboard input? The keyboard is connected to the computer by means of registers whose contents can be read by the computer. A keyboard typically has two registers, one to set a status bit when a key has been struck, and the other to identify the key by its character code. The value of the status bit is monitored in a continuous repetitive manner by the software via a programming technique known as 'polling'. When the user hits a key, the status bit is set and the application program is consequently interrupted to clear the status bit, followed by reading the corresponding code of the key character. The loop is repeated every time the user strikes a key. Keyboard characters are identified by their ASCII (American Standard Code for Information Interchange) codes. The ASCII codes for alphanumeric characters are 7-bit codes. The character code for a capital letter, say A, is different from that for a small letter, say a. EBCDIC (Extended Binary Coded Decimal Interchange Codes) for alphanumeric characters are 8-bit codes and do not have this distinction, that is, capital letters are always used.

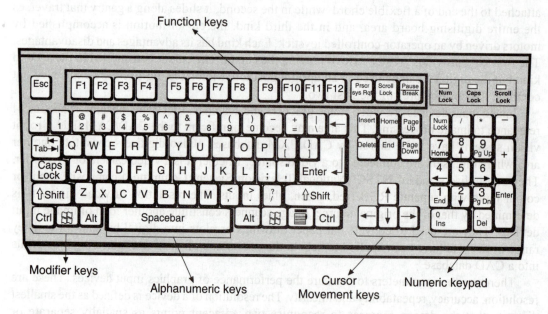

Fig. 2.12   A keyboard.

2.7.2   Mouse

The mouse (Figure 2.13) is a pointing device which has been gaining importance with the advent of microprocessors and the pull-down menus associated with application software. The mouse operates on three principles: mechanical, optical and optomechanical. The mechanical mouse contains a free-floating ball with rubber coating on the underside which, when moved on a firm plane surface, is able to follow the movement of the hand. The motion of the ball is resolved into X- and Y-motions by means of the two rollers pressed against the ball. They, in turn, control the cursor on the screen, which can then be utilised for any desired applications by means of the clicking of the buttons on the mouse. This can only suffice to point on the screen but not for giving positional data. Further, the mouse is a relative device and not an absolute pointing device.

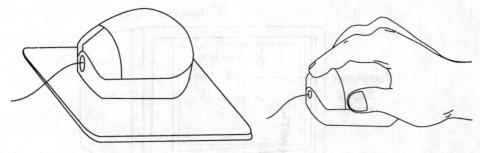

Fig. 2.13 A mouse.

Unlike the mechanical one, the optical mouse is used in conjunction with a special surface (the mouse pad). Movements over this surface are measured by a light beam modulation and optical encoding techniques. Since the light source is located at the bottom, the mouse must be in contact with the surface for the screen cursor to follow its movements. Pushbuttons may be mounted on top of the mouse and programmed to execute various functions.

2.7.3 Lightpen

A lightpen (Figure 2.14) resembles a fountain pen in the method of holding, but it works on the principle of light rather than ink, from which it derives its name. The lightpen is a pointing or picking device that enables the user to select a displayed graphics item on a screen by directly touching its surface in the vicinity of the item. The application program processes the information generated from the touching to identify the selectable item to operate on. The lightpen itself does not emit light but rather detects it from the graphics items displayed on the screen. Using the emitted light as an input, it sends an interrupt signal to the computer to determine which was seen by the pen (Figure 2.15). The lightpen normally operates as a logical pick in conjunction with a vector refresh display.

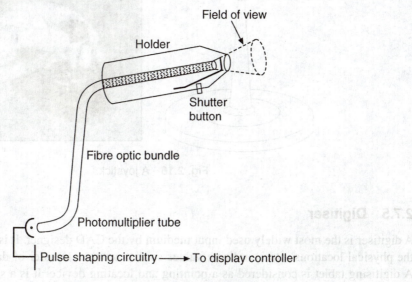

Fig. 2.14 Schematic of a lightpen.

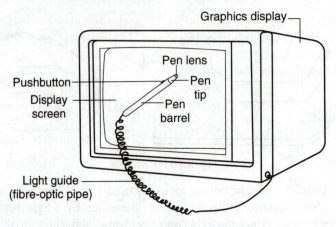

Fig. 2.15   Location by a lightpen.

2.7.4   Joystick

Vertical and horizontal displacements of a joystick produce corresponding movements of the cursor on the screen. The extreme positions of these displacements correspond to the four corners of the screen. A joystick (Figure 2.16) may be equipped with a rotating knob on the top, which can be used to enter a third axis value, thus making the joystick a three-dimensional input device. Springs are often provided to return the joystick to its position at the centre. Joysticks are suitable for raster display systems and have become very popular in the home computer market. In CAD systems, they are most effectively used in conjunction with screen display type menu facilities.

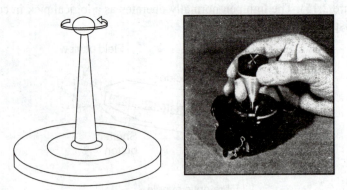

Fig. 2.16   A joystick.

2.7.5   Digitiser

A digitiser is the most widely used input medium by the CAD designer. It is used for converting the physical locations into coordinate values so that accurate transfer of data can be achieved. A digitising tablet is considered as a pointing and locating device. It is a small, low-resolution digitising board often used in conjunction with a graphics display. The tablet is a flat surface over which a stylus or a puck can be moved by the user. The close resemblance of the tablet and stylus to paper and pencil contributes to its popularity as an input device. The puck contains a rectile and at least one pushbutton. The engraved cross-hairs of rectile help locate a point for digitising. Pressing the pushbutton sends the coordinates at the cross-hairs to the computer. The sizes of digitising tablets range from 11×11 to 36×36 inches. The resolution of a tablet is 0.005 inch or 200 dots per inch.

The tablet operation is based on sensitising its surface area to be able to track the pointing element (stylus or puck) motion on the surface. There are two types of tablets. These are:

- Magnetic tablet
- Acoustic tablet

Magnetic tablet: The surface of the tablet is magnetised and is embedded with wires in the x and y directions. The physical motion of the stylus is converted by the wires into a digital location signal, which is then routed to the computer and displayed on the graphics terminal. Figure 2.17 shows the magnetic tablet.

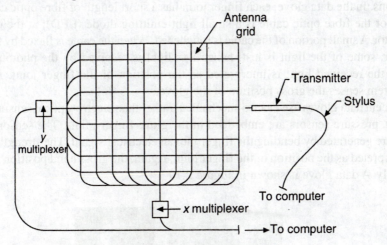

Fig. 2.17   A magnetic tablet.

Acoustic tablet: The pointing element has a sound generator with strip microphones along the edges of the tablet to pick up the periodic sound to determine the x and y values. Figure 2.18 shows the acoustic tablet.

The operation of the digitising tablet is simple. The user moves the pointing element to the desired position and then interrupts the computer to accept the coordinate value of this position. In the case of the stylus, the user presses it against the tablet surface or depresses a pushbutton near its tip. This, in turn, activates a switching mechanism inside the stylus that picks (or sends) signals from (to) the tablet position and sends them to the stylus decoding logic that stores the corresponding coordinates in the buffer registers of the tablet. These registers are read by the application program as soon as it is interrupted by the depression of the stylus or its pushbutton. All digitising tablets provide an origin, typically in the lower left corner, for the x and y coordinates, the x-axis being horizontal and the y-axis being vertical.

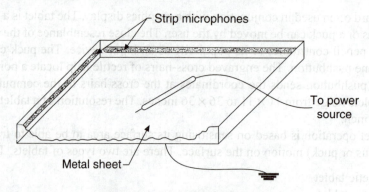

Fig. 2.18 An acoustic tablet.

2.7.6 Data Glove

The data glove records three-dimensional hand and finger positions, and therefore, the hand and finger motions. In the data glove, each finger joint has a short length of fibre optic cable attached. At one end of the fibre optic cable is a small light-emitting diode (LED); at the other end is a phototransistor. A small portion of the cable is roughened. When the cable is flexed by the movement of the finger, some of the light is lost; hence less light is received by the phototransistor. The intensity of the received light is interpreted as the position of the finger joint. In addition, a separate system senses the gross position of the glove.

More recent data gloves use electro-mechanical rather than electro-optical sensing techniques. In particular, pressure sensors are embedded in the glove finger joints. The sensor converts the small pressure generated by bending the finger into an electrical signal. The strength of the signal is again interpreted as the position of the finger joint. Again, the gross hand position is determined independently. A data glove is shown in Figure 2.19.

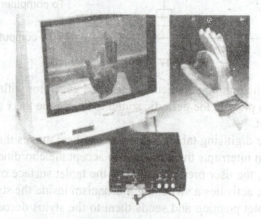

Fig. 2.19 A data glove.

2.7.7 Trackball

A trackball (Figure 2.20) is similar in principle to a joystick but it allows more precise fingertip control. The ball rotates freely within its mount. The trackball is used in radar and flight control systems. The trackball is used to navigate the screen display cursor.

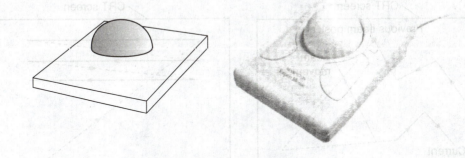

Fig. 2.20 A trackball.

2.7.8 Thumbwheels

Two thumbwheels are usually required to control the screen cursor, one for its horizontal position and the other for its vertical position. Each position is indicated on the screen by a cross-hair. Thumbwheels are usually mounted on the keyboard.

2.8 OUTPUT DEVICES

Graphics output devices are divided into soft and hard devices. The former refer to the graphics displays or terminals, which only display information on a screen. Hard output devices refer to hardcopy printers and plotters that can provide permanent copies of the displayed information.

2.8.1 Graphics Displays

The graphics display enables the user to view images and to communicate with the displayed image by adding, deleting, blanking, and moving graphics entities on the display screen. Various display technologies are now available based on the concept of converting the computer electrical signals into visible images at high speed. The graphics display can be divided into two types based on the scan technology used to control the electron beam when generating graphics on the screen. These are:

- Random scan
- Raster scan

In random scan, graphics can be generated by drawing vectors or line segments on the screen in a random order, which is controlled, by the user input and the software. The principle of random scan is illustrated in Figure 2.21(a).

In raster scan, the screen is canned from left to right, top to bottom, all the time to generate graphics. The principle of random scan is illustrated in Figure 2.21(b).

The graphics display technologies include:

- CRT (cathode ray tube) display
- Liquid crystal display
- Plasma panel display

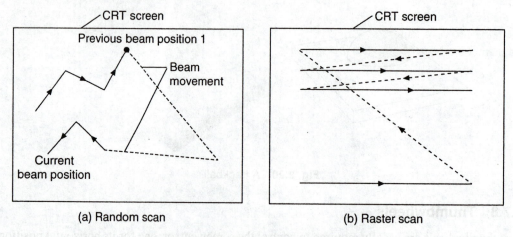

(a) Random scan   (b) Raster scan

Fig. 2.21 Graphics scanning techniques.

The CRT (Figure 2.22) is basically an evacuated glass tube in which a beam of electrons is fired from an electron gun onto a phosphor-coated screen, resulting in an illuminated trace being displayed on the screen. Various types of CRT displays are broadly categorised into:

- Direct view storage tube (DVST)
- Vector refresh
- Raster refresh

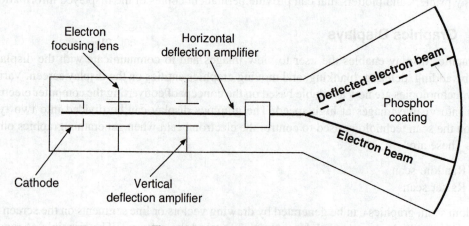

Fig. 2.22 Schematic of a CRT..

The **DVST** (Direct View Storage Tube) (Figure 2.23) has the standard CRT electron gun and deflection system for location of the beam onto the screen. The picture is stored as a charge in the phosphor mesh located behind the screen surface. Once displayed, the picture remains on the screen until it is explicitly erased. Therefore, complex pictures can be drawn without flicker at high resolution. One cannot alter a DVST picture except by erasing the entire screen and drawing it again. The inability to erase and edit individual areas of the drawing is a major drawback of the DVST system. Coloured pictures are not usually available with a DVST. This can be a distinct disadvantage, particularly for three-dimensional drawings. Animation is also difficult to achieve, a factor that effectively disallows such vital facilities as tool-path simulation, and dynamic analysis of mechanisms.

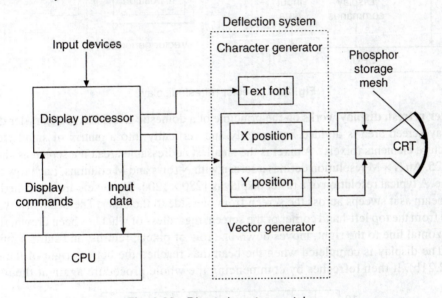

Fig. 2.23   Direct view storage tube.

In **vector refresh display** (Figure 2.24), the deflection system of the CRT is controlled and driven by the vector and character generators and digital-to-analog converters. The refresh buffer stores the display file that contains points, lines, characters, and other attributes of the picture to be drawn. These commands are interpreted and processed by the display processor. The electron beam accordingly excites the phosphor that glows for a short period. In order to maintain a steady flicker-free image, the screen must be refreshed or re-drawn at least 30 or 60 times per second. Vector refresh displays are particularly noted for their bright, clear image, and high drawing speed. The refresh operation is well-suited to fast moving animation of the screen display in either 2D or 3D. The chief disadvantages of vector refresh displays are their high cost, and their tendency to flicker on complex drawings if the refresh rate becomes less than the flicker threshold of the eye. Colour displays are possible, but again are only available at high cost.

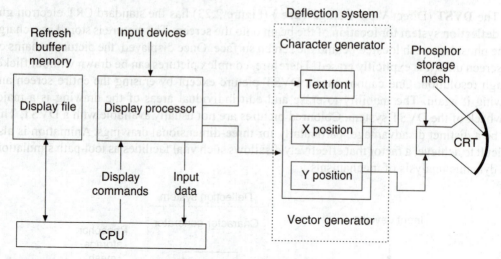

Fig. 2.24 Vector refresh display.

Raster refresh display works on the principle of a domestic television set. In raster display, the display screen area is divided horizontally and vertically into a matrix of small elements called picture elements (pixels). A pixel is the smallest addressable area on a screen as shown in Figure 2.25. An N × M resolution defines a screen with N rows and M columns. Each row defines a scan line. A typical resolution of a raster display is 1280 × 1204. The pixels are controlled by the electron beam as it sweeps across the screen from one side to the other. The beam always starts its sweep from the top left-hand corner of the screen, regardless of what has been drawn, finishes on a horizontal line to the right, moves down one row of pixels, returns, and starts again from the left. The display is completed when the beam has reached the bottom right of the screen (Figure 2.21b). It then refreshes by commencing the whole procedure again at the top left.

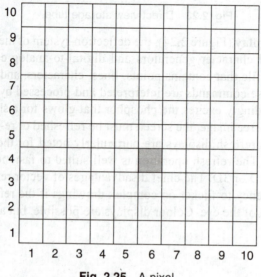

Fig. 2.25 A pixel.

Each refresh operation takes about 0.02 seconds. Images are displayed by converting geometric information into pixel values, which are then converted into electron beam deflection through the display processor and the deflection system. The creation of a raster format from geometric information is known as *rasterisation*. The raster display has become most popular due to its low cost and versatility. The principal advantage of the refresh display is its high resolution. As with vector refresh, there is no problem in erasing individual elements of a raster drawing. Unlike vector refresh, there is no flicker of the display, and the creation of filled-in areas of the drawing is easily achieved. The main disadvantage of the raster refresh display is the calculation of sequence of the pixel display pattern for each stroke, and thus the raster system needs high memory.

In a **colour raster display** (Figure 2.26), there are three electron guns, one for each of the primary colours, red, green and blue. The electron guns are frequently arranged in a triangular pattern corresponding to a similar triangular pattern of red, green and blue phosphor dots on the face of the CRT (Figure 2.27). In order to ensure that the individual electron guns excite the correct phosphor dots (e.g., the red gun excites only the red phosphor dot), a perforated metal grid is placed between the electron guns and the face of the CRT. The perforations in the shadow mask are arranged in the same triangular pattern as the phosphor dots (Figure 2.28). The distance between perforations is called the pitch. The colour guns are arranged so that the individual beams converge and intersect at the shadow mask. Upon passing through the hole in the shadow mask, the red beam, for example, is prevented or masked from intersecting either the green or blue phosphor dot; it can only intersect the red phosphor dot. By varying the strength of the electron beam for each individual primary colour, different shades (intensities) are obtained. These primary colour shades are combined into a number of colours for each pixel.

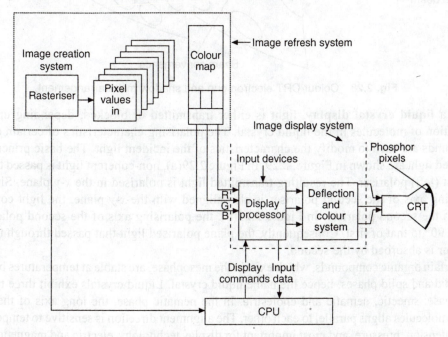

Fig. 2.26 Colour raster refresh display.

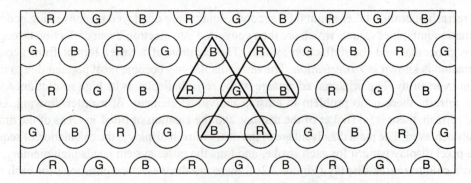

Fig. 2.27   Phosphor dot pattern for a shadow mask CRT.

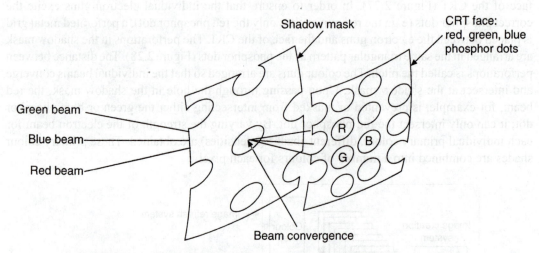

Fig. 2.28   Colour CRT electron gun and shadow mask arrangement.

In a **liquid crystal display**, light is either transmitted or blocked, depending upon the orientation of molecules in the liquid crystal. The polarising characteristics of certain organic compounds are used to modify the characteristics of the incident light. The basic principles of polarised light are shown in Figure. 2.29. In Figure 2.29(a), non-coherent light is passed through the first (left) polariser. The resulting transmitted light is polarised in the *x-y* plane. Since the polarising axis of the second polariser is also aligned with the *x-y* plane, the light continues through the second polariser. In Figure 2.29(b), the polarising axis of the second polariser is rotated 90° to that of first. Consequently, the plane polarised light that passed through the first polariser is absorbed by the second.

Certain organic compounds, which exist in the mesophase, are stable at temperatures between the liquid and solid phases, hence the name liquid crystal. Liquid crystals exhibit three types of mesophase: smectic, nematic and cholestric. In the nematic phase, the long axis of the liquid crystal molecules aligns parallel to each other. The alignment direction is sensitive to temperature, surface tension, pressure, and most important for display technology, electric and magnetic fields. The optical characteristics of the liquid crystal are also sensitive to these effects.

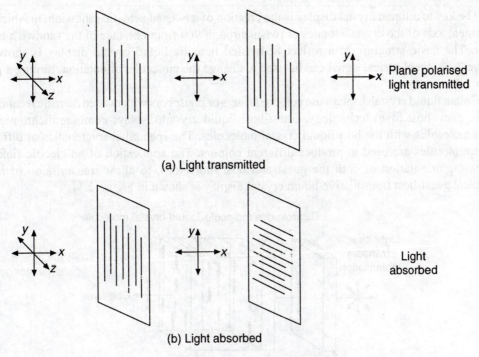

(a) Light transmitted

Plane polarised
light transmitted

Light
absorbed

(b) Light absorbed

Fig. 2.29 Polarisation of light.

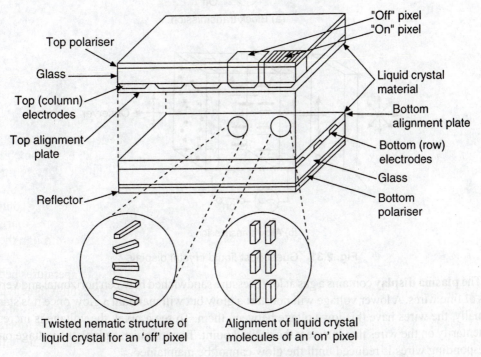

Top polariser

Glass

Top (column)
electrodes

Top alignment
plate

Reflector

"Off" pixel
"On" pixel

Liquid crystal
material

Bottom
alignment plate

Bottom (row)
electrodes

Glass

Bottom
polariser

Twisted nematic structure of
liquid crystal for an 'off' pixel

Alignment of liquid crystal
molecules of an 'on' pixel

Fig. 2.30 Basic structure of a twisted nematic liquid crystal display.

The key to a liquid crystal display is the creation of a twisted nematic sandwich, in which the alignment axis of the crystals rotates or twists through 900 from one face of the sandwich to the other. The basic structure of a reflective twisted nematic liquid crystal display is shown in Figure 2.30. An electrical signal can be used to change the molecular orientation, turning a pixel on or off.

Colour liquid crystal displays use coloured filters or phosphors with twisted nematic technology or use guest-host (dye) technology. Guest-host liquid crystal displays combine dichromic-dye guest molecules with the host liquid crystal molecules. The spectral characteristics of different guest molecules are used to produce different colours. The application of an electric field re-aligns the orientation of both the guest and host molecules, to allow transmission of light. A typical guest-host transmissive liquid crystal display is shown in Figure 2.31.

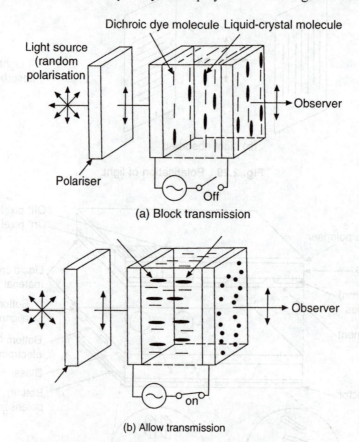

(a) Block transmission

(b) Allow transmission

Fig. 2.31 Guest-host liquid crystal display.

The **plasma display** contains a gas at low pressure sandwiched between horizontal and vertical grids of fine wires. A lower voltage will not start a glow but will maintain a glow once it is started. Normally, the wires have this low voltage between them. To see a pixel, the voltage is increased momentarily on the wires that intersect the desired point. To extinguish a pixel, the voltage on the corresponding wires is reduced until the glow cannot be maintained.

Plasma displays can be AC or DC or hybrid AC/DC activated. AC and DC plasma displays are shown in Figure 2.32(a) and Figure 2.32(b), respectively. The DC-activated display consists of a dielectric spacer plate, which contains the gas cavities sandwiched between plates containing the row–column conductors. The electric field is applied directly to the gas. A DC-activated plasma display requires continuous refreshing.

In the AC-activated plasma display, a dielectric layer is placed between the conductors and the gas. Thus, the only coupling between the gas and the conductors is capacitive. Hence, an AC-voltage is required to dissociate the gas. AC-activated plasma displays have bistable memory; thus, the necessity to continuously refresh the display is eliminated. Bistable memory is obtained by using a low AC voltage to keep alive voltage. The characteristic capacitive coupling provides enough voltage to maintain the activity in the conducting pixels, but not enough to activate non-conducting pixels.

A hybrid AC/DC plasma display uses DC voltage to prime the gas and make it more easily activated by the AC voltage. The principal advantage of the hybrid AC/DC plasma display is reduced driver circuitry.

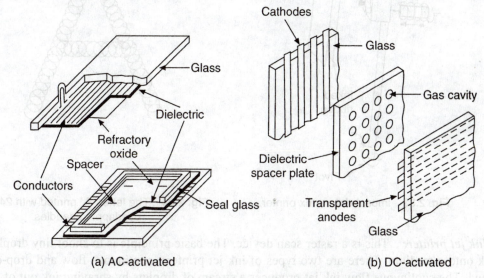

(a) AC-activated   (b) DC-activated

Fig. 2.32   Basic structure of gas discharge plasma displays.

2.8.2 Hardcopy Printers and Plotters

Printers and plotters are used to create checkplots for offline editing and producing final drawings and documentation on paper. Printers usually provide hard copies of text as well as graphics.

Printers are classified as follows on the basis of three principal technologies used for their operation:

- Impact dot matrix printer
- Ink jet printer
- Laser printer

Impact dot matrix printer: This is an electromechanical device, which creates images on paper from thousands of tiny dots when thin wires create an impact on an ink ribbon. The working principle of dot matrix printer is shown in Figure 2.33. Text characters and graphics elements are not displayed as separate items. The complete display is built up from reciprocating horizontal sweeps of the printing head as the paper winds around a rotating drum. Thus, the hard copy is constructed from dots in a similar manner to a raster screen display, with the resulting appearance being much the same. The resolutions that are available vary but range from 60 dots per inch to 240 dots per inch. Their cost is comparatively low, but a major disadvantage is their noise because of the impact of the pins on the paper. For example, the letter '**A**' is printed with 24 overlapping needles shown in Figure 2.34.

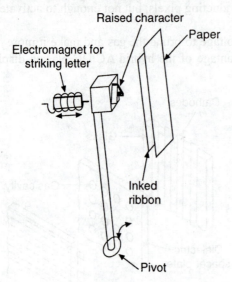

Fig. 2.33   Impact dot matrix printer.

Fig. 2.34   The letter '**A**' printed with 24 overlapping needles.

Ink jet printer: This is a raster scan device. The basic principle is to shoot tiny droplets of ink onto a medium. There are two types of ink jet printers, continuous flow and drop-on-demand. The continuous flow ink jet produces a stream of droplets by spraying ink out of the nozzle. The stream of ink from the nozzle is broken up into droplets by ultrasonic waves. If ink is desired on the medium, selected droplets are electrostatically charged. Deflection plates are then used to direct the droplet onto the medium. If not, the droplet is deflected into a gutter, from which the ink is returned to the reservoir. Paper and transparency film are typical media. This system is shown in Figure 2.35(a).

A drop-on-demand printer fires ink at the medium only if a dot is required at a particular location. Here, ink from a reservoir is supplied to a nozzle under pressure. The ink is fired on demand by applying an electric voltage to a piezoelectric crystal as the head makes a pass across the medium. When a voltage is applied, the piezoelectric crystal expands, decreasing the volume of the ink chamber. This causes a drop of ink to squirt out of the nozzle. Release of the voltage causes the piezoelectric crystal to contract, decreasing the volume of the reservoir and sucking the ink back into the nozzle. This system is shown in Figure 2.35(b).The resolution of ink jet printers is determined by the size of the droplet, and hence by the size of the nozzle. Because of the extremely small nozzle size required, nozzle clogging, ink contamination and air bubbles in the ink can be significant problems.

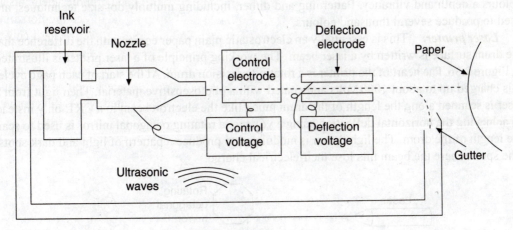

(a) Continuous

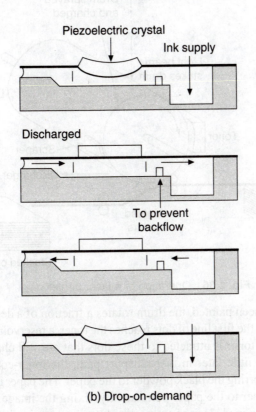

(b) Drop-on-demand

Fig. 2.35 Schematics of various ink jet printers.

Colour ink jet printers typically use four nozzles, three for the subtractive primary colours cyan, magenta and yellow, and one for black. One of the advantages of colour ink is used in a single pass across the medium, when the droplets blend together before drying. This gives ink jet colours a depth and vibrancy. Patterning and dither, including multiply dot size techniques, are used to produce several thousand colours.

Laser printer: This is essentially an electrostatic plain paper copier with the difference that the drum surface is written by a laser beam. The working principle of a laser printer is illustrated in Figure 2.36. The heart of the printer is a rotating precision drum. At the start of each page cycle, it is charged up to about 1000 volts and coated with a photosensitive material. Then light from a laser is scanned along the length of the drum much like the electron beam in a CRT, only instead of achieving the horizontal deflection using a voltage, a rotating octagonal mirror is used to scan the length of the drum. The light beam is modulated to produce a pattern of light and dark spots. The spots where the beam hits lose their electrical charge.

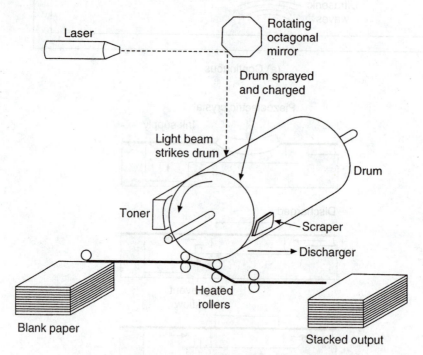

Fig. 2.36 Operation of a laser printer.

After a line of dots has been painted, the drum rotates a fraction of a degree to allow the next line to be painted. Eventually, the first line of dots reaches the toner, a reservoir of an electrostatically sensitive black powder. The toner is attracted to those dots that are still charged, thus forming a visual image of that line. A little later in the transport path, the toner-coated drum is pressed against the paper, thus transferring the black powder to the paper. The paper is then passed through heated rollers to bind the toner to the paper permanently, fixing the image. Later in its rotation, the drum is discharged and scraped clean of any residual toner, preparing it for being charged and coated again for the next page.

Although the laser printer is relatively expensive compared to the dot matrix printer, the quality of the output is extremely good and it works at 8 pages (A4) per minute.

Plotter: This is a widely accepted output device for CAD/CAM applications. A large range (A0-A4) of plotters of varying sizes and prices are available. The accuracies achievable are very high and the plots can be made on all types of media such as paper, tracing paper and acetate film.

There are three common types of conventional pen plotters: flatbed, drum and pinch roller. Pens may be of wet ink, ballpoint, or felt-tip type. The basic mechanisms are shown in Figure 2.37.

In a moving-arm flatbed plotter (Figure 2.37a), the medium is fixed in position on the bed of the plotter. Two-dimensional motion of the plotting head is obtained by the movement of an arm suspended across the width of the plotter bed. This provides motion in one direction. Motion in the second direction is obtained by moving the plotting head along the suspended arm.

A moving head flatbed head plotter (Figure 2.37b) uses a plotting tool carriage suspended above the bed by magnetic forces that are counter-balanced by an air bearing. This arrangement provides nearly frictionless movement. Movement of the head in two dimensions is controlled electromagnetically, by using the Sawyer motor principle.

In the drum plotter (Figure 2.37c), the paper is attached to a drum that rotates back and forth, thereby providing movement in one axis. The pen mechanism moves in the transverse direction to provide movement along the other axis.

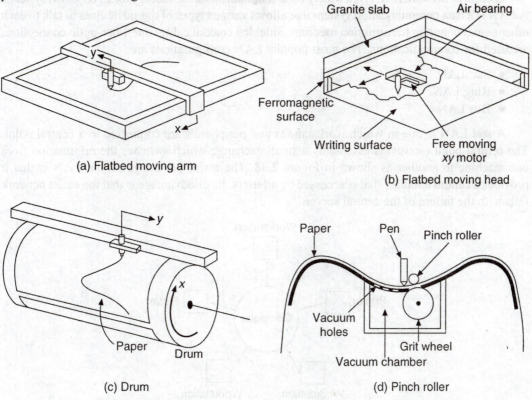

(a) Flatbed moving arm

(b) Flatbed moving head

(c) Drum

(d) Pinch roller

Fig. 2.37 Schematic diagrams of pen and ink plotters.

The pinch roller plotter (Figure 2.37d) is a hybrid of the flatbed and drum plotters. The drawing medium is held at each edge between a pinch wheel and the plotting surface. The plotting surface is cylindrical. As the pinch wheel rotates, the medium moves back and forth under a fixed arm on which the plotting head moves. These plotters use either cut or roll stock, which is usually limited to paper, vellum or transparency film.

2.9 HARDWARE INTEGRATION AND NETWORKING

The integration and networking between the various components and peripherals of a system ensures the success of CAD/CAM installations. The need for hardware integration and networking is as follows:

- CAD/CAM is inter-disciplinary by nature. Its functions are distributed among various departments like the design department, manufacturing department, etc. The hardware components in these departments must communicate together and have access to common databases.
- The common resources and peripherals like plotters and printers can be shared by networking

Local area network (LAN) is a widely used communication technology for CAD/CAM systems. A LAN is a data communication system that allows various types of digital devices to talk to each other over a common transmission medium. Shielded coaxial cables and fibre-optic connections are used for communications. The most popular LAN configurations are:

- Star LAN
- Ring LAN
- Bus LAN

A star LAN is one in which workstations and peripherals are connected to a central point. The central point (server) is essentially a small exchange which switches the information from one machine to another as shown in Figure 2.38. The major advantage of star LAN is that it provides a central database that is accessed by all users. Its disadvantage is that the entire network fails with the failure of the central server.

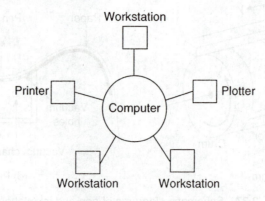

Fig. 2.38 Star LAN.

Ring LAN is one in which the devices are connected in the form of a ring-like structure as shown in Figure 2.39. The data moves in the ring and when the correct address comes up, it is picked by the device. There is no single system that acts as a server and all the nodes can transmit and receive data through the network.

The advantages of ring LAN are:

- The databases on one workstation can be shared by others in the network
- If one workstation fails, the rest remain operational.

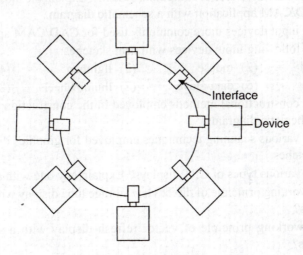

Fig. 2.39 Ring LAN.

The bus LAN is an open-loop system, which may take the form of a main bus or branched or tree systems. This network is particularly suitable when devices to be connected are dissimilar. Bus LAN is shown in Figure 2.40.

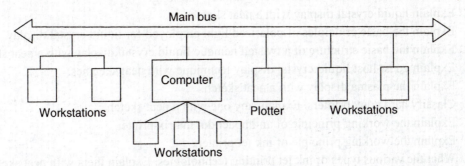

Fig. 2.40 Bus LAN.

QUESTION BANK

A. Descriptive Questions

1. What is the basic architecture computer system?
2. Describe the functioning of a CPU with a neat sketch.
3. What is the importance of ALU in a computing system?
4. Classify various architectures of computing systems. Explain the most suitable architecture used for CAD/CAM application with a schematic diagram.
5. What are the input devices more commonly used for CAD/CAM applications?
6. Describe the following input devices with neat sketches:
   (1) keyboard   (2) mouse   (3) lightpen   (4) joystick
   (5) digitizer   (6) data glove   (7) thumbwheels   (8) trackball
7. What are the constructional methods employed in the construction of digitizer? Explain them with schematic diagrams.
8. What are the various scanning techniques employed for graphics display? Explain them with neat sketches.
9. What are the various types of CRT displays? Explain any one with a neat sketch,
10. Explain the working principle of direct view storage tube display with a sketch. What are its limitations?
11. Explain the working principle of vector refresh display with a sketch. What are its disadvantages?
12. Explain the working principle of raster refresh display with a sketch. What are its advantages?
13. Explain the working principle of colour raster refresh display with a sketch.
14. What is the arrangement provided for triangular pattern of red, green and blue dots on the face CRT? Explain the importance of shadow masking.
15. Explain liquid crystal display with a neat sketch.
16. Explain the basic principles of polarized light employed for liquid crystal display.
17. Explain the basic structure of a twisted nematic liquid crystal display with a neat sketch.
18. Explain guest-host liquid crystal display technique with neat sketches.
19. Explain the plasma display with a neat sketch.
20. Classify hard copy printers. Explain any one with a neat sketch.
21. Explain the working principle of an impact dot matrix printer.
22. Explain the working principle of ink jet printer.
23. What the various types of ink jet printing technologies. Explain them with neat sketches.
24. Explain the working principle of laser printer.
25. Classify the plotters. Explain any one with a neat sketch.
26. Explain the working principles flatbed plotters with neat sketches.
27. Explain the working principles of drum and pinch roller plotters.
28. What is the importance hardware integration and networking in the computer-aided manufacturing environment?

29. Classify the various networking techniques. Enumerate their advantages and disadvantages.
30. Explain the various networking techniques with simple sketches.

B. Multiple Choice Questions

1. The heart of a computer is:
   (a) CPU   (b) ALU   (c) Monitor   (d) Keyboard
2. The widely employed computer architecture for CAD/CAM applications is:
   (a) Mainframe-based system   (b) Minicomputer-based system
   (c) Microcomputer-based system   (d) Workstation-based system
3. Keyboard is a _____ input device.
   (a) Graphical   (b) Text   (c) Games   (d) All of the above
4. Locating devices are classified as:
   (a) Text input devices   (b) Graphics input devices
   (c) Both a and b   (d) None of the above
5. Mouse is a _____ type of input device.
   (a) Text   (b) Graphics   (c) Locating   (d) All of the above
6. Lightpen is a:
   (a) Writing device   (b) Drawing device   (c) Locating device   (d) Lighting device
7. Digitizer is constructed on the basis of:
   (a) Magnetic tablet mechanism   (b) Acoustic tablet mechanism
   (c) Optical tablet mechanism   (d) Both (a) and (b)
8. Thumbwheels are usually mounted on:
   (a) Keyboard   (b) Monitor   (c) CPU   (d) Mouse
9. The screen is scanned from left to right, top to bottom all the time to generate graphics by:
   (a) Raster scan   (b) Random scan   (c) Vector scan   (d) Stroke scan
10. Colour raster display uses three electron guns, namely:
    (a) Red, green and blue   (b) Red, green and yellow
    (c) White, blue and black   (d) Red, black and white
11. Liquid crystal display is based on the principle of:
    (a) Polarization   (b) Reflection   (c) Refraction   (d) Transmission
12. Plasma display contains:
    (a) Gas at low pressure   (b) Gas at high pressure
    (c) Liquid at low pressure   (d) Liquid at high pressure
13. Impact dot matrix printer is a:
    (a) Electromechanical device   (b) Electropneumatic device
    (c) Electrochemical device   (d) Mechanical device
14. Which of the following is not networking technique:
    (a) Star network   (b) Sun network   (c) Ring network   (d) Bus network

Chapter 3

CAD/CAM Software

OBJECTIVES

After reading this chapter, the reader will be able to understand the following concepts:

- ➲ Operating system
- ➲ Graphics software
- ➲ Requirements of graphics software
- ➲ Application software
- ➲ Programming languages
- ➲ CAD/CAM evaluation criteria
- ➲ Graphics standards

3.1 INTRODUCTION

CAD/CAM software has progressed steadily since the development of interactive computer graphics in the 1960s. The software is an interactive program typically written in a standard programming language such as FORTRAN, or C. A CAD/CAM system contains different categories of software as follows:

1. Operating system
2. Graphics software
3. Application software
4. Programming support software

54

The database structure and database management system of the software determines its quality, speed and ease of information retrieval.

3.2 OPERATING SYSTEM

The major function of an operating system is to allocate the resources of a digital computer to the various programs needing them. Typical functions such as file manipulations (save, save as, rename, copy, delete, etc), managing directories and sub-directories, programming and accounts set-ups are supported by the operating system.

Computing time, memory space, input and output devices are controlled and allocated by the operating system. The operating system also detects programming errors and provides an orderly recovery or re-start when one is encountered. The operating system also classifies the files that are generated by the CAD/CAM software into text files and graphics files. The general purpose operating systems are:

- UNIX
- LINUX
- Windows-based operating systems such as Windows XP, Windows 2000.

3.3 GRAPHICS SOFTWARE

The graphics software provides users with various functions to perform geometric modelling and construction, editing and manipulation of existing geometry, drafting and documentation. The standard graphics software provides geometric building blocks such as point, line, curve, circle, rectangle, ellipse, box, cylinder, prism, wedge, sphere, torus and surface of revolution. The shaded images, wireframe models, dimensions and tolerances can also be generated by using graphics software.

3.3.1 Requirements of Graphics Software

The graphics software should fulfil the following requirements for engineering applications:

1. **Simplicity:** The graphics software should be easy to use.
2. **Consistency:** The graphics software should be consistent in generating the geometric models.
3. **Completeness:** The graphics software should be able to provide model creation, clean-up, editing, documentation, shading, rendering, optimisation and plotting.
4. **Robustness:** The graphics software should be tolerant of minor instances of misuse of graphics tools by the operator.
5. **Performance:** Within the limitations imposed by the CAD/CAM hardware, the graphics software should be efficient and fast.
6. **Economy:** The cost of the graphics software is as low as possible. The perpetual licenses should be available at a rate cheaper than that for other periodical licenses. The regular updating of graphics software should be economically feasible to the user.

3.3.2 Functions of Graphics Software

The graphics software must perform a variety of functions to fulfil the CAD/CAM requirements. Some common functions are as follows:

1. **Generation of graphic primitives:** The graphical primitives are two-dimensional and three-dimensional geometrical elements (Figure 3.1). The two-dimensional graphic primitives are line segment, arcs, circle, parabola, hyperbola and ellipse. The three-dimensional elements are box, cylinder, prism, sphere, cone and torus. The graphics software should generate the basic primitives and should also have a library of regularly used geometric features such as involute gear tooth, various types of threads, etc.

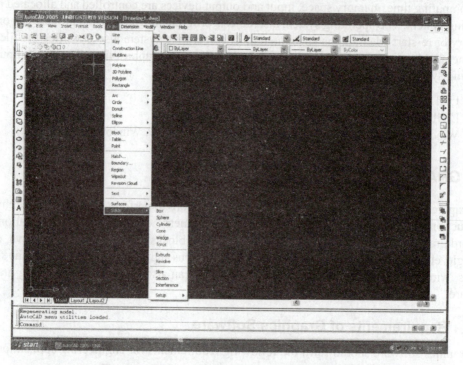

Fig. 3.1 Pop-up window for graphics primitives.

2. **Transformations:** These are used to modify the image on the display screen or to re-position the graphics item in the database. The transformations are scaling, translation, and rotation. These transformations help the user in constructing a geometrical model fast.

3. **Viewing and windowing:** While model construction involves the creation of the model database, viewing affects the way the model is displayed on the screen. Views are defined by the various angles from which a model can be observed. The views are isometric view, orthogonal view, perspective view, front view, top view, left side view, right side view, rear view and bottom view (Figure 3.2). If the object is too complex to show its entirety, windowing is often used. An imaginary box is created around the portion of the object of user's interest, windowing results in displaying the portion of the object encompassed by the imaginary box (Figure 3.3).

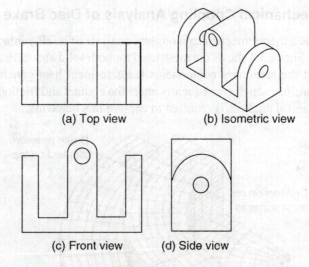

(a) Top view   (b) Isometric view

(c) Front view   (d) Side view

Fig. 3.2   Illustration of different views of an object.

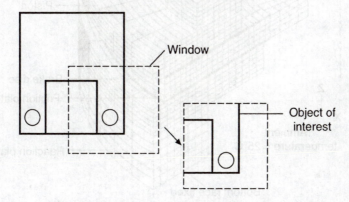

Window

Object of interest

Fig. 3.3   Windowing.

4. **Segmenting:**   This function provides the user with the capability to selectively edit the text such as deleting or modifying portions of the geometric model.

5. **User input functions:**   The user input functions should be accomplished to maximize the benefits of the interactive feature of interactive computer graphics. The user input functions permit the user to enter commands or data into the system.

3.4 APPLICATION SOFTWARE

The creation of the geometric model of an object is not the end-goal of the user. The ultimate goal is to use the geometric model for design analysis and manufacturing. Several application software packages are commercially available for the purpose of mass property calculations, assembly analysis, tolerance analysis, finite element analysis, mechanisms analysis, sheet metal design, analysis of plastic injection moulding, and animation techniques. The following sections represent some examples of engineering applications.

3.4.1   Thermomechanical Coupling Analysis of Disc Brake System

This example involves a thermomechanical coupling analysis of a full-contact disc brake system for heavy duty trucks. Figure 3.4 shows the mesh used for both solid and thermal analyses. Friction between the disc and the stationary components leads to local heat generation, causing non-uniform thermal expansion, which consequently alters the contact and friction conditions. A fully coupled thermomechanical analysis is required to capture this behaviour.

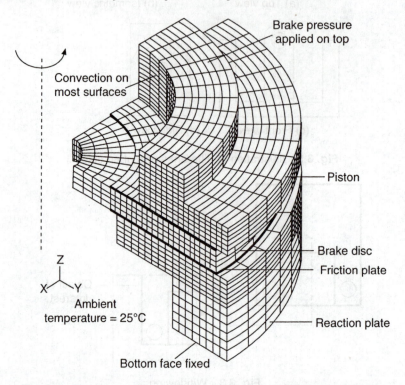

Fig. 3.4   Mesh generation used for both solid and thermal analyses.

Figure 3.5 shows the temperature variation during braking. Figure 3.6 shows the variation of contact pressure between the upper friction plate and the piston at different times. A significant change in contact pressure distribution occurs as the brake system heats up, leading to more severe contact conditions at the inner surface.

3.4.2   Sheet Metal Manufacturing Model

The sheet metal manufacturing model is an assembly that consists of a sheet metal workpiece with one or more design (reference) models attached to it. The sheet metal workpiece (Figure 3.7) represents the raw sheet metal stock which is machined by the NC sequences. It is the base component of the sheet metal manufacturing assembly.

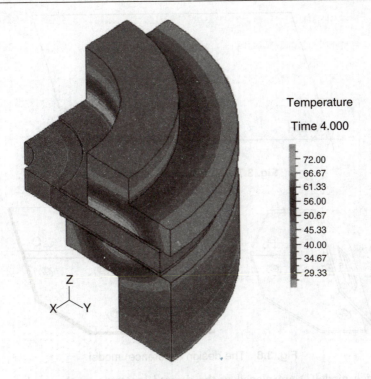

Fig. 3.5 Temperature variation during braking.

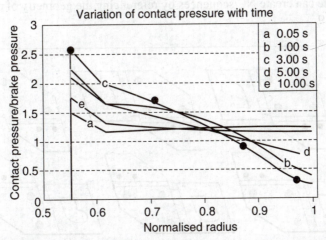

Fig. 3.6 Variation of contact pressure between the upper friction plate and the piston.

The Design (Reference) Model (Figure 3.8) represents the finished product and is used as the basis for all NC sequences. Select features, surfaces, grain orientation and edges on the design model as references for each NC sequence. Referencing the geometry of the design model sets up a parametric relationship between the design model and the workpiece. When the design model is changed, all associated NC sequences are updated to reflect the change.

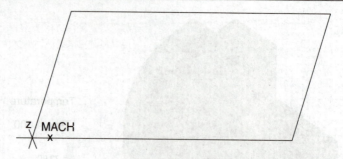

Fig. 3.7   Sheet metal workpiece.

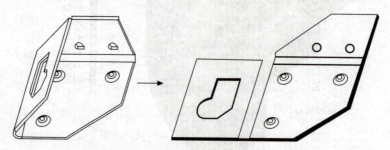

Fig. 3.8   The design (reference) model.

The reference model(s) are placed in the desired locations on the workpiece to create a manufacturing model. Either the nesting functionality or the regular assembly placement commands should be used. One can create NC sequences by referencing the geometry of design model(s) as shown in Figure 3.9.

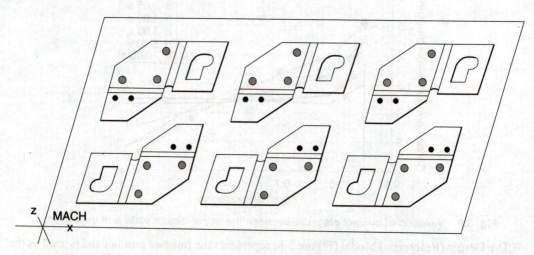

Fig. 3.9   Sheet metal manufacturing model

One can use different design models as reference parts within a single manufacturing model as shown in Figure 3.10.

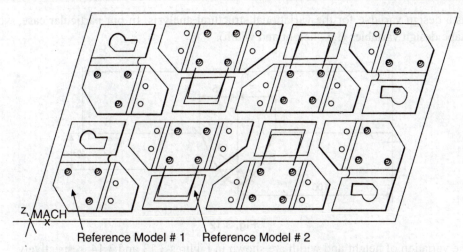

Fig. 3.10 Sheet metal manufacturing model using multiple reference models.

3.4.3 Automatic Assembling of Components

The objective is to perform a complete sensitivity and parametric analysis using variational analysis on the component shown in Figure 3.11. The mechanical properties of the component are as follows:

Elastic modulus of plate [7×10^7; 21×10^7 mN/mm^2]
Elastic modulus of rib [7×10^7; 21×10^7 mN/mm^2]
Thickness of plate [1; 3 mm]
Thickness of rib [1; 3 mm]
Width [15; 35 mm]
Height [10; 40 mm]

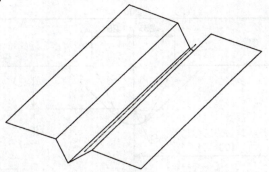

Fig. 3.11

The goal is to minimise the model mass with given limitations. We want to work with six design variables: two physical parameters (shell thickness), two material parameters (modulus of elasticity), and two shape design variables (height and width).

Variational analysis includes finite element analysis, sensitivity analysis and parametric analysis. The part geometry is shown in Figure 3.12. Each dimension of the part geometry can be used as a design variable for the variational structural analysis. In our particular case, we have two shape design variables (i.e., height and width).

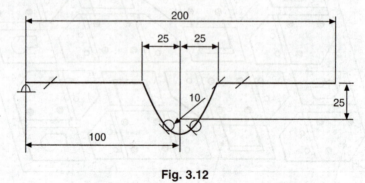

Fig. 3.12

The variation of height and width are shown in Figures 3.13 and 3.14, respectively.

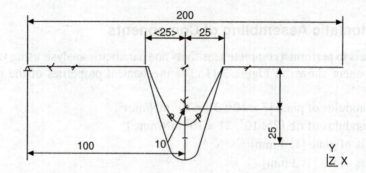

Fig. 3.13   Variation of height.

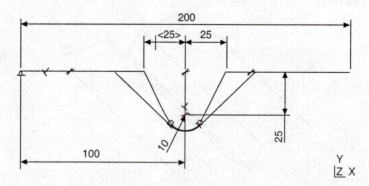

Fig. 3.14   Variation of width.

The finite element (structural) analysis is carried out with variable parameters (viz., height and width). The mesh generation of the component is shown in Figure 3.15.

The histogram shown in Figure 3.16 illustrates the influence of each parameter with respect to the criterion maximum displacement on model. For example, if the design variable 'height' varies from its minimum to maximum value, the maximum displacement varies with 0.24 mm.

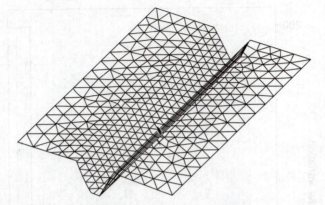

Fig. 3.15 Mesh generation.

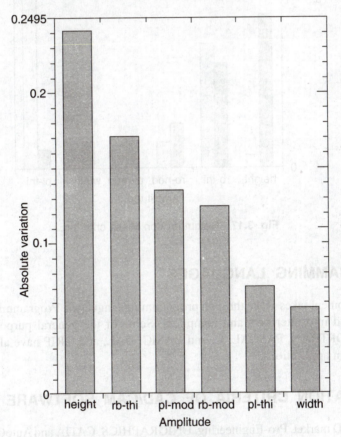

Fig. 3.16 Maximum displacement criterion.

The histogram (Figure (3.17)) shows the influence of each parameter with respect to the maximum Von Mises criterion. For example, if the design variable 'height' varies from its minimum to maximum value, the Max Von Mises criterion varies with 83 per cent for the first load case and only 7 per cent for the second one.

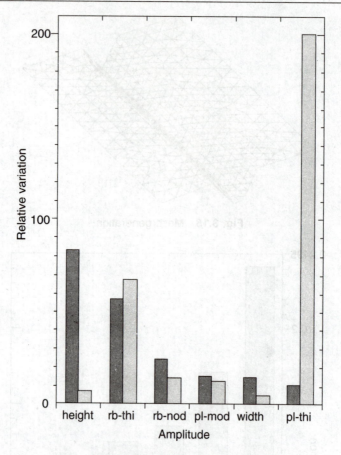

Fig. 3.17 Maximum Von Mises criterion.

3.5 PROGRAMMING LANGUAGES

Software development takes place through programming languages. Programming languages are broadly classified into interprets and compilers. Some of the general purpose programming languages are FORTRAN, PASCAL, C, and BASIC. DAL, and GRIP have also been used for graphics or design applications.

3.6 EVALUATION CRITERIA OF CAD/CAM SOFTWARE

In the current CAD market, Pro-Engineering, UNIGRAPHICS, CATIA and AutoCAD are arguably among the most dominating CAD software. AutoCAD is basically a two-dimensional program, with some capability to create three-dimensional models, whereas Pro-Engineering, UNIGRAPHICS, CATIA are truly three-dimensional CAD packages. ANSYS and NASTERAN constitute the finite element analysis software. MasterCAM and H-CAM constitute the computer-aided machining software. Besides these, there are several other CAD/ CAM software packages. No single CAD/CAM package is suitable for all the CAD/CAM users in the world. The product being designed dictates the type of CAD/CAM package needed. A good CAD/CAM package includes good software, as well as, a compatible hardware. Following is a brief description of the general criteria for evaluating a CAD/CAM package.

Hardware: The most desirable features in a good hardware are:

- Open architecture
- High speed, large storage
- Compact size
- Inexpensive components
- Inexpensive upgrading

Software: In general, the most comprehensive software are written to satisfy almost all the modelling needs of a modeller. Consequently, the software tends to be very complex and hard to learn. In order to create a simple model, one has to go through several unnecessary steps, which lack the intuitiveness of a simple, straightforward program. Pro-Engineering, UNIGRAPHICS, and CATIA are good examples, where we have to go through several layers of menus to create a simple solid. On the other hand, if we were to use a simpler CAD program, the same solid can be created by only a few simple commands. There are several other factors that we should consider when evaluating software.

Following is a brief description of these factors:

1. **Operating system:** PCs in general use Microsoft Windows, where as, operating system for Workstations is Unix. For a large organization, Workstations are preferable.
2. **User interface:** Most popular CAD/CAM software have menu driven commands, which is preferable to the old system of non-menu driven, where user interface was completely by responding to software commands. The most popular CAD/CAM programs work with menu driven interface, with some input/action required through command prompts.
3. **Documentation and support:** Learning software can be very difficult if the software lacks good documentation. Documentation usually comes in the form of a user's manual, a tutorial book, commands manual, and on-line help. The recent trend is to provide access to the above-mentioned documentation through the Internet, or provide the manuals on a CD ROM. Some CAD/CAM vendors provide additional technical support help through phone.
4. **Maintenance:** Cost of the hardware and software upgrades can significantly impact the small and medium size companies' decision to choose one software over the others. Most CAD/CAM vendors go through an upgrade, on the average, every two years. Usually, hardware upgrade is not as frequent.
5. **Modelling capabilities:** In general, a CAD/CAM software can be classified as either a 2-D or a 3-D program. If we were basically involved in 2-D drawings, any well established 2-D software, similar to AutoCAD would suffice our needs. On the other hand, if we need to create 3-D models and assemblies, we will be better off with a 3-D molder— Pro-Engineering, SOLIDWORKS, UNIGRAPHICS, CATIA, etc.
6. **Ease of modelling:** As a rule-of-thumb, a general, all-purpose type CAD/CAM software is much more complex and difficult to learn than a special purpose CAD or CAM package.

7. **Interface with other CAD/CAM packages and data transferability:**   A CAD package is used to create models that will be used for analysis, manufacturing, or some other applications. Therefore, a CAD software should be capable of transferring and accepting files from other FEM or CAM programs, without this provision, the CAD program has only a very limited use.

8. **Design documentation:**   Besides creating a model, the software should be capable of creating drawings, assemblies, dimensioning, various views (isometric, orthogonal, etc.), labels and attributes, etc.

3.7   GRAPHICS STANDARDS

There are several CAD/ CAM software. No one CAD/CAM package is suitable for all the CAD/CAM users in the world. In general, the geometric modelling is practiced using the CAD software. The geometric model is then imported to the CAM software. The exporting from CAD software or importing to the CAM software is only possible if CAD and CAM software have the same syntax. It is not always possible. A good CAD/CAM package includes good software, as well as, a compatible hardware. The source code of graphics software is embedded with several subroutine calls. Thus, the graphics software is hardware dependent. If input/output devices change or become obsolete, its related software becomes obsolete. These problems are very serious to both CAD/CAM vendors as well as users.

Both CAD/CAM vendors as well as users identified some needs to have some graphics standards. The needs are as follows:

1. **Software portability:**   This avoids hardware dependence of the software. If the program is written originally for random scan display, when the display device is changed to raster scan display the program should work with minimum effort.

2. **Image data portability:**   Information and storage of images should be independent of different graphics devices.

3. **Text data portability:**   The text associated with graphics should be independent of different input/output devices.

4. **Model database portability:**   Transporting of design and manufacturing data from one application software to another should simple and economical.

The search for standards began in 1974 to fulfill the above needs both at the USA and International levels. As a result of worldwide efforts, various standards at different levels of the graphics systems were developed. The standards are as follows:

1. **GKS (Graphics kernel system):**   It is an ANSI (American National Standards Institute) and ISO (International Standards Organization) standard. It interfaces the application program with graphics support package.

2. **IGES (Initial graphics exchange specification):**   It is an ANSI standard. It enables an exchange of model database among CAD/CAM software.

3. **PHIGS (Programmer's hierarchical interactive graphics system):**   It supports workstations and their related CAD/CAM applications. It supports 3-dimensional modelling of geometry, segmentation and dynamic display.

4. **CGM (Computer graphics metafile):** It defines functions needed to describe an image. Such description can be stored or transported from one graphics device to another.

5. **CGII (Computer graphics interface):** It is designed to interface plotters to GKS or PHIGS. It is the lowest device independent interface in a graphics system.

QUESTION BANK

A. Descriptive Questions

1. What are the functions of operating system? Give examples.
2. What are the requirements of graphics software?
3. What are the functions of graphics software?
4. Explain viewing and windowing with examples.
5. What are the functions of application software?
6. Explain the use of application software with an example.
7. What are the programming languages?
8. Describe the evaluation criteria of CAD/CAM software.
9. What are the needs of graphics standards?
10. What are the various types of graphics standards?

B. Multiple Choice Questions

1. The software that is used for file manipulations, managing directories and subdirectories, programming and accounts setups is known as:
   (a) Graphics software
   (b) Operating system
   (c) Application software
   (d) Programming language

2. The software that provides users with various functions to perform geometric modelling and construction, editing and manipulation of existing geometry, drafting and documentation is known as:
   (a) Operating system
   (b) Application software
   (c) Graphics software
   (d) Programming language

3. The software used for the purpose of mass property calculations, assembly analysis, tolerance analysis, finite element analysis, mechanisms analysis, sheet metal design, analysis of plastic injection molding, and animation techniques, is:
   (a) Graphics software
   (b) Operating system
   (c) Application software
   (d) Programming language

4. The software that enables the user to implement custom applications or modify the system for specialized needs is known as:
   (a) Programming language
   (b) Operating system
   (c) Application software
   (d) Graphics software

5. The following is not a graphics standard:
   (a) GKS
   (b) IGES
   (c) UNIX
   (d) PHIGS

Chapter 4

Interactive Computer Graphics

After reading this chapter, the reader will be able to understand the following concepts:

- ➲ Raster scan graphics
- ➲ Line drawing algorithm
- ➲ Mid-point circle algorithm
- ➲ Scan conversion
- ➲ Rasterising polygons
- ➲ Anti-aliasing
- ➲ Coordinate systems
- ➲ Windowing
- ➲ View generation
- ➲ Clipping
- ➲ Transformations of geometry
- ➲ Mathematics of projections
- ➲ Hidden surface removal
- ➲ Shading
- ➲ Rendering
- ➲ Database structure for graphics modelling

4.1   INTRODUCTION

The purpose of a graphics system is to make programming easier for the user. Raster scan graphics devices require special procedures to generate the display, to draw lines or curves and to fill polygons to give the impression of solid areas. This chapter deals with the techniques of raster technology.

4.2   RASTER SCAN GRAPHICS

The most common type of a computer output device capable of displaying graphical output in use today is the raster scan cathode ray tube (CRT). Since the CRT raster display is the most widely used monitor, it is considered a matrix of discrete finite area cells (pixels), each of which can be made bright, it is not possible to draw a straight line from one point to another. Each pixel on the graphics display does not represent a mathematical point. Rather, it represents a region, which theoretically can contain an infinite number of points. The process of determining which pixels provide the best approximation to the desired line is known as *rasterisation*. When combined with the process of generating the picture in scan line order, it is known as scan conversion. Scan conversion of a point involves illuminating the pixel that contains the point.

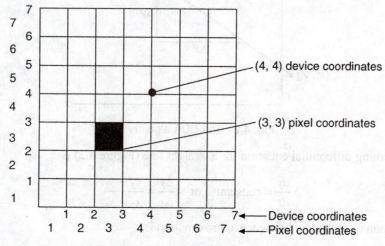

Fig. 4.1   Device and pixel coordinates.

The device coordinate points (2.5, 2.75) and (2.75, 2.25) would both be represented by pixel (3,3). The pixel is represented by [INY(x), INT(y)]. The process of turning on the pixels for a line segment is called *vector generation*. If the end points of the line segment are known, there are several schemes for selecting the pixels between the endpoints.

4.3   LINE DRAWING ALGORITHMS

The primary design criteria for line drawing displays are as follows:

1. Lines should appear straight.
2. Lines should start and end accurately.

3. Lines should have constant brightness along their length.
4. Displayed lines should be independent of line length and orientation.
5. Lines should be drawn rapidly.

The line drawing algorithms are:

- Digital differential analyser (DDA) algorithm
- Bresenham's algorithm

4.3.1 DDA Algorithm

The digital differential analyser generates lines from their differential equations. The DDA works on the principle that x and y are simultaneously incremented by small steps proportional to the first derivatives of x and y.

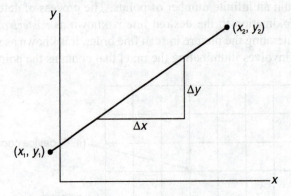

Fig. 4.2 The DDA algorithm.

The governing differential equation for a straight line (Figure 4.2) is

$$\frac{dy}{dx} = \text{constant} \quad \text{or} \quad \frac{\Delta y}{\Delta x} = \frac{y_2 - y_1}{x_2 - x_1} \tag{4.1}$$

The solution of the finite difference approximation is

$$y_{i+1} = y_i + \Delta y$$

$$y_{i+1} = y_i + \left(\frac{y_2 - y_1}{x_2 - x_1} \right) \Delta x \tag{4.2}$$

where (x_1, y_1) and (x_2, y_2) are the end points of the required straight line, and y_i is the initial value for any given step along the line. Equation 4.2 represents a recursion relation for successive values of y along the required line. For simple DDA algorithm, either Δx or Δy, which ever is larger, is chosen as one raster unit. The DDA algorithm, which works in all quadrants, is given by:

```
digital differential algorithm (DDA)
// The line end points are (x₁,y₁) and (x₂,y₂) assume not equal //
Integer is the integer function.
```

```
// For example (-6.5) = -7 rather than -6 //
```

```
Sign returns -1, 0, 1 for arguments <0, = 0, >0, respectively
// Approximate the line length //
```

```
if abs (x₂ - x₁) > abs (y₂ - y₁) then
length = abs (x₂ - x₁)
else
    length = abs (y₂ - y₁)
endif
```

```
// Select the larger of Δx or Δy to be one raster unit //
Δx = (x₂ - x₁) /length
Δy = (y₂ - y₁) /length
```

```
//round the values rather than truncate, so that centre pixel addressing
is handled correctly //
```

```
x = x₁ + 0.5
y = y₁ + 0.5
```

```
begin main loop
    i = 1
while (if ≤ length )

    setpixel (Integer (x), Integer (y))
x = x + Δx
y = y + Δy
i = i + 1
end while

finish
```

The flowchart of a DDA algorithm is shown in Figure 4.3.

Example 4.1   The end points of a line are (0, 0) and (4, 4). Use the DDA algorithm to rasterize the line.

Solution
The initial calculations are:

$$x_1 = 0$$
$$y_1 = 0$$
$$x_2 = 4$$
$$y_2 = 4$$
$$\text{Length} = 4$$
$$\Delta x = 1$$
$$\Delta y = 0.5$$
$$x = 0.5$$
$$y = 0.5$$

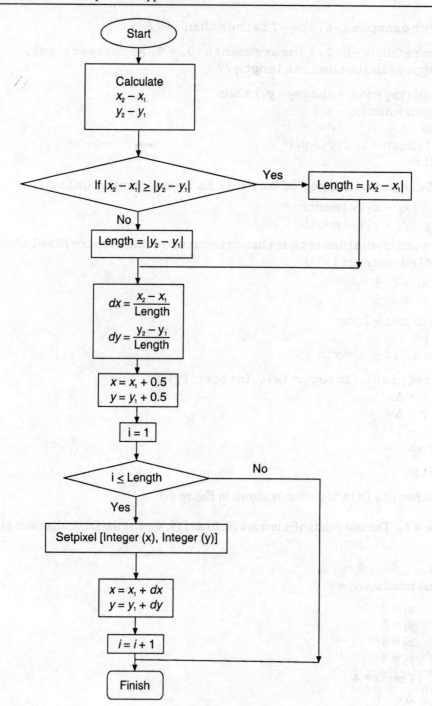

Fig. 4.3   Flowchart of a DDA algorithm.

Incrementing through the main loop yields.

Iterations	Setpoint	X	Y
		0.5	0.5
1	(0, 0)		
		1.5	1.5
2	(1, 1)		
		2.5	2.5
3	(2, 2)		
		3.5	3.5
4	(3, 3)		
		4.5	4.5

The results are shown in Figure 4.4

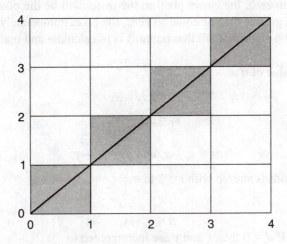

Fig. 4.4 Display of a line.

4.3.2 Bresenham's Algorithm

This is an efficient method for scan converting a straight line which uses only integer addition, subtraction, and multiplication by 2. The computer can perform the operations of integer addition and subtraction very rapidly. The computer is also time-efficient when performing integer multiplication and division by powers of 2.

The algorithm seeks to select the optimum raster locations that represent a straight line. The algorithm increments by one unit in either x or y depending on the slope of the line. The increment in the other variable, is either zero or one, and is determined by examining the distance between the actual line and the nearest grid location. The algorithm identifies the decision variable:

$$d_i = S_i - T_i \tag{4.3}$$

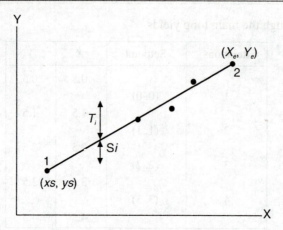

Fig. 4.5   Bresenham's algorithm.

When d_i is less than zero, the closet pixel in the raster will be the pixel below the true line. Conversely, when d_i is greater than or equal to zero, the pixel immediately above the true line is closet. To implement the algorithm, all that remains is to calculate and update the various values of d_i as follows:

Initially set first value of d as

$$d_1 = 2dy - dx \tag{4.4}$$

$$x_1 = x_s, y_1 = y_s \tag{4.5}$$

where

$$dx = x_e - x_s \text{ and } dy = y_e - y_s$$

The cycle for calculations is started with $i = 1$ to n
where

$$n = x_e - x_s$$

In the recursion cycle, if $d_i > 0$ then x and y are incremented to

$$x_{i+1} = x_i + 1 \text{ and } y_{i+1} = y_i + 1 \tag{4.6}$$

The next d is calculated as:

$$d_{i+1} = d_i + 2 (d_y - d_x) \tag{4.7}$$

If $d_i < 0$ then x and y are incremented to:

$$x_{i+1} = x_i + 1 \tag{4.8}$$

The next d is calculated as:

$$d_{i+1} = d_i + 2d_y \tag{4.9}$$

```
# include "conio.h"
# include "math.h"
# include "studio.h"
# include "graphics.h"
/* Bresenham's algorithm */
main()
```

```
{
int driver, mode, x1, y1, x2, y2;
void line(int x1, int y1, int x2, int y2, int z);
detectgraph(7driver, and mode);
printf("enter the values of x1, y1, x2, y2\n");
scanf("%d%d%d%d,and x1,and y1,and x2,and y2);
initgraph(&driver,&mode,\\tc);
line(x1,y1,x2,y2,5);
getch();
restorecrtmode();
}
void line(int x1, int yi, int x2, int y2, intz);
{
register int i, distance,t;
int x = 0, y = 0, dx, dy;
int incx, incy;
dx = x2 - x1;
dy = y2 - y1;
/* Compute the direction of the increment */
if(dx>0) incx = 1;
else
if(dx == 0) incx = 0;
else
incx = -1;
if(dy>0) incy = 1;
else
if(dy == 0) incy = 0;
else
incy = -1;
/* Determine greater distance */
dx = abs(dx);
dy = abs(dy);
if dx>dy)
dist =dx;
else
dist = dy;
/*Draw the line */
for (n = 0; n <=dist + 1; n++)
{
        put pixel (x1, y1, z);
        x+ = dx;
y+ = dy;
if(x>dist)
        {
```

```
x- = dist;
x1+ = incx;
}
if(y>dist)
{
y- = dist;
y1+ = incy:
}}
}
```

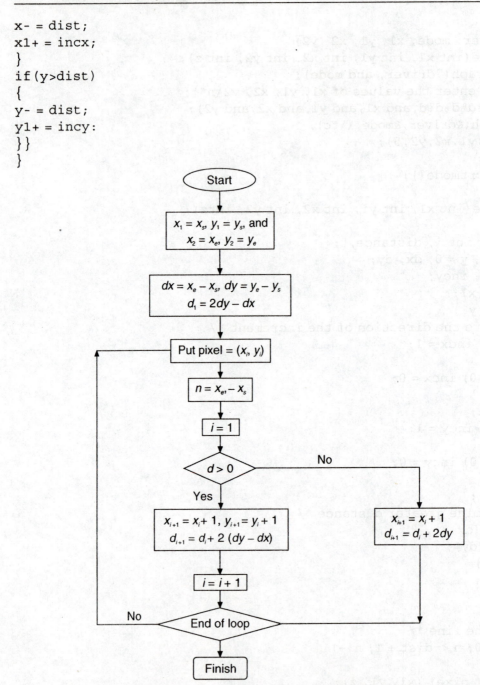

Fig. 4.6 Flowchart of Bresenham's algorithm.

Example 4.2 Find out the raster locations by Bresenham's algorithm for the end points of a straight line (20,10), (30,18).

Solution

$$m = \frac{y_2 - y_1}{x_2 - x_1} = \frac{18 - 10}{30 - 20} = 0.8 \, (<1)$$

$$d_1 = 2dy - dx = 2 \times 8 - 10 = 6$$

$$2dy = 16$$

$$2dy - 2dx = 2 \times 8 - 2 \times 10 = -4$$

If $d_i > 0$, then x and y are incremented to:

$$x_{i+1} = x_i + 1 \text{ and } y_{i+1} = y_i + 1$$

The next d is calculated as:

$$d_{i+1} = d_i + 2 \, (d_y - d_x)$$

If $d_i < 0$ then x and y are incremented to:

$$x_{i+1} = x_i + 1$$

$$d_{i+1} = d_i + 2d_y$$

I	d_i	x_{i+1}, y_{i+1}
0	6	(21, 11)
1	2	(22, 12)
2	−2	(23, 12)
3	14	(24, 13)
4	10	(25, 14)
5	6	(26, 15)
6	2	(27, 16)
7	−2	(28, 16)
8	14	(29, 17)
9	10	(30, 18)

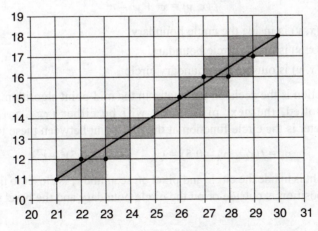

Fig. 4.7 Display of a line.

4.4 MID-POINT CIRCLE ALGORITHM

A circle is a symmetric geometric primitive. Any circle-generating algorithm takes the advantage of the symmetry of the circle to plot eight points (Figure 4.8).

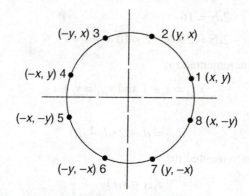

Fig. 4.8 The circle.

If x and y are coordinates of a point on the circle, then the relationship between (x, y) and the radius r is given by:

$$y = \sqrt{r^2 - x^2} \tag{4.10}$$

For a given radius r and screen position (x_c, y_c), set up the algorithm to calculate pixel positions around a circle path centred at the coordinate origin $(0, 0)$. Then each calculated position (x, y) is moved to its proper screen position by adding x_c to x and y_c to y. Along the circle section from $x = 0$ to $x = y$ in the first quadrant, the slope of the curve varies from 0 to -1. Therefore, unit steps are taken in a positive x-direction over this octant and use a decision parameter to determine which of the two possible y positions closer to the circle path at each step. Positions in the other seven octants are obtained by symmetry.

To apply the mid-point method, the circle is defined as:

$$f(x, y) = x^2 + y^2 - r^2 \tag{4.11}$$

$$f(x, y) \quad \begin{cases} > 0 \text{ if } (x, y) \text{ is inside the circle boundary} \\ = 0 \text{ if } (x, y) \text{ is on the circle boundary} \\ < 0 \text{ if } (x, y) \text{ is outside the boundary circle} \end{cases}$$

Thus, the circle function is the decision parameter in the mid-point algorithm. Assuming that the pixel (x_k, y_k) is plotted, the next pixel point will be either (x_{k-1}, y_{k+1}) or (x_{k+1}, y_{k-1}). The decision parameter is the circle function at the mid-point between these two pixels.

$$p_k = f(x_{k+1}, y_k - 0.5) = (x_{k+1})^2 + (y_k - 0.5)^2 - r^2 \tag{4.12}$$

If $p_k < 0$, the mid-point is inside the circle and pixel on scan line y_k is closer to the circle boundary. Otherwise the mid-position is outside or on the circle boundary and the pixel on scan line y_{k-1} is selected.

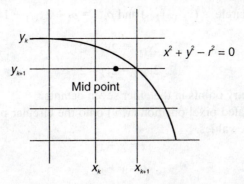

Fig. 4.9 Mid-point circle algorithm.

Successive decision parameters are obtained by using incremental calculations. A recursive expression for the next decision parameter is obtained by evaluating the circle function at the sampling position $x_{k+1} + 1 = x_k + 2$.

$$p_{k+1} = f(x_{k+1} + 1, y_{k+1} - 0.5) = (x_{k+1} + 1)^2 + (y_{k+1} - 0.5)^2 - r^2 \qquad (4.13)$$

where

y_{k+1} is either y_k or y_{k-1} depending on the sign of p_k.

The initial decision parameter is obtained by evaluating the circle function at the start position $(x_0, y_0) = (0, r)$.

$$p_0 = f(1, r - 0.5) + 1 + (r - 0.5)^2 + r^2 \qquad (4.14)$$

$$p_0 = \frac{5}{4} - r$$

If the radius t is specified as an integer, then

$$p_0 = 1 - r \qquad (4.15)$$

since all increments are integers.

The mid-point algorithm is given by:

1. Input radius r and circle centre (x_c, y_c) and obtain the first point on the circumference of a circle centred on the origin as:

$$(x_0, y_0) = (0, r)$$

2. Calculate the initial value of decision parameter as:

$$p_0 = \frac{5}{4} - r$$

$$p_0 = 1 - r$$

3. At each x_k position starting at $k = 0$, perform the following test:

If $p_k < 0$, the next point along the circle centred on $(0, 0)$ is (x_{k+1}, y_k) and $p_{k+1} = p_k + 2x_{k+1}$ $+ 1 - 2y_{k+1}$

else

The next point along the circle is (x_{k+1}, y_{k-1}) and $p_{k+1} = p_k + 2x_{k+1} + 1 - 2y_{k+1}$
where

$$2x_{k+1} = 2x_k + 2$$

$$2y_{k+1} = 2y_k - 2$$

4. Determine symmetry points in the other seven octants.
5. Move each calculated pixel position (x, y) onto the circular path centred on (x_c, y_c) and plot the coordinate values.

$$x = x + x_c$$

$$y = y + y_c$$

6. Repeat Steps 3 to 5 until $x \geq y$.

Example 4.3   Given a circle of radius $r = 15$ cm, determine the pixel positions along the circle octant using the mid-point algorithm in the first quadrant from $x = 0$ to $x > y$.

Solution

$$R = 15$$

$$p_0 = 1 - r = 1 - 15 = -14$$

$$(x_0, y_0) = (0, 15)$$

$$2x_0 = 0 \text{ and } 2y_0 = 30$$

k	p_k	(x_{k+1}, y_{k+1})	$2x_{k+1}$	$2y_{k+1}$
0	−14	(1, 15)	2	30
1	−11	(2, 15)	4	30
2	−6	(3, 15)	6	30
3	1	(4, 14)	8	28
4	−18	(5, 14)	10	28
5	−7	(6, 14)	12	28
6	6	(7, 13)	14	26
7	−6	(8, 13)	16	26
8	11	(9, 12)	18	24
9	6	(10, 11)	20	22
10	5	(11, 10)	22	20

4.5 SCAN CONVERSION

In order to display the raster image by using video technology, it is necessary to organise the picture into the precise pattern required by the graphics display. This process is called *scan conversion*. The display information is organised and presented at appropriate frame rates in scan line order (i.e., from the top to the bottom and from left to right). There are three ways of scan conversion. These are:

1. Real-time scan conversion
2. Run-length encoding
3. Frame buffer memory

4.5.1 Real-Time Scan Conversion

In real-time scan conversion, the picture is randomly represented in terms of geometric properties and visual attributes. The typical geometrical properties are x, y coordinates, slopes and text. The visual attributes are colour, shade and intensity. The processor scans through this information and calculates the intensity of every pixel on the screen during the presentation of each frame. A small amount of memory is sufficient for the real-time scan conversion. In addition, it is easy to add or delete information in this scheme.

For example, the picture consists of four edges (AB, BC, CD, and DA) as shown in Figure 4.10. Because every edge may not be intersected by the scan line, the active edge list is prepared. The active edge list contains only those lines in the picture, which intersect the scan line. The edges are sorted by the largest value of y. A begin pointer is used to indicate the beginning of the active edge list, and an end pointer is used to indicate the end of the active edge list. The active edge list is given in Table 4.1.

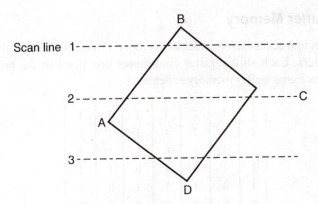

Fig. 4.10 Active edge list.

Table 4.1 Active edge list.

Edges	Scan line		
	1	2	3
BC	BC		
BA	BA	BA	
CD		CD	CD
AD			AD

4.5.2　Run-Length Encoding

In run-length encoding, the number of successive pixels of same intensity or colour on a given scan line is specified. The encoding records intensity along the run length. For pictures having black and white colours, the intensity for black is 1 and for white is 0. The recording consists of intensity and run length. Run length is expressed in terms of number of pixels. The first scan line has 9 pixels of zero intensity.

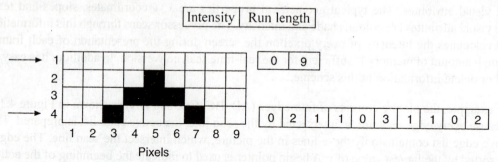

Fig. 4.11　Run-length encoded image.

4.5.3　Frame Buffer Memory

Frame buffer uses random access semiconductor memory. Frame buffers can also be implemented by using shift registers. Each shift register contributes one pixel in the horizontal line scan. Figure 4.12 illustrates frame buffer memory scheme.

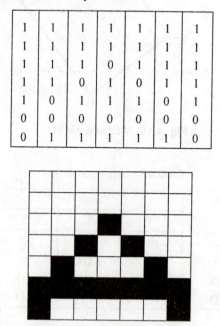

Fig. 4.12　Frame buffer memory scheme using shift registers.

4.6 RASTERISING POLYGONS

The simplest method of filling a polygon is to find the pixel coordinates of the interior points of the polygon and to assign a value calculated from the incremental shading schemes. The techniques used for polygon filling are as follows:

1. Scan-converting polygons
2. Edge flag algorithm
3. Seed fill algorithm

4.6.1 Scan-Converting Polygons

On a given scan line, the characteristics of pixels change only where a polygon edge intersects the scan line. These intersections divide the scan line into regions. For the simple polygon shown in Figure 4.12, the scan line 8 intersects the polygon at $x = 4$ and $x = 6$. These intersections divide the scan line into three regions:

$x < 4$ outside the polygon
$4 \leq x \leq 6$ inside the polygon
$x > 6$ outside the polygon

In order to determine the intensity, colour or shade of the pixels on the scan line, the sorted intersections are considered in pairs. From the beginning of the scan line until the first intersection, and from the last intersection to the end of the scan line, the intensity or colour is specified as the background. For each interval formed by the pair of intersections, the intensity or colour is that of the polygon. For the polygon in Figure 4.13, the pixels from 0 to 3, 4 to 6 and 7 to 10 on scan line 4 are set at the background colour, while those from 3 to 4 and 6 to 7 are set at the polygon colour.

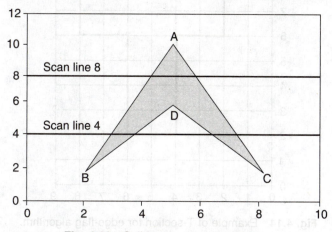

Fig. 4.13 Solid area scan conversion.

4.6.2 Edge Flag Algorithm

This is a two-step process. The first step is to outline the polygon to establish pairs of span-bounding pixels on each scan line. The second step is to fill in between these bounding pixels. The algorithm is as follows:

`Contour outline`

> Using the half scan line convention for each edge intersecting
> the scan line, set the left most pixel whose mid point lies to the
> right of the intersection lines to the right of the intersection
> to the boundary value.

`Fill`

> For each scan line intersecting the polygon
> Interior = FALSE
> for x = 0 to x = x_{max}
>   if the pixel at x is set to the boundary value then
>   negate Interior
>   end if
>   if Interior = TRUE then
>   set the pixel at x to the polygon value
>   else
>   reset the pixel at x to the background value
>   end if
>   next x

Example 4.4   Consider the picture shown in Figure 4.14. Fill in the picture by using the edge flag algorithm.

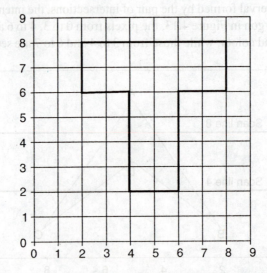

Fig. 4.14   Example of T-section for edge-flag algorithm.

Solution

First the contour is outlined: the result is shown in Figure 4.14(a). Pixels at (2, 6), (2, 7), (4, 2), (4, 3), (4, 4), (4, 5), (6, 2), (6, 3), (6, 4), (6, 5), (8, 6) and (8, 7) are activated.

The polygon is then filled. To illustrate this, scan line at 4 is extracted and shown in Figure 4.14(b). Pixels at $x = 4$, 6 on this scan line are activated to outline the contour. Applying the edge flag algorithm yields:

Initially

Interior = FALSE			
For $x = 0$	The pixel is not set to the boundary value and Interior	= FALSE, so the polygon is set to the background value	
For $x = 1$	The pixel is not set to the boundary value and Interior	= FALSE, so the polygon is set to the background value	
For $x = 2$	The pixel is not set to the boundary value and Interior	= FALSE, so the polygon is set to the background value	
For $x = 3$	The pixel is not set to the boundary value and Interior	= FALSE, so the polygon is set to the background value	
For $x = 4$	The pixel is set to the boundary value and Interior	= TRUE, so the polygon is set to the polygon value	
For $x = 5$	The pixel is set to the boundary value and Interior	= TRUE, so the polygon is set to the polygon value	
For $x = 6$	The pixel is set to the boundary value and Interior	= FALSE, so the polygon is set to the background value	

The result is shown in Figure 4.15(c). The final result for the complete polygon is shown in Figure 4.16.

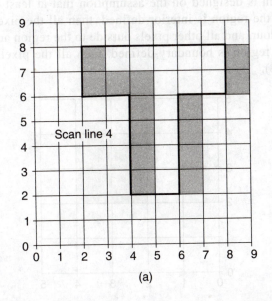

(a)

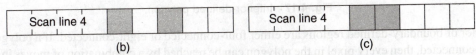

(b)   (c)

Fig. 4.15 Illustration of edge flag algorithm.

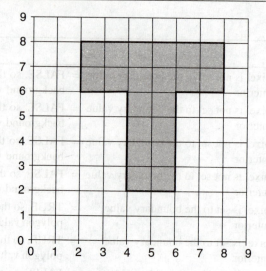

Fig. 4.16 Illustration of complete polygon.

4.6.3 Seed Fill Algorithm

The seed fill algorithm is designed on the assumption that at least one pixel interior to a polygon is known. If the region is interior-defined, then all the pixels in the inside of the polygon are of one colour, and all other pixels outside to the region are given another colour (Figure (4.17). If the region is boundary-defined, then all the pixels on the boundary are given one colour (4.18).

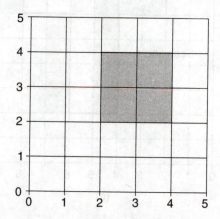

Fig. 4.17 Interior-defined polygon.

Interior or boundary-defined regions are either four-connected or eight-connected. If a polygon is four-connected, then every pixel in the polygon can be reached by a combination of moves in four direction: left, right, up and down. Figure 4.17 shows the four-connected interior-defined polygon. The four-connected boundary-defined polygon is shown in Figure 4.18.

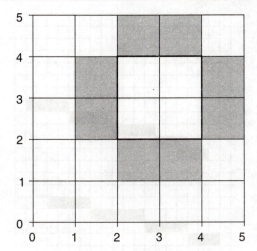

Fig. 4.18 Boundary-defined polygon.

The simple seed fill algorithm for a boundary-defined polygon is developed by using a stack. The algorithm is based on the principle of first-in-last-out (FILO) concept. The simple seed fill algorithm is as follows:

```
Push the seed pixel onto the stack
While the stack is not empty
      Pop the stack from the stack
      Set the pixel to the required value
```

For each of the four-connected pixels adjacent to the current pixel check if it is a boundary pixel or if it is already given the required value. In either case, ignore it, otherwise push it onto the stack.

4.7 ANTI-ALIASING

Many displays allow only two pixel states, on or off. For such displays, lines may have a jagged or stair-step appearance when they step from one row or column to the next. If the resolution is low, the effect is more apparent. This phenomenon is called *aliasing*. Aliasing produces the defects, which occur when the display scene changes faster. The rasterisation algorithms generate the pixels by rounding off to the nearest integer. As a result the inclined lines have the staircase effect.

Displays, which allow setting pixels to gray levels between white and black, provide a means to reduce this effect. The technique is called *anti-aliasing*. Anti-aliasing is carried out in the following two ways:

1. Increase the sample rate by increasing the resolution of the counter.
2. Calculate the raster at higher resolution and display it at lower resolution.

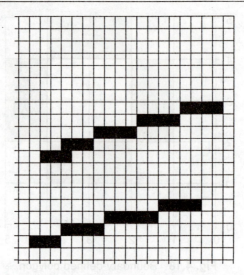

Fig. 4.19   Staircase effect of pixels when drawing inclined lines.

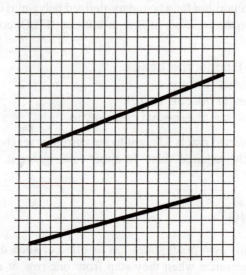

Fig. 4.20   Anti-aliasing of pixels proportional to the portion of pixel occupied by the line.

Super sampling is an anti-aliasing technique in which the image is rasterised at a higher resolution of the pseudoraster and groups of sub-pixels are averaged to obtain the attributes of individual physical pixels. The pseudoraster is superimposed on the physical raster. The process of dividing each physical pixel into 2×2 sub-pixels and rastering the line within the physical pixel is shown in Figure 4.21. The intensity of the physical pixel is made proportional to the ratio

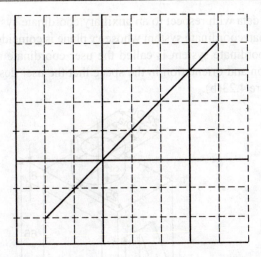

Fig. 4.21 Super sampling of straight lines.

of the number of activated sub-pixels to the total number of possible activated sub-pixels in a physical pixel. The intensity of the physical pixel of the anti-aliased line is

$$I = \frac{s}{n} I_{max} \qquad (4.16)$$

where

s is the number of rasterised sub-pixels

n is the total number of possible activated sub-pixels in a physical pixel

i_{max} is the maximum number of intensities supported by the system.

4.8 COORDINATE SYSTEMS

Three types of coordinate systems are needed to input, store and display model geometry and graphics. They are the world coordinate system (WCS), user coordinate system (UCS) and screen coordinate system (SCS).

4.8.1 World Coordinate System (WCS)

The world coordinate system is the reference space of the model with respect to which all the model geometrical data is stored. Figure 4.22 shows a typical model, which is to be modelled. Figure 4.23(a) illustrates the model with its associated world coordinate system x, y, and z. It is also called the *model coordinate system*. It is the default coordinate system. The WCS is the only coordinate system that the software recognises when storing or retrieving geometrical information.

4.8.2 User Coordinate System (UCS)

If the model has complex geometry, the desired feature of construction can be easily defined with respect to the world coordinate system. It is often convenient in the development of geometric models and the input of data with respect to an auxiliary coordinate system instead of WCS. The user can define a Cartesian coordinate system whose *xy* plane is coincident with the desired plane of construction. This coordinate system is called the user coordinate system. The UCS can be positioned at any position and orientation in the space that the user desires. The user coordinate system is shown in Figure 4.23(b).

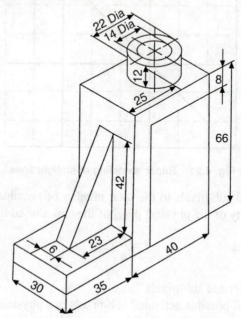

Fig. 4.22   Typical component to model.

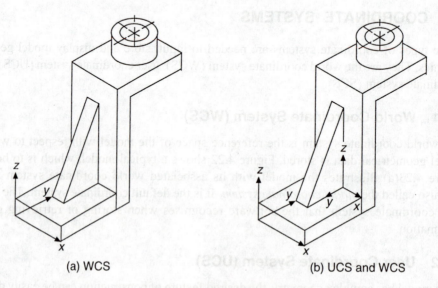

(a) WCS   (b) UCS and WCS

Fig. 4.23   Coordinate systems.

4.8.3 Screen Coordinate System (SCS)

The screen coordinate system is a two-dimensional Cartesian coordinate system whose origin is located at the lower left corner of the graphics display (Figure 4.24). It is a device-dependent coordinate system. For raster graphics displays, the pixel gird is the screen coordinate system. A 1024 × 1024 display as a range of (0, 0) to (1024, 1024). The centre of the screen is at (512, 512). The SCS is used to display graphics by converting from WCS coordinates to SCS coordinates. The transformation from WCS coordinates to SCS coordinates is performed by the software before displaying the model views and graphics.

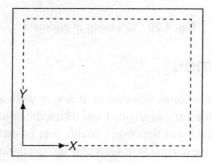

Fig. 4.24 Screen coordinate system.

4.9 WINDOWING

When drawings are too complex, they become difficult to read. In such situations, it is useful to display only those portions of the drawings that are of interest. This gives the effect of looking at the image through a window. it is desirable to zoom in on these portions. The technique of selecting and enlarging portions of a drawing is called *windowing*. The application of windowing is shown in Figures 4.25 and 4.26.

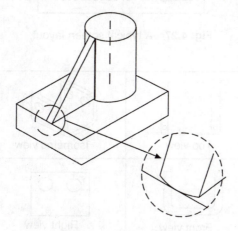

Fig. 4.25 A window to view only part of an object.

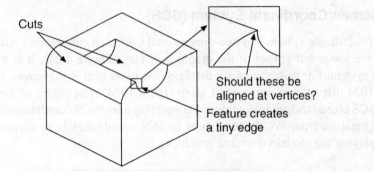

Fig. 4.26   Checking of geometry.

4.10   VIEW GENERATION

The display screen is two-dimensional. Sometimes, it is very difficult to view all the details of an object. Views are defined by the various angles from which the object can be observed. The most common views required to represent the object details are: isometric view, orthographic view, front view, top view, left side view, right side view and sectional views. In order to accommodate the display of several views simultaneously, the display screen is divided into viewports. A typical screen layout with four viewports is shown in Figure 4.27.

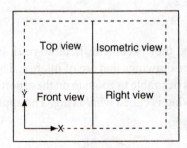

Fig. 4.27   A typical screen layout.

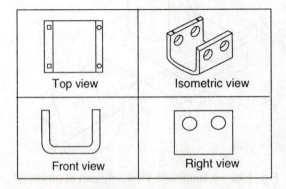

Fig. 4.28   Illustration of different views of an object.

Auxiliary views (Figure 4.29) discern the true size and shape of a planar surface on a part. The system makes a projection of the model perpendicular to a selected edge.

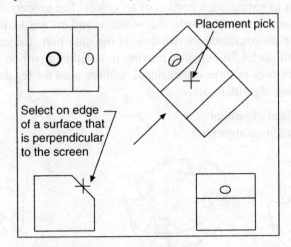

Fig. 4.29 Illustration of auxiliary view of an object.

Sectional views are used to see the inner details of a part or an assembly. A cross-section in part or assembly modes can be created and shown in a drawing. A full cross-section displays the whole view while a half cross-section shows a portion of the model on one side of a cutting plane, but not on the other side. A full cross-sectional view is illustrated in Figure 4.30.

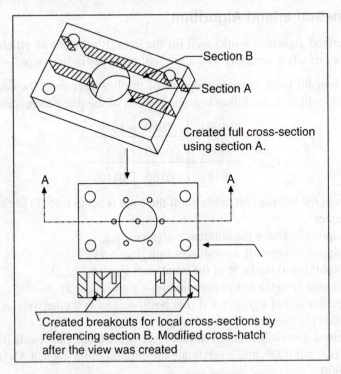

Fig. 4.30 Full cross-sectional view of an object.

4.11 CLIPPING

Clipping is the process of extracting a portion of an object. The process of clipping determines which elements of the picture lie inside the window and so are visible. For example, in Figure 4.31, the image shown inside the window is the only part (Figure 4.31c) that will be visible. Clipping is also useful for copying, moving or deleting a portion of a scene or picture. Clipping algorithms are two- or three-dimensional, and are used for regular or irregular regions or volumes. The clipping algorithms are:

1. Cohen–Sutherland algorithm
2. Sutherland–Hodgman algorithm

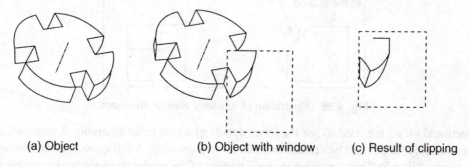

| (a) Object | (b) Object with window | (c) Result of clipping |

Fig. 4.31   Illustration of clipping.

4.11.1 Cohen–Sutherland Algorithm

The Cohen–Sutherland algorithm works well for the lines. It provides an efficient procedure for finding the category of a line segment. The algorithm proceeds in two steps:

1. Assign a four-bit code to each endpoint of the line segment. The code is determined according to which of the following nine regions of the plane the endpoint lies in:

$$
\begin{array}{c|c|c}
1001 & 1000 & 1010 \\
\hline
0001 & 0000 & 0010 \\
\hline
0101 & 0100 & 0110
\end{array}
$$

Y_{max} ... Y_{min}

Starting from the leftmost bit, each bit of the code is set to true (1) or false (0) according to the scheme:

Bit 1 = endpoint is above the window = sign $(y - y_{max})$
Bit 2 = endpoint is below the window = sign $(y_{min} - y)$
Bit 3 = endpoint is to the right of the window = sign $(x - x_{max})$
Bit 4 = endpoint is to the left of the window = sign $(x_{min} - x)$
The convention is that sign $a = 1$ if a is positive, and is 0 otherwise. A point with code 0000 is inside the window.

2. The line segment is visible if both endpoint codes are 0000, not visible if the logical AND of the codes is not 0000, and a candidate for clipping if the logical AND of the endpoint codes is 0000.

4.11.2 Sutherland–Hodgman Algorithm

It works the clipping test against each of the four boundaries individually. In this algorithm, all line-segment endpoints lying within the boundary and all points where lines intersect the boundary are passed on, while points lying outside the boundary are filtered out (Figure 4.32). This algorithm works well for two-dimensional objects. It can be extended for three-dimensional objects too.

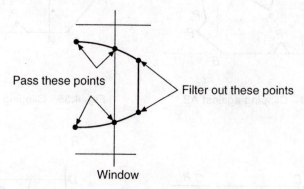

Fig. 4.32 Working of Sutherland–Hodgman algorithm for clipping against an edge.

Example 4.5 Clip the polygon shown in Figure 4.33 against the window *ABCD* by using the Sutherland–Hodgman algorithm.

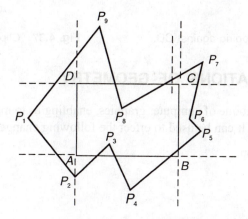

Fig. 4.33 An example to illustrate Sutherland-Hodgman algorithm.

Solution
Clipping against *AB* is given in Figure 4.34.
Clipping against *BC* is given in Figure 4.35.
Clipping against *CD* is given in Figure 4.36.
Clipping against *DA* is given in Figure 4.37.

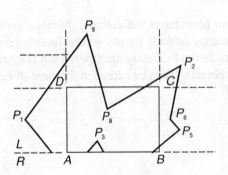

Fig. 4.34 Clipping against AB.

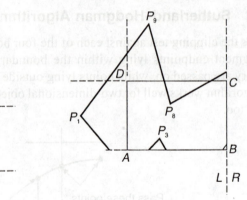

Fig. 4.35 Clipping against BC.

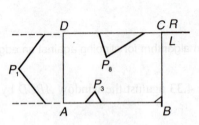

Fig. 4.36 Clipping against CD.

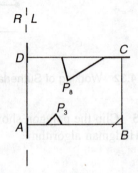

Fig. 4.37 Clipping against DA.

4.12 TRANSFORMATIONS OF GEOMETRY

Transformation is the backbone of computer graphics, enabling us to manipulate the shape, size, and location of the object. It can be used to effect the following changes in a geometric object:

1. Change the location
2. Change the shape
3. Change the size
4. Rotate
5. Copy
6. Generate a surface from a line
7. Generate a solid from a surface
8. Animate the object

The basic transformations are translation, scaling, rotation and combination of one or more of these basic transformations. Examples of these transformations can be easily found in any commercial CAD software. For instance, AutoCAD uses MOVE, SCALE, and ROTATE commands for translation, scaling, and rotation transformations, respectively.

4.12.1 Translation

In translation, every point on an object translates exactly the same distance as shown in Figure 4.38. The effect of a translation transformation is that the original coordinate values increase or decrease by the amount of the translation along the x, and y-axes.

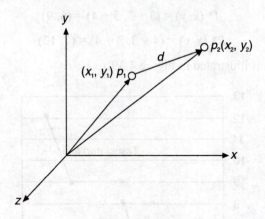

Fig. 4.38 Translation.

The point p_1 moves to p_2 by a distance d. The translation is expressed mathematically as:

$$p_2 = p_1 + d \tag{4.17}$$

This equation can be written in scalar form as follows:

$$x_2 = x_1 + d_x$$
$$y_2 = y_1 + d_y \tag{4.18}$$

In matrix form, the translation is expressed as:

$$\begin{Bmatrix} x_2 \\ y_2 \end{Bmatrix} = \begin{Bmatrix} x_1 \\ y_1 \end{Bmatrix} + \begin{Bmatrix} d_x \\ d_y \end{Bmatrix} \tag{4.19}$$

The translation matrix is given by:

$$T = \begin{Bmatrix} d_x \\ d_y \end{Bmatrix} \tag{4.20}$$

Example 4.6 If line $A(3, 5)$, $B(4, 8)$ is translated into three units along the positive x-axis and four units along the positive y-axis, find the new coordinates of the line.

Solution

Given $A(3, 5)$, $B(4, 8)$.

$$d_x = 3 \text{ and } d_y = 4$$

The new points are given by:

$$A^* (x, y) = (3 + 3, 5 + 4) = (6, 9)$$

$$B^* (x, y) = (4 + 3, 8 + 4) = (7, 12)$$

The effect of translation is illustrated in Figure 4.39.

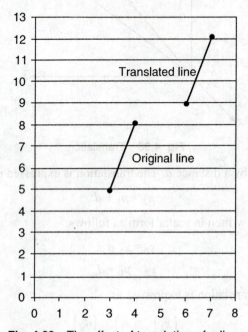

Fig. 4.39 The effect of translation of a line.

4.12.2 Scaling

In scaling transformation, the original coordinates of an object are multiplied by the given scale factor (Figure 4.40). There are two types of scaling transformations: uniform and non-uniform. In the uniform scaling, the coordinate values change uniformly along the x, and y coordinates, whereas in non-uniform scaling, the change is not necessarily the same in all the coordinate directions.

Uniform Scaling

For uniform scaling, the scaling transformation matrix is given as:

$$S = \begin{bmatrix} s & 0 \\ 0 & s \end{bmatrix} \tag{4.21}$$

Here, s is the scale factor.

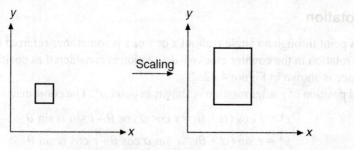

Fig. 4.40 Scaling.

Non-uniform Scaling

Matrix equation of a non-uniform scaling has the form:

$$S = \begin{bmatrix} s_x & 0 \\ 0 & s_y \end{bmatrix}$$ (4.23)

where s_x and s_y are the scale factors for the x and y coordinates of the object.

Example 4.7 If the triangle $A(1, 1)$, $B(2, 1)$, $C(1, 3)$ is scaled by a factor 2, find the new coordinates of the triangle.

Solution

Given: $A(1, 1)$, $B(2, 1)$, $C(1, 3)$

The uniform scale factor is 2.

The new coordinates of $A = \begin{Bmatrix} x \\ y \end{Bmatrix} = \begin{Bmatrix} 1 \\ 1 \end{Bmatrix} \begin{bmatrix} 2 & 0 \\ 0 & 2 \end{bmatrix} = \begin{Bmatrix} 2 \\ 2 \end{Bmatrix}$

The new coordinates of $B = \begin{Bmatrix} x \\ y \end{Bmatrix} = \begin{Bmatrix} 2 \\ 1 \end{Bmatrix} \begin{bmatrix} 2 & 0 \\ 0 & 2 \end{bmatrix} = \begin{Bmatrix} 4 \\ 2 \end{Bmatrix}$

The new coordinates of $C = \begin{Bmatrix} x \\ y \end{Bmatrix} = \begin{Bmatrix} 1 \\ 3 \end{Bmatrix} \begin{bmatrix} 2 & 0 \\ 0 & 2 \end{bmatrix} = \begin{Bmatrix} 2 \\ 6 \end{Bmatrix}$

The graphical representation of scaling is shown in Figure 4.41.

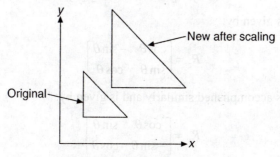

Fig. 4.41 Effect of scaling.

4.12.3 Rotation

Rotation of a point through an angle θ about x or y or z is sometimes referred to as rotation about the origin. A rotation in the counter-clockwise direction is considered as positive. The rotation of a point in space is shown in Figure 4.42.

The final position of p after rotation is shown as point p^*. The coordinates of p^* are given by:

$$x^* = r \cos (\alpha + \theta) = r \cos \alpha \cos \theta - r \sin \alpha \sin \theta$$
$$y^* = r \sin (\alpha + \theta) = r \sin \alpha \cos \theta - r \cos \alpha \sin \theta$$

$$(4.23)$$

where

$$x = r \cos \alpha \text{ and } y = r \sin \alpha \qquad (4.24)$$

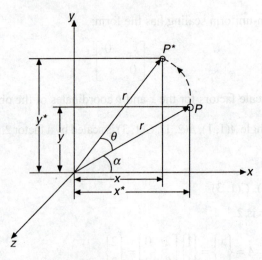

Fig. 4.42 Rotation.

Substituting Equation 4.24 into Equation 4.25 gives:

$$x^* = x \cos \theta - y \sin \theta \text{ and } y^* = x \cos \theta + y \sin \theta \qquad (4.25)$$

Rewriting Equation 4.25 in a matrix form gives:

$$\begin{Bmatrix} x^* \\ y^* \end{Bmatrix} = \begin{bmatrix} \cos \theta & -\sin \theta \\ \sin \theta & \cos \theta \end{bmatrix} \begin{Bmatrix} x \\ y \end{Bmatrix} \qquad (4.26)$$

Rotation about z-axis is given by:

$$R_z = \begin{bmatrix} \cos \theta & -\sin \theta \\ \sin \theta & \cos \theta \end{bmatrix} \qquad (4.27)$$

Rotation about y-axis is accomplished similarly and is given by:

$$R_y = \begin{bmatrix} \cos \theta & \sin \theta \\ -\sin \theta & \cos \theta \end{bmatrix} \qquad (4.28)$$

Rotation about *x*-axis is accomplished similarly and is given by:

$$R_x = \begin{bmatrix} \cos\theta & -\sin\theta \\ \sin\theta & \cos\theta \end{bmatrix} \tag{4.29}$$

Example 4.8 The line defined by two endpoints $A(1, 1)$ and $B(2, 4)$ is rotated by 30°. Determine the transformed line.

Solution
The rotation matrix is given by:

$$A(x^*, y^*) = \begin{bmatrix} \cos\theta & -\sin\theta \\ \sin\theta & \cos\theta \end{bmatrix} \begin{Bmatrix} 1 \\ 1 \end{Bmatrix} = (0.37, 1.37)$$

$$B(x^*, y^*) = \begin{bmatrix} \cos\theta & -\sin\theta \\ \sin\theta & \cos\theta \end{bmatrix} \begin{Bmatrix} 2 \\ 4 \end{Bmatrix} = (-0.27, 4.46)$$

The effect of rotation is shown in Figure 4.43

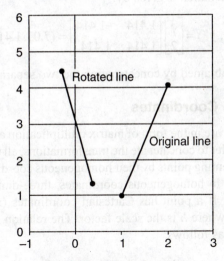

Fig. 4.43 Effect of rotation.

4.12.4 Concatenation

Most applications require the use of more than one basic transformation to achieve the desired results. In such cases, the combined transformation matrix is obtained by multiplying the respective transformation matrices. This process is called concatenation. The concatenation matrix is given by:

$$C = T_n T_{n-1} \dots T_2 T_1 \tag{4.30}$$

Example 4.9 In the text, a point (3, 2) is to be scaled by a factor of 2 and rotated by 45°. Determine the transformed position using (i) sequential transformations and (ii) concatenated transformation matrix.

Solution

(i) Sequential transformations:

The effect of scaling is given by:

$$(x', y') = \begin{Bmatrix} 3 \\ 2 \end{Bmatrix} \begin{bmatrix} 2 & 0 \\ 0 & 2 \end{bmatrix} = (6, 4)$$

The effect of rotation is given by:

$$(x'', y'') = \begin{Bmatrix} 6 \\ 4 \end{Bmatrix} \begin{bmatrix} \cos 45 & -\sin 45 \\ \sin 45 & \cos 45 \end{bmatrix} = (7.07, 1.41)$$

(ii) Using the concatenation matrix:

The concatenation matrix is given by:

$$C = \begin{bmatrix} 2 & 0 \\ 0 & 2 \end{bmatrix} \begin{bmatrix} \cos 45 & -\sin 45 \\ \sin 45 & \cos 45 \end{bmatrix} = \begin{bmatrix} 1.414 & 1.414 \\ 1.414 & 1.414 \end{bmatrix}$$

The effect of concatenation is given by:

$$(x'', y'') = \begin{bmatrix} 3 \\ 2 \end{bmatrix} \begin{bmatrix} 1.414 & -1.414 \\ 1.414 & 1.414 \end{bmatrix} = (7.07, 1.41)$$

The same result is obtained by concatenating the two separate transformations.

4.12.5   Homogeneous Coordinates

Scaling and rotation matrices are in the form of matrix multiplication and the translation takes the form of vector addition. In order to concatenate the transformations, all the transformation matrices should be multiplied. Representing points by their homogeneous coordinates provides an effective way to apply concatenation. In homogeneous coordinates, three-dimensional space is mapped into four-dimensional space. If a point has Cartesian coordinates (x, y, z), the homogeneous coordinates are (x', y', z', h) where h is the scale factor. The relation between the Cartesian and homogeneous coordinates is as follows:

$$x = \frac{x'}{h}, y = \frac{y'}{h} \quad \text{and} \quad z = \frac{z'}{h} \tag{4.31}$$

For the geometric transformations, the scale factor h is taken as unity to avoid unnecessary division.

The translational transformation matrix in homogeneous coordinates is given by:

$$\begin{Bmatrix} x* \\ y* \\ z* \\ 1 \end{Bmatrix} = \begin{bmatrix} 1 & 0 & 0 & d_x \\ 0 & 1 & 0 & d_y \\ 0 & 0 & 1 & d_z \\ 0 & 0 & 0 & 1 \end{bmatrix} \begin{Bmatrix} x \\ y \\ z \\ 1 \end{Bmatrix} \tag{4.32}$$

If a point has Cartesian coordinates (x, y), the homogeneous coordinates are (x', y', h),
The translational matrix is given by:

$$T = \begin{bmatrix} 1 & 0 & d_x \\ 0 & 1 & d_y \\ 0 & 0 & 1 \end{bmatrix} \quad (4.33)$$

The scaling matrix is given by:

$$S = \begin{bmatrix} s_x & 0 & 0 \\ 0 & s_y & 0 \\ 0 & 0 & 1 \end{bmatrix} \quad (4.34)$$

The rotational matrix about the z-axis is given by:

$$R_z = \begin{bmatrix} \cos\theta & -\sin\theta & 0 \\ \sin\theta & \cos\theta & 0 \\ 0 & 0 & 1 \end{bmatrix} \quad (4.35)$$

4.12.6 Rotation about an Arbitrary Point

The rotation of a point about the origin is given by:

$$R_z = \begin{bmatrix} \cos\theta & -\sin\theta & 0 \\ \sin\theta & \cos\theta & 0 \\ 0 & 0 & 1 \end{bmatrix}$$

The rotation of a point or an object about an arbitrary point is useful in simulation of mechanisms, linkages, and robotics where links must rotate about their respective joints.

Figure 4.44 shows the rotation of point P about point A in the xy plane. Thus, the rotation of the point or object about an arbitrary point involves three steps:

Step 1: Translate the point or object to the origin (Figure 4.45a).
Step 2: Rotate the point or object by the given angle (Figure 4.45b).
Step 3: Translate the point or object back to the original position (Figure 4.45c).

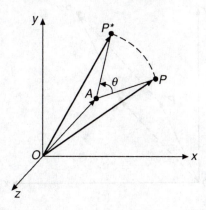

Fig. 4.44 Rotation of a point about an arbitrary point.

The concatenated transformation matrix is given by:

$$T_c = T_3 R_2 T_1 \tag{4.36}$$

where

$$T_1 = \begin{bmatrix} 1 & 0 & -d_x \\ 0 & 1 & -d_y \\ 0 & 0 & 4 \end{bmatrix}$$

$$R_2 = \begin{bmatrix} \cos\theta & -\sin\theta & 0 \\ \sin\theta & \cos\theta & 0 \\ 0 & 0 & 1 \end{bmatrix}$$

$$T_3 = \begin{bmatrix} 1 & 0 & d_x \\ 0 & 1 & d_y \\ 0 & 0 & 1 \end{bmatrix}$$

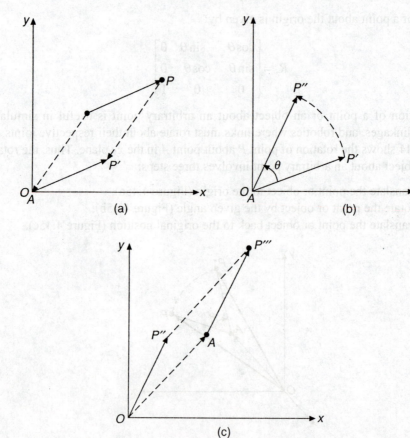

(a)

(b)

(c)

Fig. 4.45 Illustration of steps followed for the rotation of a point about an arbitrary point.

4.12.7   Three-dimensional (3-D) Transformations

A three-dimensional object has a three-dimensional geometry, and therefore, it requires a three-dimensional coordinate transformation. A right-handed coordinate system is used to carry out a three-dimensional transformation. The scaling and translation transformations are essentially the same as two-dimensional transformations. However, the points matrix will have a non-zero third column. Additionally, the transformation matrices contain some non-zero values in the third row and third column, as shown below.

The translational transformation matrix in homogeneous coordinates is given by:

$$\begin{Bmatrix} x^* \\ y^* \\ z^* \\ 1 \end{Bmatrix} = \begin{bmatrix} 1 & 0 & 0 & d_x \\ 0 & 1 & 0 & d_y \\ 0 & 0 & 1 & d_z \\ 0 & 0 & 0 & 1 \end{bmatrix} \begin{Bmatrix} x \\ y \\ z \\ 1 \end{Bmatrix} \tag{4.37}$$

The translational matrix is given by:

$$T = \begin{bmatrix} 1 & 0 & 0 & d_x \\ 0 & 1 & 0 & d_y \\ 0 & 0 & 1 & d_z \\ 0 & 0 & 0 & 1 \end{bmatrix} \tag{4.38}$$

The scaling matrix is given by:

$$S = \begin{bmatrix} s_x & 0 & 0 & 0 \\ 0 & s_y & 0 & 0 \\ 0 & 0 & s_z & 0 \\ 0 & 0 & 0 & 1 \end{bmatrix} \tag{4.39}$$

The rotational matrix about the *z*-axis is given by:

$$R_z = \begin{bmatrix} \cos\theta & -\sin\theta & 0 & 0 \\ \sin\theta & \cos\theta & 0 & 0 \\ 0 & 0 & 1 & 0 \\ 0 & 0 & 0 & 1 \end{bmatrix} \tag{4.40}$$

The rotational matrix about the *y*-axis is given by:

$$R_y = \begin{bmatrix} \cos\theta & 0 & \sin\theta & 0 \\ 0 & 1 & 0 & 0 \\ -\sin\theta & 0 & \cos\theta & 0 \\ 0 & 0 & 0 & 1 \end{bmatrix} \tag{4.41}$$

The rotational matrix about the z-axis is given by:

$$R_x = \begin{bmatrix} 1 & 0 & 0 & 0 \\ 0 & \cos\theta & -\sin\theta & 0 \\ 0 & \sin\theta & \cos\theta & 0 \\ 0 & 0 & 0 & 1 \end{bmatrix} \qquad (4.42)$$

Example 4.10 The coordinates of a cube are (0, 0, 0), (2, 0, 0), (2, 2, 0), (0, 2, 0), (0, 0, 2), (2, 0, 2), (2, 2, 2), (0, 2, 2). Scale the cube uniformly by 1/2.

Solution
The effect of scaling is given by:

$$\begin{bmatrix} 0 & 0 & 0 & 1 \\ 2 & 0 & 0 & 1 \\ 2 & 2 & 0 & 1 \\ 0 & 2 & 0 & 1 \\ 0 & 0 & 2 & 1 \\ 2 & 0 & 2 & 1 \\ 2 & 2 & 2 & 1 \\ 0 & 2 & 2 & 1 \end{bmatrix} \begin{bmatrix} 1/2 & 0 & 0 & 0 \\ 0 & 1/2 & 0 & 0 \\ 0 & 0 & 1/2 & 0 \\ 0 & 0 & 0 & 1 \end{bmatrix} = \begin{bmatrix} 0 & 0 & 0 & 1 \\ 1 & 0 & 0 & 1 \\ 1 & 1 & 0 & 1 \\ 0 & 1 & 0 & 1 \\ 0 & 0 & 1 & 1 \\ 1 & 0 & 1 & 1 \\ 1 & 1 & 1 & 1 \\ 0 & 1 & 1 & 1 \end{bmatrix}$$

The results of scaling of the cube are shown in Figure 4.46.

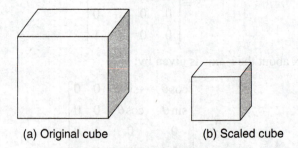

(a) Original cube   (b) Scaled cube

Fig. 4.46 Effect of scaling.

4.12.8 Rotation of a Three-dimensional Object about an Arbitrary Axis

A three-dimensional rotation of a geometric model about an arbitrary axis is complex, and involves several rotation and translation transformations. Following is a step-by-step procedure to accomplish the transformation:

1. Translate the given axis so that it will pass through the origin.
2. Rotate the axis about the x-axis (or y-axis) so that it will lie in the xz-plane (angle α).
3. Rotate the axis about the y-axis so that it will coincide with the z-axis (angle ϕ).
4. Rotate the geometric object about the z-axis (angle θ).

5. Reverse of Step 3.
6. Reverse of Step 2.
7. Reverse of Step 1.

4.12.9 Reflection

Reflection is also known as mirror. Reflection is useful in the construction of symmetric objects. If the model is symmetric with respect to a plane, only half the geometry is created. The half model is copied by reflection to develop the full model. The principle of reflection is shown in Figure 4.47.

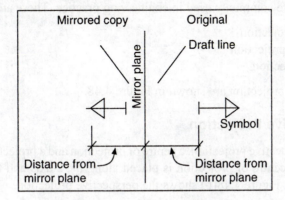

Fig. 4.47 Illustration of reflection.

The reflection transformation is expressed as follows:

$$P^* = MP \tag{4.43}$$

where

$$M = \begin{bmatrix} \pm m_{11} & 0 & 0 \\ 0 & \pm m_{22} & 0 \\ 0 & 0 & \pm m_{33} \end{bmatrix} = \begin{bmatrix} \pm 1 & 0 & 0 \\ 0 & \pm 1 & 0 \\ 0 & 0 & \pm 1 \end{bmatrix} \tag{4.44}$$

P is the given point.

P^* is the reflected point.

For reflection through $x = 0$ plane:

$$M = \begin{bmatrix} -1 & 0 & 0 \\ 0 & 1 & 0 \\ 0 & 0 & 1 \end{bmatrix} \tag{4.45}$$

For reflection through $x = 0$ plane:

$$M = \begin{bmatrix} 1 & 0 & 0 \\ 0 & -1 & 0 \\ 0 & 0 & -1 \end{bmatrix} \tag{4.46}$$

For reflection through $z = 0$ plane:

$$M = \begin{bmatrix} 1 & 0 & 0 \\ 0 & 1 & 0 \\ 0 & 0 & -1 \end{bmatrix}$$

(4.47)

4.13 MATHEMATICS OF PROJECTIONS

In computer graphics, a three-dimensional object is viewed on a two-dimesional screen. The projection transforms a three-dimensional object onto the two-dimensional screen. Three types of projections are commonly used in engineering practice. These are:

1. Perspective projection
2. Orthographic projection
3. Isometric projection

The principles of projection are shown in Figure 4.48.

4.13.1 Perspective Projection

In order to define perspective projection, a centre of projection and a projection plane are required. More commonly, the centre of projection is placed along the z-axis and the image is projected onto $z = 0$ or xy plane. Figure 4.48(b) shows the perspective projection.

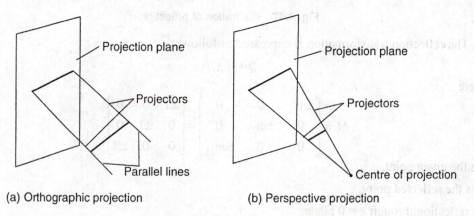

(a) Orthographic projection   (b) Perspective projection

Fig. 4.48 Principles of projection.

The transformation of perspective projection is given by:

$$P^* = P_0 P$$

(4.48)

where

$$P_p = \begin{bmatrix} 1 & 0 & 0 & 0 \\ 0 & 1 & 0 & 0 \\ 0 & 0 & 0 & 0 \\ 0 & 0 & -1/d & 1 \end{bmatrix}$$

(4.49)

P is the given point.

P^* is the reflected point.

d is the distance between the centre of projection to the projection plane.

The perspectives create only an artistic effect. Perspective projections are not popular because actual dimensions and angles of objects preserved.

4.13.2 Orthographic Projection

In orthographic projection, the projectors are parallel. The centre of projection is at infinity. The orthographic projection of a view is obtained by setting to zero the coordinate value that coincides with the direction of projection after the object rotation. The orthographic projection system consists of six projecting planes. The orthographic projection is shown in Figure 4.48a.

The front view is obtained by setting $z = 0$. The transformation of orthographic projection is given by:

$$P^* = P_0 P \tag{4.50}$$

where

P is the given point.

P^* is the reflected point.

$$P_0 = \begin{bmatrix} 1 & 0 & 0 & 0 \\ 0 & 1 & 0 & 0 \\ 0 & 0 & 0 & 0 \\ 0 & 0 & 0 & 1 \end{bmatrix} \tag{4.51}$$

For the top view, the object is rotated at 90° about the *x*-axis and setting $y = 0$. The transformation of orthographic projection is given by:

$$P^* = P_0 P \tag{4.52}$$

where

$$P_0 = \begin{bmatrix} 1 & 0 & 0 & 0 \\ 0 & 0 & -1 & 0 \\ 0 & 0 & 0 & 0 \\ 0 & 0 & 0 & 1 \end{bmatrix} \tag{4.53}$$

Unlike perspective projection, the orthogonal projection preserves actual dimensions and angles of objects.

4.13.3 Isometric Projection

The isometric projection of an object is a single orthographic projection, with the object so placed with respect to the plane of projection, that all the three axes of the object are equally inclined to it. The three front edges are called the isometric axes and their angle of inclination with the vertical plane of projection is 35°16′. The front view obtained in this way shows three faces of the cube equal in shape and is called isometric projection. The transformation of isometric projection is given by:

$$P^* = P_i P \qquad (4.54)$$

where

$$P_i = \begin{bmatrix} 0.7071 & 0 & 0.7071 & 0 \\ 0.4082 & 0.8165 & -0.4082 & 0 \\ -0.5774 & 0.5774 & 0.5774 & 0 \\ 0 & 0 & 0 & 1 \end{bmatrix}$$

The isometric, front, top and right views of an object are shown in Figure 4.49.

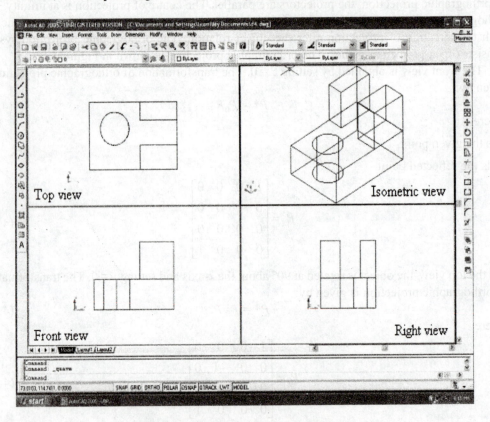

Fig. 4.49   Different views of an object.

4.14   HIDDEN SURFACE REMOVAL

The need for eliminating hidden lines, edges, surfaces or volumes is illustrated in Figure 4.50.

The complexity of the visible lines results ambiguity. There is no best solution to the visible surface problem. All visible surface algorithms involve sorting. The order in which sorting of the geometric coordinates occurs is generally immaterial to the efficiency of the algorithm. The principal sort is based on the geometrical distance of a volume, surface or point from the viewpoint. After the distance priority is established, it remains to be sorted laterally and vertically.

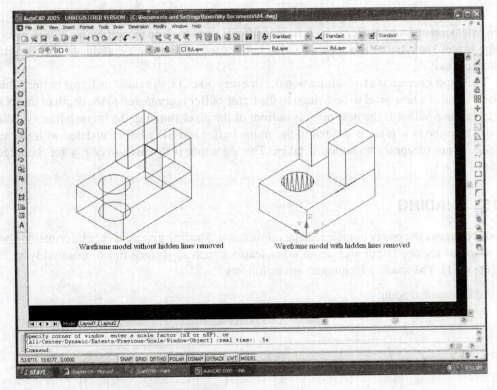

Fig. 4.50 Need for hidden line removal.

The hidden line removal algorithms are:

1. Floating horizon algorithm
2. Roberts algorithm
3. Image space algorithm
4. Warnock algorithm
5. Appel algorithm
6. Haloed line algorithm
7. List priority algorithm

The hidden surface removal algorithms are:

1. Z-buffer algorithm
2. A-buffer algorithm
3. List priority algorithm
4. Newell-Newell-Snacha algorithm
5. Binary space portioning algorithm
6. Scan line algorithms
7. Visible surface ray tracing algorithm
8. Object space algorithm
9. Warnock algorithm

The z-buffer algorithm is a popular hidden surface removal algorithm. The z-buffer algorithm is an extension of frame buffer idea. A frame buffer is used to store the attributes of each pixel in image space. The z-buffer is a separate depth buffer used to store the z-coordinate of every pixel in image space.

The display screen is a two-dimensional. For every pixel, (x, y) values are frame buffer values. If the z-value of a new pixel to be written to the frame buffer is compared to the depth of that pixel stored in the z-buffer. If the new pixel is in front of the pixel stored in the frame buffer (smallest depth), then the new pixel is written to the frame buffer and the z-buffer updated with the new z-value. If not (deepest), no action is taken. The algorithm is a search over x, y for the largest value of $z (x, y)$.

4.15 SHADING

Shaded images can convey complex shape information. Shading gives not only information about the shape of the object but also about other features such as surface finish, material type, etc. (Figure 4.51). The shading techniques are as follows:

1. Gouraud shading
2. Phong shading

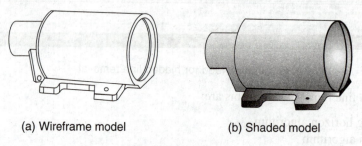

(a) Wireframe model   (b) Shaded model

Fig. 4.51   Shading.

Gouraud shading involves bilinear intensity interpolation over a polygon mesh. This technique shades the objects and smoothens the edges between polygon faces, giving the objects a smooth, realistic appearance. In this technique, the intensity at each vortex is calculated by assuming that the light source is at infinity. The intensity of the light reflected over the polygon surface is then obtained by integrating the interpolation process with the scam conversion process.

Phong shading uses the bilinear interpolation for the incremental interpolation of points interior to polygons. A separate intensity is evaluated for each pixel from the interpolated normals. In this technique, vertex normals are calculated by averaging normal vectors. Phong shading incorporates specular reflection. The Phong technique is superior to Gouraud shading.

4.16 RENDERING

Rendering is the process of producing realistic images or pictures (Figure 4.52). CAD software uses geometry, lighting, and materials to render a realistic image of a model. Rendering often requires the most computer time in a three-dimensional project. It generally involves three steps:

1. **Preparing models:** This includes following proper drafting techniques, removing hidden surfaces, constructing meshes for smooth shading, and setting view resolution.
2. **Illuminating:** This includes creating and placing lights and creating shadows.
3. **Adding colour:** This includes defining the reflective qualities of materials and associating these materials with the visible surfaces.

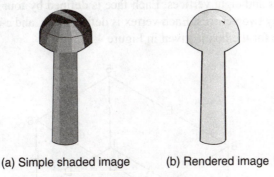

(a) Simple shaded image   (b) Rendered image

Fig. 4.52   Rendering.

A rendered model cannot move or rotate on the screen in real time. A shaded image rendering is employed to move or rotate in real time. Shaded image renderings are limited. They always have a matte appearance, because they do not reflect the environment on the surface. Texture maps do not show up in a shaded tile rendering on many hardware platforms. The number of lights available for shaded image renderings is limited by the platform. The maximum is 12 on a Sun Solaris. It is 8 on other platforms like SGI, IBM, HP, etc.

The effects of light on rendering are as follows:

1. **Effect of point light:** A point light is similar to a light bulb in a room. The light radiates from the centre. The light reflection off a surface varies, depending on the surface position with respect to the light (Figure 4.53).
2. **Effect of light direction:** A directional light casts parallel light rays, illuminating all surfaces at the same angle, regardless of the position. This type of light simulates the sun or any other distant light source.
3. **Effect spot light:** A spot light is a point light whose rays are confined within a cone. Use the sliders when defining light colour to set the light intensity. Spot determines the size of the spot in the Direction option. Valid entries are 0 to 180°.

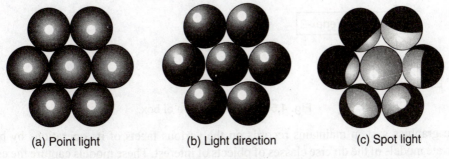

(a) Point light   (b) Light direction   (c) Spot light

Fig. 4.53   Effect of light on rendering.

4.17 DATABASE STRUCTURE FOR GRAPHICS MODELLING

The *data structure* is a set of data elements that are related to each other by a set of relations. The data items are geometrical elements like point, line, arc, circle, face, box, cylinder, wedge, prism, etc. The relations consist of topology. For example, a box shown in Figure 4.54 is defined by six faces, twelve edges and eight vertices. Each face is defined by four edges and four vertices. Each edge is defined by two vertices. Each vertex is defined by x, and z-coordinates in the space. The data structure tree for the box is given in Figure 4.55.

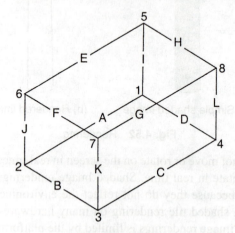

Fig. 4.54 Box.

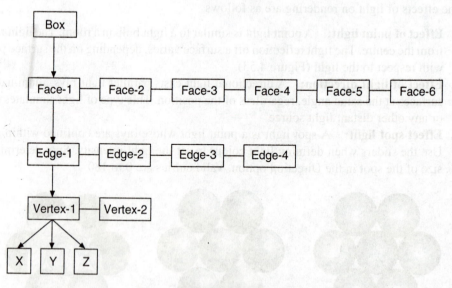

Fig. 4.55 Data structure of box.

The graphics system maintains records on the various facets of its operations by building appropriate models of the diverse classes of objects of interest. These models capture the essential properties of the objects and record relationships among them. Such a related data is called a *database*. A database system is an integrated collection of related files, along with details of the interpretation of the data contained therein. Database is the art of storing or the implementation of data structure into the computer. The database consists of an organised collection of graphics and non-graphics stored on secondary storage in the computer.

The functions of a database are to:

1. Manipulate the data on the display device e.g., zooming
2. Interact with the user e.g., clipping, windowing, copying, deleting, trimming
3. Evaluate mass properties e.g., area, volume, density
4. Provide design attributes e.g., shape, size
5. Evaluate assembly attributes e.g., fits, tolerances
6. Provide manufacturing specifications e.g., tools, cutting speeds
7. Eliminate redundancy The data should be shared by all engineering applications
8. Enforce standards of National and International to adopt interchangeability
9. Balance conflicting requirements e.g., between the topology and geometry
10. Apply security restrictions. Access to sensitive data is checked and controlled
11. Maintain integrity for the purpose accuracy and consistency.

CAD/CAM systems employ a relational database to store geometric, graphical and other data that defines the model. The *relation* is the only data structure used in the relational data model to represent both entities and the relationships between them. A relation may be visualised as a names *table*. Each column of the table corresponds to an attribute of the relation and is named.

Rows of the relation are referred to as *records* of the relation and the columns are its attributes. Each attribute of a relation has a distinct name. The values for an attribute or a column are drawn from a set of values known as a domain. In the relational model, note that no two rows of a relation are identical and the ordering of the rows is not significant. A correspondence between two relations is implied by the data values of attributes in the relation defined on common domains. Such correspondence is used for navigating through the relational database.

For example, consider a two-dimesional model shown in Figure 4.56. The relational database of the model is shown in Figure 4.57.

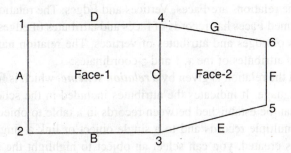

Fig. 4.56 A two-dimensional model.

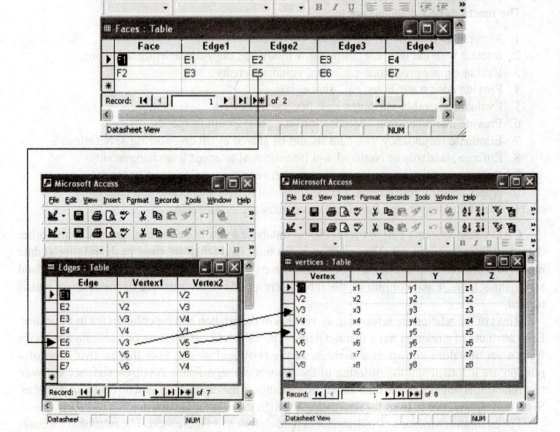

Fig. 4.57 A relational database model.

In the example, the relations are Faces, Vertices and Edges. The relations are in the form of tables. The relation named Faces has records of faces and attributes of edges. The relation named Edges has the records of edges and attributes of vertices. The relation named Vertices has the records of vertices and attributes of the *x*, *y* and *z*-coordinates.

The description of the relation is given by a ***relation scheme***. which is like a type declaration in a programming language. It indicates the attributes included in the scheme, their order, and their domain. A link can be established between records in a table to objects in a drawing. It is also possible to link multiple records and to a single object or link a single record to multiple objects. After a link is created, you can select an object to highlight the record to which it is attached (Figure 4.58), or you can select a record to highlight the object to which it is linked. A link template is defined for a drawing; you can link records to objects, and then view their link associations.

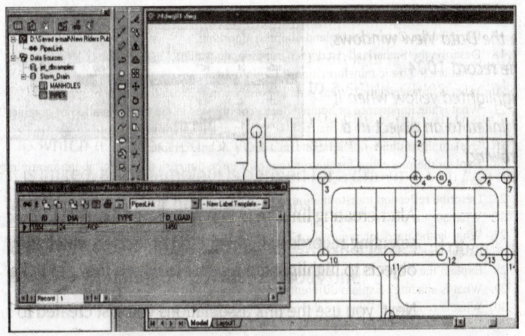

Fig. 4.58 The selected object is used to locate and display the record to which it is linked.

QUESTION BANK

A. Descriptive Questions

1. Explain raster scan graphics.
2. What is the design criteria used for line drawing algorithms?
3. Describe DDA algorithm.
4. Describe Bresenham's algorithm.
5. Describe mid-point algorithm.
6. Explain real-time scan conversion with an example.
7. Explain real-length encoding scan conversion with an example.
8. Explain frame buffer memory scan conversion with an example.
9. Explain the scan converting polygon technique for polygon filling with an example.
10. Explain the edge flag algorithm for polygon filling with an example.
11. Explain the seed fill algorithm for polygon filling with an example.
12. What is aliasing? Describe different methods of carrying out anti-aliasing.
13. What are the various types of coordinate systems used to input, store and display geometry and graphics? Explain them.
14. What is windowing? Explain with an example.
15. Explain view generation with an example.

16. What is clipping? Describe any one clipping algorithm.
17. Describe the Cohen–Sutherland clipping algorithm.
18. Describe the Sutherland–Hodgman clipping algorithm.
19. What are the basic transformations? Explain them.
20. What is concatenation? What is its importance in the transformation of graphics?
21. What is the importance of homogeneous coordinates in the transformation of graphics?
22. Derive the transformation matrix for rotation about an arbitrary point.
23. Explain three-dimensional transformations with an example.
24. Explain the procedure for the rotation of a three-dimensional object about an arbitrary axis.
25. Describe reflection transformation.
26. What are the projections commonly used in engineering practice? Explain them.
27. What is the need for removal of hidden lines and surfaces? List out various types of hidden line and hidden surface removal algorithms.
28. Explain the Z-buffer algorithm for hidden surface removal.
29. What is shading? Explain different shading techniques.
30. What is rendering? What are the effects of light on rendering?
31. What is data structure? Explain with an example.
32. What is database? Explain the popular database model with an example.
33. The endpoints of a given line are (0, 0) and (6, 18). Use the DDA algorithm to rasterise the line.
34. Find out the raster locations by Bresenham's algorithm for the endpoints of a straight line (1, 1), and (8, 5).
35. Given a circle of radius $r = 12$ cm, determine the pixel positions along the circle octant using mid-point algorithm in the first quadrant from $x = 0$ to $x \geq y$.
36. Magnify the triangle with vertices $A(0, 0)$, $B(1, 1)$, and $C(5, 2)$ to twice its size while keeping $C(5, 2)$ fixed.
37. Perform a 45° of rotation of a triangle $A(0, 0)$, $B(1, 1)$, and $C(5, 2)$ (a) About the origin (b) About $(-1,-1)$.
38. Reflect the polygon whose vertices are $A(-1, 0)$, $B(0, -2)$, $C(1, 0)$ and $D(0, 2)$ about the lines (a) horizontal line $y = 2$, and (b) vertical line $x = 3$.

B. Multiple Choice Questions

1. The most common type of computer output device capable of displaying graphical output in use today is:
   (a) Vector scan CRT   (b) Raster scan CRT
   (c) Random scan CRT   (d) Liquid crystal CRT
2. The digital differential analyser generates lines from their _____ equations.
   (a) Algebraic   (b) Trigonometric   (c) Differential   (d) All the above
3. Bresenham's Algorithm generates a straight line for the given _____ coordinates.
   (a) Integer   (b) Real   (c) Complex   (d) All the above

4. The seed fill algorithm is based on the assumption that the number of interior pixels is known to be _____ .

    (a) Two   (b) Four   (c) Eight   (d) One

5. The simple seed fill algorithm is based on the principle of _____ .

    (a) First-in-last-out   (b) Last-in-first-out

    (c) Just-in-time   (d) None of the above

6. The screen coordinate system is a _____ coordinate system.

    (a) Three-dimensional cartesian   (b) Two-dimensional cartesian

    (c) Spherical   (d) Cylindrical

7. The technique of selecting and enlarging portions of a drawing is called:

    (a) Viewing   (b) Clipping   (c) Sorting   (d) Windowing

8. Translation is the transformation technique in the form of _____ .

    (a) Matrix multiplication   (b) Vector addition

    (c) Matrix division   (d) Matrix inversion

9. In orthographic projection, the projectors are _____ .

    (a) Parallel   (b) Perpendicular   (c) Inclined   (d) Intersecting

10. The logical representation of a collection of data elements is known as:

    (a) Data record   (b) Data structure   (c) Data item   (d) Database

11. The data structure in which the data is stored in tables, called relations, is known as:

    (a) Network model   (b) Hierarchical model

    (c) Relational model   (D) Object-oriented model

Chapter 5

Basics of Geometric Modelling

After reading this chapter, the reader will be able to understand the following concepts:

- ➲ Requirements of geometric modelling
- ➲ Geometric models
- ➲ Geometric construction methods
- ➲ Modelling facilities desired

5.1 INTRODUCTION

Computer graphics, computer-aided design and computer-aided manufacturing have been and continue to be the driving forces behind the development of most of geometric modelling. Now robotics, computer vision, virtual reality, scientific visualisation and artificial intelligence are making new demands on geometric modelling capabilities. Engineering analysis is an area undergoing change with the increasing sophistication of solid modellers. They also permit automatic static and dynamic structural analysis of mechanical parts subjected to a variety of loading conditions.

5.2 REQUIREMENTS OF GEOMETRIC MODELLING

The requirement of geometric modelling is manifold. The conceptual design is the basis for the generation of a geometric model. The choice of the geometric model depends on the mechanical functioning to be performed by it. A valid geometric model is created by the CAD system and its model database is stored. The database of geometric modelling is used for engineering analysis and for design optimisation. Design testing and evaluation may necessitate changing the geometric model before finalising it. When the final design is achieved, it is documented and used for subsequent manufacturing applications, quality and cost analyses. The requirements of geometric modelling are as follows:

1. Evaluation of geometrical properties such as centroid, cross-sectional area, surface area, volume.
2. Evaluation of mass properties such as mass, density, inertia.
3. Finite element analysis and optimisation—parametric design studies by considering different complex shapes or geometries, materials, loads and selecting the optimum design.
4. Volume visualisation—the presentation of not just surface data to present a three-dimensional model, but of interior points in a structure.
5. Animation of graphics—obstacle avoidance in robotics, verification of NC tool paths, car-crash analysis, nuclear weapon simulation and many others.
6. Automatic assembly—modelling and representing assemblies, generating assembly sequences, inference checking.
7. Tolerance analysis for process planning, assembly operations, part inspection and interchangeable manufacturing.
8. Manufacturing—generation of part families, NC code generation, inventory control, E-manufacturing, net-shape manufacturing, and scheduling.
9. Computer-aided inspection and control—comparison of product with geometry in the database, re-engineering of complex products, etc.

Having established the requirements for geometric modelling, one has to decide what the best useful geometric model is for engineering applications?

From a strictly geometric modelling point of view, it depends on:

1. The intellectual selection of geometric entities for the model to meet the requirement of engineering applications.
2. Decision-making process
3. Evaluation criteria of CAD/CAM systems

In design and drafting, the engineer's role may soon be more like sculpting than drafting. The new sculpting tools, using combinations of simple solid shapes and sophisticated shape transformations, will mimic not only those of the artist but also the forming processes available in manufacturing, thereby extending a designer's ability to rapidly create and evaluate highly complex models.

5.3 GEOMETRIC MODELS

The geometric models are broadly classified on the basis of geometric construction into the following categories:

1. Two dimensional
2. Three dimensional

The two-dimensional modelling includes the construction of geometrical faces, plane drawings, two-diemensional views (top, front right and left views) of objects. Presently, the application of two-dimensional models is limited to drafting, sheet metal manufacturing, spot welding, laser cutting, etc. The two-dimensional objects are shown in Figure 5.1.

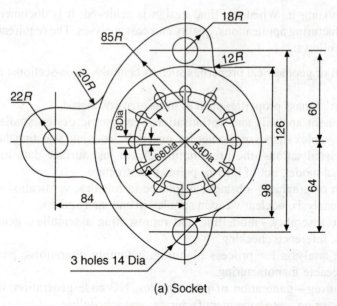

(a) Socket

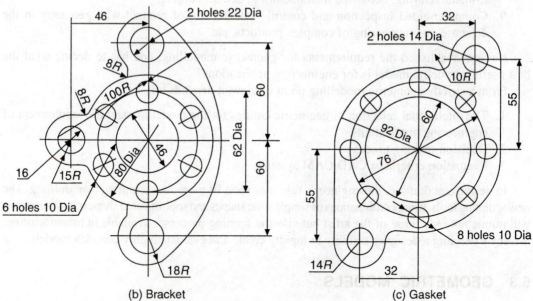

(b) Bracket   (c) Gasket

Fig. 5.1 Two-dimensional objects.

Three-dimensional modelling is widely used for engineering applications. It provides all the information required for animation, design analysis and manufacturing. The three-dimensional objects are shown in Figure 5.2.

The three-dimensional modes are further sub-divided into the following groups:

1. Wireframe models
2. Surface models
3. Solid models

It does not require much computer time and memory. Wireframe models are also used for simple graphic generation and interface detection.

There are many disadvantages of wireframe modelling. The wireframe models lack visual information. The orientation of the true model and any edge are very difficult. They cannot model curved elements.

Wireframe is wrong. It does not give a clear representation of complex profiles, overlap, interference, numerical control, prohibited tooling, etc. Surface models are unambiguous. Figure 5.2. Surface models are less ambiguous as compared to wireframe models.

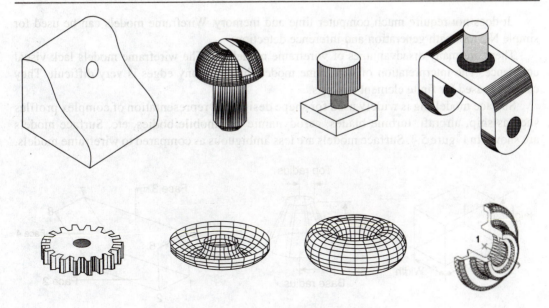

Fig. 5.2 Three-dimensional objects.

Wireframe models are also known as line models (Figure 5.3). Wireframe modelling is an extension of the traditional method of drafting. The construction of a wireframe model is simple.

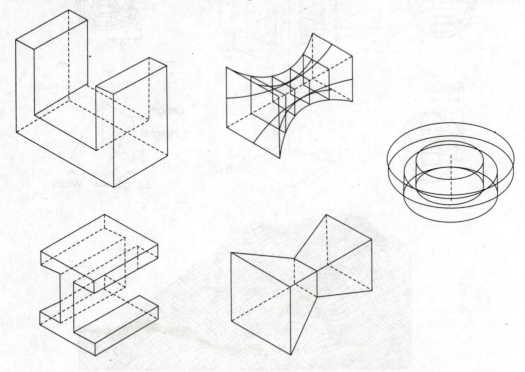

Fig. 5.3 Wireframe models.

It does not require much computer time and memory. Wireframe models can be used for simple NC tool path generation and inference detection.

There are many disadvantages of wireframe modelling. The wireframe models lack visual coherence. The interpretation of wireframe models having many edges is very difficult. They cannot be used for finite element analysis.

Surface modelling is widely used for shape design and representation of complex profiles such as ship, aircraft, turbine blades, aerodynamic automobile bodies, etc. Surface models are shown in Figure 5.4. Surface models are less ambiguous as compared to wireframe models.

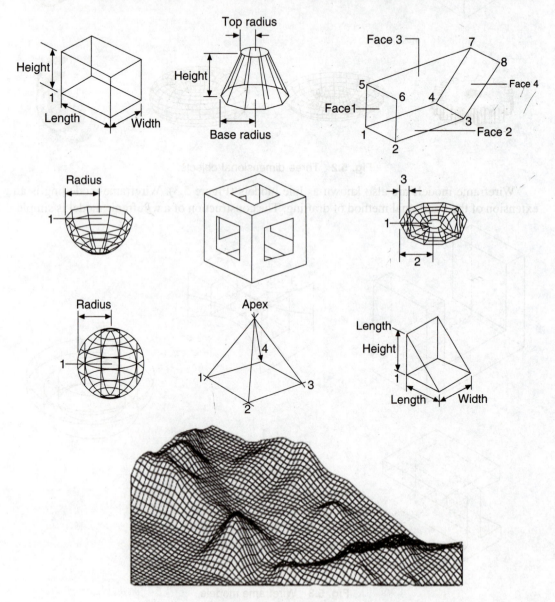

Fig. 5.4 Surface models.

They support hidden line and surface removal algorithms to add realism to the displayed geometry. Surface models are utilised for mass property calculations, creation of finite element meshes, NC tool path generation and for checking interference between mating parts.

Surface models are more complex than other types of models. They require higher computer time and memory than wireframe models. Even though surface models appear like solid models, there is a fundamental difference between surface models and solid models. Surface models define only the geometry of their corresponding objects. They do not specify the topology of their corresponding objects.

Solid modelling is the best technological solution for parametric design and manufacturing applications. Solid modelling represents complete, valid and unambiguous objects. Solid modelling is also called volumetric modelling. The database of solid models contains both geometrical and topological information. The solid models are shown in Figure 5.5. They are less ambiguous as compared to wireframe and surface models. Solid models support hidden line and surface removal algorithms to add realism to the displayed geometry. They support shading and rendering. Solid models are constructed on the basis of both geometry and topology.

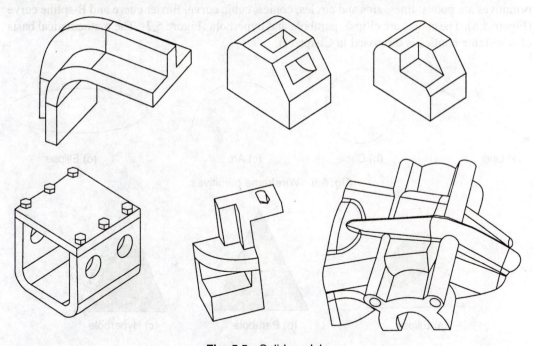

Fig. 5.5 Solid models.

Solid models are used for the evaluation of mass and geometric properties, finite element analysis, kinematic analysis, NC tool path generation and verification, process planning, implementing implementation of form features such as tolerances and surface finish, assembly, planning, the robotics kinematics and dynamics, and the inference analysis for checking mating parts.

The disadvantage of solid models is that they need larger computer time and memory than surface and wireframe models.

5.4 GEOMETRIC CONSTRUCTION METHODS

The three-dimensional construction methods are:

1. Wireframe modelling
2. Surface modelling
3. Solid modelling
4. Extrusion
5. Sweeping
6. Feature modelling
7. Lofting
8. Tweaking

5.4.1 Wireframe Modelling

Wireframe modelling uses geometric primitives for the construction of models. The geometric primitives are points, lines, arcs and circles, conics, cubic curve, Bezier curve and B-spline curve (Figure 5.6). The conics are ellipse, parabola and hyperbola (Figure 5.7). The mathematical basis of wireframe entities is discussed in Chapter 6.

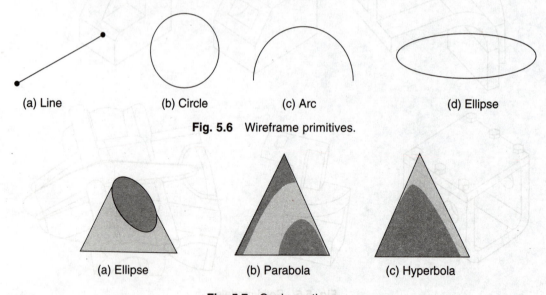

   (a) Line   (b) Circle   (c) Arc   (d) Ellipse

Fig. 5.6 Wireframe primitives.

   (a) Ellipse   (b) Parabola   (c) Hyperbola

Fig. 5.7 Conic sections.

5.4.2 Surface Modelling

Surface models are generated by using surface primitives such as plane surface, ruled surface, surface of revolution, tabulated cylinder, fillet surface, offset surface, Bezier surface, B-spline surface and coons patch (Figure 5.8). The detail mathematical basis of surface entities is discussed in Chapter 7.

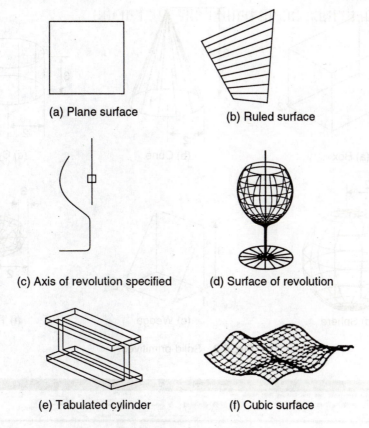

(a) Plane surface   (b) Ruled surface

(c) Axis of revolution specified   (d) Surface of revolution

(e) Tabulated cylinder   (f) Cubic surface

Fig. 5.8 Surface entities.

5.4.3 Solid Modelling

Solid models are constructed by the boundary representation (B-rep) method or by constructive solid geometry (CSG). The solid entities of CSG modelling are box, cone, sphere, cylinder, prism, wedge and torus (Figure 5.9). CSG modelling constructs solid models through Boolean operations (union, subtraction and intersection) on solid entities. The mathematical basis of solid modelling is discussed in Chapter 8.

5.4.4 Extrusion

In extrusion, a three-dimensional solid is created by extruding the face in a direction perpendicular to it as shown in Figure 5.10.

5.4.5 Sweeping

Sweeping is based on the notation of moving a point, curve, or a surface along a given path. A sweep may be linear or non-linear. The linear sweep may involve extrusion or revolving. The non-linear sweep is shown in Figure 5.11.

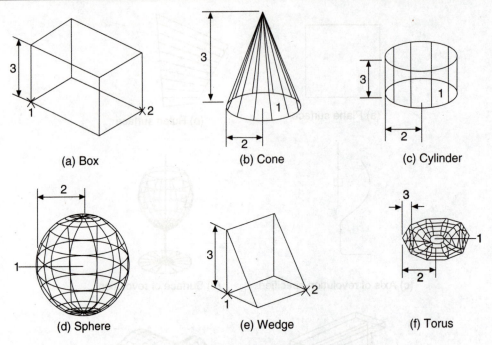

(a) Box   (b) Cone   (c) Cylinder

(d) Sphere   (e) Wedge   (f) Torus

Fig. 5.9   Solid primitives.

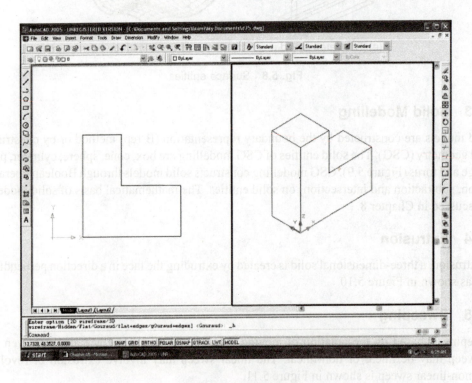

Fig. 5.10   Extrusion.

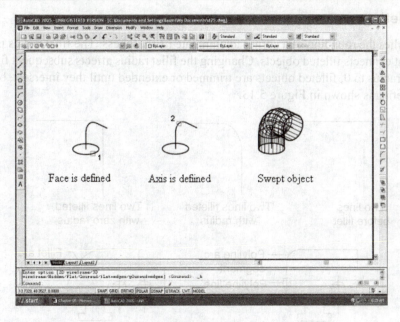

Fig. 5.11   Sweeping.

5.4.6   Feature Modelling

This creates solid models from a shape by an operation. The shape is a two-dimensional sketch, for example, ribs, bosses, cuts and holes. The operation may involve extrusion, sweeping, revolving, etc. Feature modelling is shown in Figure 5.12.

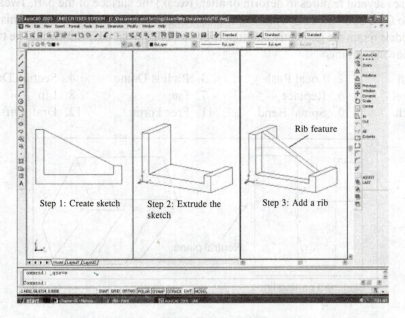

Fig. 5.12   Feature modelling.

5.4.7   Filleting

Filleting implies the rounding of a corner to eliminate its sharpness. The fillet radius is the radius of the arc that connects filleted objects. Changing the fillet radius affects subsequent fillets. If you set the fillet radius to 0, filleted objects are trimmed or extended until they intersect, but no arc is created. Filleting is shown in Figure 5.13.

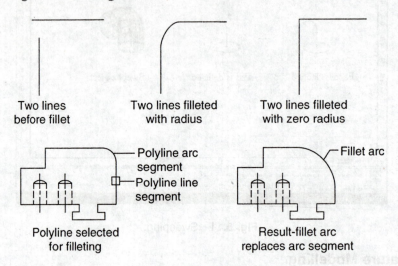

Two lines   Two lines filleted   Two lines filleted
before fillet   with radius   with zero radius

Polyline arc segment
Polyline line segment

Fillet arc

Polyline selected   Result-fillet arc
for filleting   replaces arc segment

Fig. 5.13   Filleting.

5.4.8   Tweaking

Tweaking uses several features to deform or alter (tweak) the surface of the part. Tweaking is not applicable to CSG solid models. Splitting sketch drafts is shown in Figure 5.14. This is because the CSG models retain the geometry and topology modelled from the primitives. The tweak menu lists the following options:

1. Draft	2. Local Push	3. Radius Dome	4. Section Dome
5. Offset	6. Replace	7. Ear	8. Lip
9. Patch	10. Spinal Bend	11. Free Form	12. Draft Offset

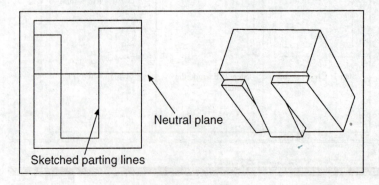

Neutral plane

Sketched parting lines

Fig. 5.14   Tweaking.

5.4.9 Lofting

Lofting is used to create a model with a variant cross-section along a linear/non-linear axis. The lofting procedure is illustrated in Figure 5.15.

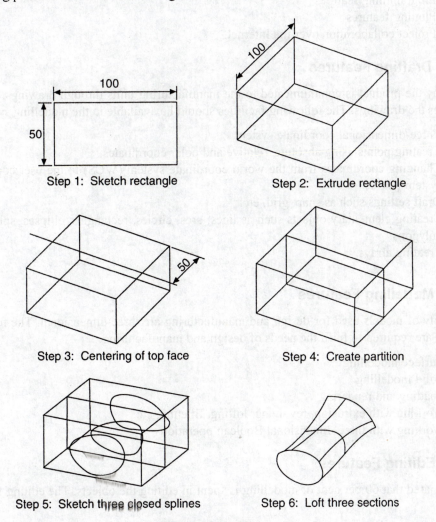

Fig. 5.15   Lofting.

5.5 MODELLING FACILITIES DESIRED

Accurate models are highly essential for precise finite element analysis and qualitative manufacturing. The facilities required to generate accurate models are:

1. Drafting features
2. Modelling features
3. Editing features

4. Annotations, dimensioning, tolerancing and hatching features
5. Display control features
6. Analysis and optimisation features
7. Programming features
8. Plotting features
9. Project collaboration over the Internet.

5.5.1 Drafting Features

Till today the product is communicated to the manufacturing units through drawings. Drafting generates the drawings. The following facilities should be available in the modelling system:

- Three-dimensional coordinate system.
- Creating points using absolute, relative and polar coordinates.
- Changing coordinates from the world coordinate system (WCS) to the user coordinates system (UCS).
- Draft settings such as snap, grid, etc.
- Creating elementary objects such as lines, arcs, circles, rectangles, ellipses, splines and polygons.
- Creating arrays.

5.5.2 Modelling Features

A majority of models used for design and manufacturing are three-dimensional. The following facilities are required to fulfil the needs of design and manufacturing:

- Surface modelling
- Solid modelling
- Shading and rendering
- Working with extrusion, revolving, lofting, filleting, etc.
- Working with three-dimensional Boolean operations

5.5.3 Editing Features

It is estimated that 60 per cent of modelling is spent in editing the objects. The editing facilities are:

- Resizing
- Relocating and duplicating
- Filleting and chamfering
- Windowing, clipping and zooming
- Exploding
- Mirroring
- Lengthening and shortening
- Renaming named objects
- Editing mesh surfaces
- Editing solids

5.5.4 Annotations, Dimensioning, Tolerancing and Hatching Features

Text is a very important part of any drawing. On any given drawing, you may need to draw a single word, a sentence or even paragraphs of text. Dimensions are vital for determining the size of the objects. Tolerances are always posted on the dimensions to find the interference of components used in assembly manufacturing. Sectioning necessitaties hatching to fill areas with a repetitive pattern or solid fill. Hence, the modelling system should have the required facilities to perform annotations, dimensioning, tolerancing and hatching. Following are the essential facilities of a modelling system:

- Drawing single line text
- Editing single line text
- Drawing paragraphs
- Performing spelling check
- Variety of patterns for hatching
- Variety of solid fills for hatching
- Defining the boundaries of area to be hatched
- Controlling the visibility of hatch objects
- Unilateral tolerance system
- Bilateral tolerancing system
- Linear dimensioning
- Leader dimensioning
- Radial dimensioning

5.5.5 Display Control Features

In order to present a picture of the model, display control facilitates lights for illuminating the objects, establishes a viewpoint from which to view the model and then transforms the scene into a realistic rendering or picture. Following are the facilities required:

- Creating views
- Zooming
- Panning
- Windowing
- Creating and assigning materials
- Removal of hidden lines and surfaces
- Creating lights
- Shading and rendering the model
- Generating output

5.5.6 Analysis and Optimisation Features

The size and shape of a model are finalised by practising design and optimising techniques. The facilities required are:

- Evaluation of geometric properties such as area, volume, centroid and inertia
- Evaluation of mass properties such as mass and density

- Finite element analysis tool
- Finite volume analysis tool
- Kinematic analysis tool
- Optimisation of many parameters at a time
- Simulation tools

5.5.7 Programming Features

It is well known that modelling systems are customised for a given range of applications. Programming ability within the modelling system can allow to facilitate the development of user-defined functions. The programming facilities are in the form of MACROs, sub-routines, functions or customised programming language.

5.5.8 Plotting Features

The ultimate goal of most drawings is the final plot because the plots are what the client uses to build the model you created inside the modelling system. The following facilities are required:

- Configuring a plotter
- Defining plot styles
- Creating page set-ups

5.5.9 Project Collaboration Over the Internet

Today, product design has become a collaborative process. From concept to final construction or manufacturing, a varying range of disciplines are involved in converting an idea to reality. Effective management of the design process requires timely communication and rapid distribution of design standards. The World Wide Web (www) benefits the design process by facilitating communication and creating a collaborative environment. Internet collaborative tools are required for the design and manufacturing disciplines.

QUESTION BANK

A. Descriptive Questions

1. What are the requirements of geometric modelling?
2. How do you classify the various modelling systems on the basis of their capabilities?
3. What are the limitations of wireframe modelling? Explain with an example.
4. What are the various three-dimensional construction methods suitable for mechanical engineering applications?
5. Give a classification of the different surfaces that can be used in geometric modelling applications.
6. What are the basic elements of solid modelling?
7. What is meant by sweep? Discuss in detail the various types of sweep techniques.
8. What is feature modelling? Explain with an example.
9. What is filleting? Explain with an example.

10. What is tweaking? Explain with an example.
11. What is lofting? Explain with an example.
12. Explain the range of modelling facilities desired in any general purpose modelling system.

B. Multiple Choice Questions

1. In the following geometric modelling techniques which is not three-dimensional modelling?
   (a) Wireframe modelling   (b) Drafting
   (c) Surface modelling   (d) Solid modelling
2. In the following three-dimensional modelling techniques, which do not require much computer time and memory?
   (a) Surface modelling   (b) Solid modelling
   (c) Wireframe modelling   (d) All of the above
3. In the following geometric modelling techniques, which cannot be used for finite element analysis:
   (a) Wireframe modelling   (b) Surface modelling
   (c) Solid modelling   (d) None of the above
4. In the following geometric primitives, which is not a solid entity of CSG modelling:
   (a) Box   (b) Cone   (c) Cylinder   (d) Circle

Chapter **6**

Wireframe Modelling

After reading this chapter, the reader will be able to understand the following concepts:

➲ Wireframe entities

➲ Curve representation methods

➲ Parametric representation of analytic curves

➲ Curvature continuity

➲ Lagrange interpolation

➲ Parametric representation of synthetic curves

➲ Curve manipulations

6.1 INTRODUCTION

A wireframe model consists of points and curves only, and looks as if it is made up of a bunch of wires. A wireframe model consists of two tables, the vertex table and the edge table. Each entry of the vertex table records a vertex and its coordinate values, while each entry of the edge table has two components giving the two incident vertices of that edge. A wireframe model does not have face information. For example, the manner of representing a cube defined by eight vertices and twelve edges is given om Table 6.1. Figure 6.1 shows all eight vertices and twelve edges of a cube.

Table 6.1 Vertex			
Vertex No.	*X*	*Y*	*Z*
1	1	1	1
2	1	–1	1
3	–1	–1	1
4	–1	1	1
5	1	1	–1
6	1	–1	–1
7	–1	–1	–1
8	–1	–1	–1

Table 6.2 Edge		
Edge No.	*Start Vertex*	*End Vertex*
1	1	2
2	2	3
3	3	4
4	4	1
5	5	6
6	6	7
7	7	8
8	8	5
9	1	5
10	2	6
11	3	7
12	4	8

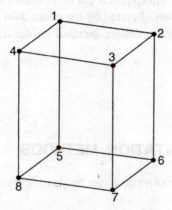

Fig. 6.1 A cube.

Curves play a very significant role in generating a wireframe model, which is the simplest form for representing a solid model. The advantages of a wireframe model include ease of creation and low level hardware and software requirements. Additionally, the data storage requirement is low. The main disadvantage of a wireframe model is that it can be very confusing to visualise. For example, a blind hole in a box may look like a solid cylinder, as shown in Figure 6.2.

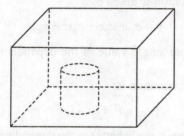

Fig. 6.2 A wireframe model of a solid object with a blind hole.

6.2 CLASSIFICATION OF WIREFRAME ENTITIES

Curves are used to draw a wireframe model which consists of points and curves. In general, curves can be classified as follows:

1. **Analytical curves:** This type of curve can be represented by a simple mathematical equation, such as a circle or an ellipse. It has a fixed form and cannot be modified to achieve a shape that violates the mathematical equations. The analytical curves are:

   - Line
   - Arc
   - Circle
   - Ellipse
   - Parabola
   - Hyperbola

2. **Synthetic curves:** An interpolated curve is drawn by interpolating the given data points and has a fixed form, dictated by the given data points. These curves have some limited flexibility in shape creation, dictated by the data points. The synthetic curves are:

   - Hermite cubic spline
   - Bezier
   - B-spline

6.3 CURVE REPRESENTATION METHODS

The mathematical representation of a curve can be classified as:

1. Non-parametric
   - Explicit
   - Implicit
2. Parametric

6.3.1 Non-parametric Representation

The explicit non-parametric equation is given by:

$$y = c_1 + c_2 x + c_3 x^2 + c_4 x^3 \tag{6.1}$$

In this equation, there is a unique single value of the dependent variable for each value of the independent variable.

The implicit non-parametric equation is:

$$(x - x_c)^2 + (y - y_c)^2 = r^2 \tag{6.2}$$

In this equation, no distinction is made between the dependent and the independent variables. The limitations of non-parametric representation are:

1. Explicit non-parametric representation is based on one-to-one mapping. This cannot be used for the representation of closed curves such as a circle or multi-valued curves such as parabola.
2. If the gradient of a curve at a point is vertical, its value is infinity, which cannot be incorporated in the computer programming.

6.3.2 Parametric Equations

A parametric curve in space has the following form:

$$f: [0, 1] \rightarrow (f(u), g(u), h(u)) \qquad (6.3)$$

where, $f(\ )$, $g(\ )$ and $h(\ )$ are three real-valued functions.

Thus, $f(u)$ maps a real value u in the closed interval [0, 1] to a point in space. The domain of these real functions and vector-valued function $f(\ )$ does not have to be [0, 1]. It can be any closed interval; but, for simplicity, we restrict the domain to [0, 1]. Thus, each u in [0, 1], corresponds to a point $[(f(u), g(u), h(u)]$ in space. The functions $f(\ )$, $g(\ )$ and $h(\ )$ are always polynomials.

Note that if function $h(\ )$ is removed from the definition of $f(u)$, then $f(u)$ has two coordinate components and becomes a curve in the coordinate plane.

Parametric equations allow great versatility in constructing space curves that are multi-valued and easily manipulated.

6.4 PARAMETRIC REPRESENTATION OF ANALYTIC CURVES

6.4.1 Points

The xyz-coordinate system has three coordinate axes, the x- y- and z-axis. They are perpendicular to each other. A point in the space is represented by three numbers (x, y, z), where x, y and z are the coordinates of the x-, y- and z-axes.

6.4.2 Vectors

Vectors have a very important advantage in geometric computing, because it is 'coordinate free.' The meaning of 'coordinate-free' will be clear in later discussions. All vectors will be in boldface like **a** and **A**.

A vector is similar to a point. If it is a vector in the plane (resp.,space), it has two (resp.,three) components. Thus, a vector in an n-dimensional space has n components. For our applications, we shall distinguish two types of vectors: *position* vectors and *direction* vectors. A position vector gives the position of a point. More precisely, a point is a vector. A direction vector gives a direction. Hence, it is not a point. In what follows, position vectors and direction vector are written with boldface upper case and lower case, respectively. For example, **A** and **a** are position and direction vectors, respectively. In many cases, such distinction is unnecessary.

As you have learnt in linear algebra or in calculus, you can add and subtract vectors; but you can only multiply or divide a vector with constants.

The length of a vector is the square root of the sum of squares of all components. A unit-length vector is a vector whose length is one. A vector can be normalised by dividing its components with its length, converting the given vector to a unit-length one while keeping its direction the same. For example, if **a** = (3, 4, 5), then the length of **a**, usually written as |**a**|, is SQRT (50) and the normalised **a** is (3/SQRT(50), 4/SQRT(50), 5/SQRT(50)).

6.4.3 Inner Product

Given two vectors **a** and **b**, its inner product, written as **a** · **b**, is the sum of the products of corresponding components. For example, if **a** = (1, 2, 3) and **b** = (2, –1, 4), then:

$$\mathbf{a} \cdot \mathbf{b} = 1 \times 2 + 2 \times (-1) + 3 \times 4 = 12.$$

The geometric meaning of the inner product of **a** and **b** is the following:

$$\mathbf{a} \cdot \mathbf{b} = |\mathbf{a}| \cdot |\mathbf{b}|\cos(\theta) \tag{6.4}$$

More precisely, the inner product of **a** and **b** is equal to the product of the length of **a**, the length of **b**, and the cosine of the angle θ between **a** and **b**. This is an important formula, because we know the following facts about **a** and **b** once the inner product becomes available:

1. If **a** · **b** is zero, where **a** and **b** are non-zero vectors, then cos(θ) must be zero and, as a result, θ must be 90 degree. Therefore, **a** and **b** are perpendicular to each other.
2. If **a** · **b** is equal to the product of lengths of **a** and **b**, the cosine of θ is 1 and θ is 0 degree. As a result, **a** and **b** are parallel to each other and point to the same direction.
3. If **a** · **b** is equal to the negative product of lengths of **a** and **b**, the cosine of θ is –1 and **a** and **b** are parallel to each other but point in opposite directions.

6.4.4 Cross Product

There is yet one more important concept about vectors: the cross-product of two vectors. Given two vectors **a** and **b**, their cross-product, written as **a** × **b**, is defined as follows:

$$\mathbf{a} \times \mathbf{b} = \left\langle \begin{vmatrix} a_2 & a_3 \\ b_2 & b_3 \end{vmatrix}, -\begin{vmatrix} a_1 & a_3 \\ b_1 & b_3 \end{vmatrix}, \begin{vmatrix} a_1 & a_2 \\ b_1 & b_2 \end{vmatrix} \right\rangle \tag{6.5}$$

where **a** = < a_1, a_2, a_3 >, **b** = < b_1, b_2, b_3 >, and | | is a 2 × 2 determinant. In other words, the cross-product is:

$$\mathbf{a} \times \mathbf{b} = < a_2 b_3 - a_3 b_2, -(a_1 b_3 - a_3 b_1), a_1 b_2 - a_2 b_1 > \tag{6.6}$$

The cross-product of **a** and **b**, **a** × **b**, is perpendicular to both **a** and **b** and points to the direction based on the right-handed system in the order of **a**, **b**, **a** × **b**. Therefore, **b** × **a** points to the opposite direction of **a** × **b**. The length of **a** × **b** is |**a**| |**b**| sin(θ), where θ is the acute angle between **a** and **b**. Hence, if **a** and **b** are perpendicular to each other, the length of **a** × **b** is simply |**a**| |**b**|.

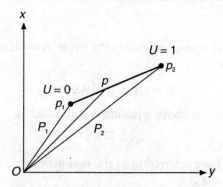

Fig. 6.3   Line connecting two points.

6.4.5   Line

A line is defined by connecting two points P_1 and P_2. A parameter u is defined such that it has the values 0 and 1 at P_1 and P_2 respectively.

The equation of the line is given by:

$$P = P_1 + u\,(P_2 - P_1) \qquad 0 \le u \le 1 \tag{6.7}$$

The length of the line is given by:

$$L = \sqrt{(x_2 - x_1)^2 + (y_2 - y_1)^2 + (z_2 - z_1)^2} \tag{6.8}$$

The unit vector is given by:

$$n = \frac{P_2 - P_1}{L}$$

In matrix form,

$$\begin{Bmatrix} x \\ y \\ z \end{Bmatrix} = \begin{Bmatrix} x_1 \\ y_1 \\ z_1 \end{Bmatrix} + u \left[\begin{Bmatrix} x_2 \\ y_2 \\ z_2 \end{Bmatrix} - \begin{Bmatrix} x_1 \\ y_1 \\ z_1 \end{Bmatrix} \right] \tag{6.9}$$

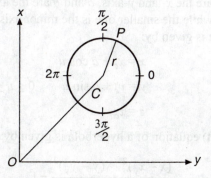

Fig. 6.4   Circle defined by centre and radius.

6.4.6 Circle

The simplest non-linear curve is unquestionably the circle. A circle with centre (x_c, y_c) and radius r has an equation as follows:

$$(x - x_c)^2 + (x - y_c)^2 = r^2 \qquad (6.10)$$

If the centre is the origin, the above equation is simplified to:

$$x^2 + y^2 = r^2 \qquad (6.11)$$

Equations 6.10 and 6.11 are referred to as the non-parametric (implicit) form of the circle. The parametric form of a circle is:

$$x = x_c + r \cos u$$
$$y = y_c + r \sin u \qquad 0 \le u \le 2\pi \qquad (6.12)$$
$$z = z_c$$

The above parametric form uses trigonometric functions.

6.4.7 Conics

A direct generalisation of the circle is the so-called conic curves or simply conics. Greeks knew about conics very well. In fact, Apollonius of Perga (262–200 B.C.) wrote a book of several volumes about conics. Conics are the intersection curves of a plane and a circular cone (i.e., a cone whose base is a circle and whose axis is perpendicular to the base and runs through the centre of the base circle).

There are three types of non-degenerate conics: ellipses, hyperbolas and parabolas. Ellipses and hyperbolas are called central conics because they have a centre of symmetry, while parabolas are non-central.

The non-parametric (implicit) equation of an ellipse is given by:

$$\frac{(x - x_c)^2}{a^2} + \frac{(y - y_c)^2}{b^2} = 1 \qquad (6.13)$$

The axes of this ellipse are the x- and y-axis, a and b are the axis lengths, and the larger one of a and b is the major axis while the smaller one is the minor axis.

The parametric equation is given by:

$$x = x_c + a \cos u$$
$$y = y_c + b \sin u \qquad 0 \le u \le 2\pi \qquad (6.14)$$
$$z = z_c$$

The non-parametric (implicit) equation of a hyperbola is given by:

$$\frac{(x - x_y)^2}{a^2} - \frac{(y - y_y)^2}{b^2} = 1 \qquad (6.15)$$

The definitions of the major axis and minor axis are identical to that of ellipses. The x-axis intersects the curve at two points $(a, 0)$ and $(-a, 0)$ while, the y-axis does not intersect the curve at all.

The parametric equation is given by:

$$x = x_v + a \cosh u$$
$$y = y_v + b \sin u \qquad\qquad (6.16)$$
$$z = z_v$$

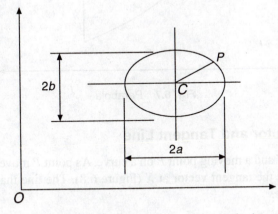

Fig. 6.5 Ellipse defined by a centre, major and minor axes.

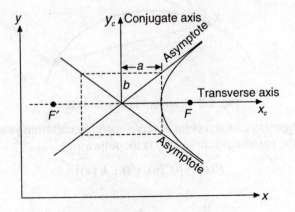

Fig. 6.6 A hyperbola.

The parametric equation of a parabola is given by:

$$x = x_v + 2\,au$$
$$y = y_v + au^2 \qquad 0 \le u \le \infty$$
$$z = z_v \qquad\qquad (6.17)$$

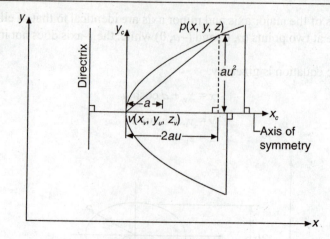

Fig. 6.7 Parabola.

6.4.8 Tangent Vector and Tangent Line

Consider a fixed point X and a moving point P on a curve. As point P moves toward X, the vector from X to P approaches the tangent vector at X (Figure 6.8). The line that contains the tangent vector is the tangent line.

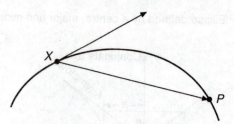

Fig. 6.8 Tangent vector and line.

Computing the tangent vector at a point is very simple. Recall from your calculus knowledge that the derivative of the parametric curve $\mathbf{f}(u)$ is the following:

$$f'(u) = [(f'(u), g'(u), h'(u)]$$

(6.18)

where

$$f'(u) = \frac{df}{du},\ g'(u) = \frac{dg}{du},\ and\ h'(u) = \frac{dh}{du}$$

(6.19)

In general, the length of the tangent vector $f'(u)$ is not one, and normalisation is required, i.e, the unit-length tangent vector at parameter u, or at point $\mathbf{f}'(u)$, is:

$$\frac{f'(u)}{|f'(u)|}$$

(6.20)

where $|\mathbf{x}|$ is the length of vector $\mathbf{x}$. The tangent line at $\mathbf{f}(u)$ is either

$$f(u) + tf'(u) \tag{6.21}$$

or if unit-length direction vector is preferred

$$f(u) + t\left(\frac{f'(u)}{f'(u)}\right) \tag{6.22}$$

where t is a parameter.

Example 6.1 Given the circle $f(u) = [r\cos(2\pi u) + p, r\sin(2\pi u) + q)\, f(u)]$, where u is in the range of 0 and 1. Find the tangent line at $f(u)$.

Solution
We have the tangent vector

$$f'(u) = [-2\pi r \sin(2\pi u),\, 2\pi r \cos(2\pi u)]$$

and the tangent line at $f(u)$:

$$f(u) + tf'(u) = f'(u) = [r\cos(2\pi u) + p, r\sin(2\pi u) + q) + t\,(-2\pi r \sin(2\pi u),\, 2\pi r \cos(2\pi u)]$$

Example 6.2 Given a space cubic curve $f(u) = (u, u^2, u^3)$. Find the tangent line.

Solution
We have the tangent vector

$$f'(u) = (1,\, 2u,\, 3u^2)$$

and the tangent line

$$f(u) + tf'(u) = (u + t,\, u^2 + 2tu,\, u^3 + 3tu^2)$$

6.4.9 Normal Vector

Consider a fixed point $\mathbf{f}(u)$ and two moving points P and Q on a parametric curve. These three points determine a plane. As P and Q move toward $\mathbf{f}(u)$, this plane approaches a limiting position. This is the *osculating plane* at $\mathbf{f}(u)$. Obviously, the osculating plane at $\mathbf{f}(u)$ contains the tangent line at $\mathbf{f}(u)$. It can be shown that the osculating plane is the plane that passes through $\mathbf{f}(u)$ and contains both $\mathbf{f}'(u)$ and $\mathbf{f}''(u)$. More precisely, any point on this plane has the following equation where p and q are parameters:

$$\mathbf{f}(u) + p\mathbf{f}'(u) + q\mathbf{f}''(u) \tag{6.23}$$

The binormal vector $\mathbf{b}(u)$ is the unit-length vector of the cross product of $\mathbf{f}'(u)$ and $\mathbf{f}''(u)$:

$$\mathbf{b}(u) = \frac{[f'(u) \times f''(u)]}{|f'(u) \times f''(u)|} \tag{6.24}$$

Thus, the binormal vector $\mathbf{b}(u)$ is perpendicular to both $\mathbf{f}'(u)$ and $\mathbf{f}''(u)$ and hence perpendicular to the osculating plane. The line $\mathbf{f}(u) + t\mathbf{b}(u)$ is the binormal line at $\mathbf{f}(u)$.

The normal vector is the vector perpendicular to both the tangent and binormal vectors with its direction determined by the right-handed system. That is, the unit-length normal vector $n(u)$ is defined to be as follows:

$$n(u) = \frac{[b(u) \times f'(u)]}{|b(u) \times f'(u)|}$$ (6.25)

The line $f(u) + tn(u)$ is the normal line at $f(u)$. Therefore, tangent vector $f'(u)$, normal vector $n(u)$ and binormal vector $b(u)$ form a coordinate system with origin $f(u)$. The tangent line, binormal line and normal line are the three coordinate axes with positive directions given by the tangent vector, binormal vector and normal vector, respectively. These three vectors are usually referred to as the moving triad or triad at point $f(u)$. The moving triad is also called *moving trihedron*. Figure 6.9 shows their relationship. Note that the tangent, normal and $f''(u)$ vectors are on the same plane.

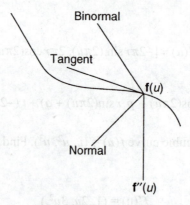

Fig. 6.9   Moving triad.

Example 6.3   Compute the tangent, binormal and normal vectors of the circular helix curve $f(u) = (a\cos(u), a\sin(u), bu)$

Solution
The first and second derivatives are as follows:

$$f'(u) = (-a\sin(u), a\cos(u), b)$$
$$f''(u) = (-a\cos(u), -a\sin(u), 0)$$

The binormal vector is the cross-product of $f'(u)$ and $f'(u)$:

$$b(u) = f'(u) \times f''(u) = (ab\sin(u), -ab\cos(u), a^2)$$

The normal vector is the cross-product of the binormal vector and the tangent vector:

$$n(u) = b(u) \times f'(u) = (-a(a^2 + b^2)\cos(u), -a(a^2 + b^2)\sin(u), 0)$$

If you compare $n(u)$ and $f''(u)$, you will see that these vectors are parallel to each other (i.e., coefficients are proportional) and are both parallel to the xy-plane. As a result, after all the vectors involved are normalised, the normal and the second derivative vectors are identical. This is shown in Figure 6.10. It is computed at $u = 1$.

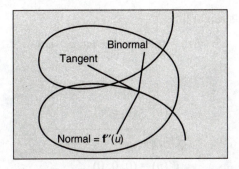

Fig. 6.10 Illustration of tangent, normal and binormal vectors.

6.4.10 Curvature

The tangent vector measures the change of 'distance' and thus gives the speed of a moving point. The speed change, or acceleration, is measured by the derivative of the tangent vector, which is the second derivative. In fact, there is one more interesting interpretation. Take *X* as a fixed point and *P* and *Q* two moving points. As long as not all of these three points lie on a line, they uniquely determine a circle. As both *P* and *Q* moves toward *X*, the circle they determine approaches a limiting position as shown with dot-line Figure 6.11. This limiting circle is called the ***circle of curvature*** at *X* and its centre and radius, *O* and *r*, are the centre and radius of the circle of curvature, respectively. More importantly, 1/*r* is the curvature at *X*. Therefore, the larger the circle of curvature, the smaller the curvature.

From the definition of osculating plane, we know that this circle of curvature must be on the osculating plane. Since the circle of curvature is a tangent to the curve and hence the tangent line, the centre of curvature lies on the normal line.

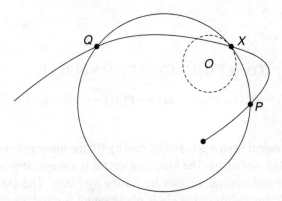

Fig. 6.11 Curvature.

The curvature at *u*, *k*(*u*), can be computed as follows:

$$k(u) = \frac{\left| f'(u) \times f''(u) \right|}{\left| f'(u) \right|^3}$$

(6.26)

Example 6.4   Consider a straight line:

$$\mathbf{f}(u) = (a + up, b + uq, c + ur)$$

Solution

We have the following:

$$\mathbf{f}'(u) = (p, q, r)$$

$$|\mathbf{f}'(u)| = \sqrt{p^2 + q^2 + r^2}$$

$$\mathbf{f}''(u) = (0, 0, 0)$$

$$\mathbf{f}'(u) \times \mathbf{f}''(u) = (0, 0, 0)$$

$$k(u) = 0$$

Therefore, the curvature of a straight line is zero everywhere.

Example 6.5   Consider a circle on the *xy*-plane:

$$\mathbf{f}(u) = (r\cos(u) + p, r\sin(u) + q, 0)$$

Solution

Since it is on the *xy*-plane, the third coordinate function is always 0. From the given circle equation we have the following:

$$\mathbf{f}'(u) = (-r\sin(u), r\cos(u), 0)$$

$$\mathbf{f}''(u) = (-r\cos(u), -r\sin(u), 0)$$

$$\mathbf{f}'(u) \times \mathbf{f}''(u) = (0, 0, r^2)$$

$$|\mathbf{f}'(u)| = r$$

$$|\mathbf{f}'(u) \times \mathbf{f}''(u)| = r^2$$

$$\mathbf{b}(u) = (\mathbf{f}'(u) \times \mathbf{f}''(u)) / |\mathbf{f}'(u) \times \mathbf{f}''(u)| = (0, 0, 1)$$

$$\mathbf{n}(u) = (\mathbf{b}(u) \times \mathbf{f}'(u)) / |\mathbf{b}(u) \times \mathbf{f}'(u)| = (-\cos(u), -\sin(u), 0)$$

$$k(u) = 1/r$$

Thus, the unit-length tangent vector is $(-\sin(u), \cos(u), 0)$, the binormal vector is $(0, 0, 1)$, and the normal vector is $(-\cos(u), \sin(u), 0)$. The binormal vector is always perpendicular to the *xy*-plane while both the tangent and normal vectors lie on the *xy*-plane. The curvature of a circle is a constant $1/r$. As a result, the radius of the circle of curvature is r and the circle of curvature is the given circle itself.

6.5 CURVATURE CONTINUITY

Two boundary curve segments shown in Figure 6.12 are meeting at a vertex X. Let these two curves be described as $\mathbf{f}(u)$ and $\mathbf{g}(v)$, where u and v are values in intervals $[a, b]$ and $[m, n]$, respectively. The problem is: how we can make sure that these curves join together in a 'smooth' way?

Consider the 'endpoint' of curve $\mathbf{f}(b)$ and the 'start point' of curve $\mathbf{g}(m)$. If $\mathbf{f}(b)$ and $\mathbf{g}(m)$ are equal as shown in Figure 6.12a, we shall say curves $\mathbf{f}()$ and $\mathbf{g}()$ are C^0 continuous at $\mathbf{f}(b) = \mathbf{g}(m)$.

If for all $i <= k$, the i-th derivatives at $\mathbf{f}(b)$ and $\mathbf{g}(m)$ are equal, we shall say that the curves are C^k continuous at point $\mathbf{f}(b) = \mathbf{g}(m)$. Intuitively, two curves are C^0 continuous at the joining point if we can go from one curve to the other without crossing a gap because these two curves connect each other. Two curves are C^1 continuous at the joining point if the first derivative does not change when crossing one curve to the other (Figure 6.12b).

Similarly, two curves are C^2 continuous at the joining point if, in addition to the first derivative, the second derivative is also the same when one curve is crossed to the other (Figure 6.12c).

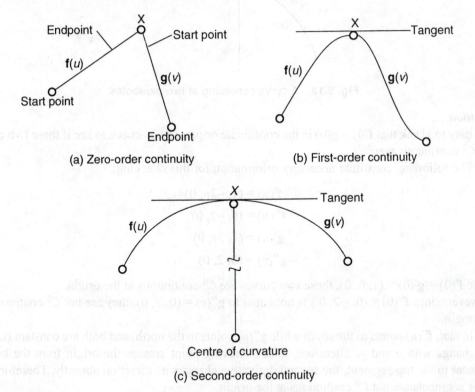

(a) Zero-order continuity   (b) First-order continuity

(c) Second-order continuity

Fig. 6.12 Continuity of curves.

Therefore, C^1 continuous is 'smoother' than C^0 continuous at the joining point, C^2 continuous is 'smoother' than C^1 continuous at the joining point, and so on. Moreover, if the curvatures of the curves at the joining point are equal, we will say they are curvature continuous at the joining point. Intuitively, two curves are curvature continuous if the turning rate is the same at the joining point; however, the second derivatives may not be the same at the joining point. In other words, curvature continuous does not guarantee C^2 continuous; but, C^2 continuous does imply curvature continuous. (Why?)

Example 6.6   Consider that the curve shown in Figure 6.13 consists of two parabolas as follows:

$$\mathbf{f}(u) = (u, -u^2, 0) \text{ and } \mathbf{g}(v) = (v, v^2, 0)$$

where $\mathbf{f}()$, the left curve, and $\mathbf{g}()$, the right curve, have domains $[-1, 0]$ and $[0, 1]$, respectively.

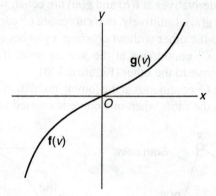

Fig. 6.13   A curve consisting of two parabolas.

Solution
It is easy to check that $\mathbf{f}(0) = \mathbf{g}(0)$ is the coordinate origin. Let us check to see if these two curves are C^2 continuous there.

The following constitute necessary information for this checking:

$$\mathbf{f}'(u) = (1, -2u, 0)$$
$$\mathbf{f}''(u) = (0, -2, 0)$$
$$\mathbf{g}'(u) = (1, 2v, 0)$$
$$\mathbf{g}''(v) = (0, 2, 0)$$

Since $\mathbf{f}'(0) = \mathbf{g}'(0) = (1, 0, 0)$, these two curves are C^1 continuous at the origin.
However, since $\mathbf{f}''(0) = (0, -2, 0)$ is not equal to $\mathbf{g}''(v) = (0, 2, 0)$, they are not C^2 continuous at the origin.

In fact, $\mathbf{f}''(u)$ points to the south while $\mathbf{g}''(u)$ points to the north, and both are constant (i.e., do not change with u and v. Therefore, once a moving point crosses the origin from the bottom segment to the top segment, the second derivative changes its direction abruptly. Therefore, the curve segments are not C^2 continuous at the origin.

Let us computes their curvatures:

$$\text{Curvature of } \mathbf{f}(u) = 2/(1 + 4u^2)^{1.5}$$
$$\text{Curvature of } \mathbf{g}(v) = 2/(1 + 4v^2)^{1.5}$$

They have the same forms, though u is in $[-1, 0]$ and v is in $[0, 1]$. Therefore, the two curve segments are ***curvature continuous*** at the joining point (i.e., $\mathbf{f}(0) = \mathbf{g}(0)$)! Thus, we see that two curve segments may be C^1 continuous and even curvature continuous, but not C^2 continuous.

6.6 LAGRANGE INTERPOLATION

The interpolation method can be applied to draw curves that pass through a set of given data points. The resulting curve can be a straight line, or a quadratic, cubic, or higher order curve. Lagrange interpolation is widely used in computer programming. When a sequence of planar points (x_0, y_0) (x_1, y_1), (x_2, y_2), $....(x_n, y_n)$ is given, the nth degree of the interpolated polynomial can be calculated by the Lagrange Polynomial equation, as follows:

$$y = f(c) = \sum_{i=0}^{n} y_i \prod_{j=0}^{n} \frac{\left[(x - x_j) \text{ omitting } (x - x_i)\right]}{[(x_i - x_j) \text{ omitting } (x_i - x_i)]} \qquad (6.27)$$

In order to understand the above expression better, note that:

1. The term $(x - x_i)$ is skipped in the numerator.
2. The denominator starts with the term $(x_i - x_0)$ and skips the term $(x_i - x_i)$, which will make the expression equal to infinity.

Example 6.7   Using the Lagrange polynomial, find the expression of the curve containing the points, $P0(1, 1)$, $P1(2, 2)$, $P2(3, 2)$.

Solution
The degree of the Lagrange polynomial $= 3 - 1 = 2$
Expanding the Lagrange polynomial, we get:

$$y = y_0 \frac{(x - x_1)(x - x_2)}{(x_0 - x_1)(x_0 - x_2)} + y_1 \frac{(x - x_0)(x - x_2)}{(x_1 - x_0)(x_1 - x_2)} + y_2 \frac{(x - x_0)(x - x_2)}{(x_2 - x_0)(x_2 - x_1)}$$

$$y = (1) \frac{(x - 2)(x - 3)}{(1 - 2)(1 - 3)} + (2) \frac{(x - 1)(x - 3)}{(2 - 1)(2 - 3)} + (1) \frac{(x - 1)(x - 2)}{(3 - 1)(3 - 2)}$$

$$y = -x^2 + 4x - 2$$

This is the explicit non-parametric equation of a circle; the given points lie on the circumference.

6.7 PARAMETRIC REPRESENTATION OF SYNTHETIC CURVES

The analytical discussed in Section 6.4 is insufficient to meet the requirements of mechanical parts that have complex curved shapes such as propeller blades, aircraft wings, ship hulls, automobile body, etc. These components require free-form or synthetic curves. The designs of curved boundaries and surfaces require curve representations that can be manipulated by changing data points, which will create bends and sharp turns in the shape of the curve. These curves are called synthetic curves, and the data points are called control points. If the curve passes through all the data points, it is called an interpolated curve. The smoothness of the curve is the most important requirement of a synthetic curve. The most popular synthetic curves are Hermite cubic, Bezier and B-spline.

6.7.1 Hermite Cubic Curve

The Hermite cubic curve is determined by defining two positions and two tangent vectors at the data points. The Hermite cubic curve is also known as a parametric cubic curve, and cubic spline. This curve is used to interpolate given data points but not a free-form curve, unlike the Bezier and B-spline curves. The most commonly used cubic spline is a three-dimensional planar curve (not twisted). It is represented by a cubic polynomial. Several cubic splines can be joined together by imposing the slope continuity at the common points.

The parametric equation of a cubic spline is given by:

$$P(u) = \sum_{i=0}^{3} a_i u^i \qquad 0 \le u \le 1 \tag{6.28}$$

where a_i are the polynomial coefficients and u is the parameter.

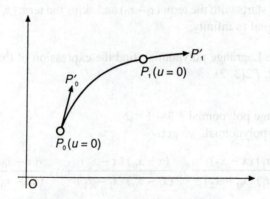

Fig. 6.14 Hermite cubic curve.

Expanding Equation 6.28 we get:

$$P(u) = a_0 + a_1 u + a_2 u^2 + a_3 u^3 \tag{6.29}$$

If (x, y, z) are the coordinates of point P, Equation 6.29 can be written as:

$$x(u) = a_{0x} + a_{1x}u + a_{2x}u^2 + a_{3x}u^3$$
$$y(u) = a_{0y} + a_{1y}u + a_{2y}u^2 + a_{3y}u^3 \tag{6.30}$$
$$z(u) = a_{0z} + a_{1z}u + a_{2z}u^2 + a_{3z}u^3$$

The tangent vector to the curve at any point is obtained by differentiating Equation 6.29 with respect to u to give:

$$P'(u) = \sum_{i=0}^{3} a_i i u^{i-1} \qquad 0 \le u \le 1 \tag{6.31}$$

Equation 6.31 at point P can be written as:

$$x'(u) = a_{1x} + 2a_{2x}u + 3a_{3x}u^2$$
$$y(u) = a_{1y} + 2a_{2y}u + 3a_{3y}u^2 \tag{6.32}$$
$$z(u) = a_{1z} + 2a_{2z}u + 3a_{3z}u^2$$

The coefficients can be evaluated by applying the boundary conditions at the end points. Substituting the boundary conditions at $u = 0$, and $u = 1$ in Equations 6.29 and 6.31, we get:

$$P_0 = P(0) = a_0$$
$$P_1 = P(1) = a_0 + a_1 + a_2 + a_3 \tag{6.33}$$
$$P'_0 = P'(0) = a_1$$
$$P'_1 = P'(1) = a_1 + 2a_2 + 3a_3$$

Solving these four equations simultaneously for the coefficients, we get:

$$a_0 = P_0$$
$$a_1 = P'_0 \tag{6.34}$$
$$a_2 = 3(P_1 - P_0) - (2P'_0 + P'_1)$$
$$a_3 = -2(P_1 - P_0) + P'_0 + P'_1$$

Substituting Equations 6.34 into Equation 6.29 and re-arranging gives:

$$P(u) = (2u^3 - 3u^2 + 1) P_0 + (-2u^3 + 3u^2) P_1 + (u^3 - 2u^2 + u) P'_0 + (u^3 - u^2)P'_1 \quad 0 \le u \le 1 \tag{6.35}$$

The tangent vector is:

$$P'(u) = (6u^2 - 6u) P_0 + (-6u^2 + 6u) P_1 + (3u^2 - 4u + 1) P'_0 + (3u^2 - 2u)P'_1 \quad 0 \le u \le 1 \tag{6.36}$$

The functions of u in Equations 6.35 and 6.36 are called blending functions. The matrix form of Equation 6.35 can be written as:

$$P(u) = [u^3 \ u^2 \ u \ 1] \begin{bmatrix} 2 & 2 & 1 & 1 \\ -3 & 3 & -2 & -1 \\ 0 & 0 & 1 & 0 \\ 1 & 0 & 0 & 0 \end{bmatrix} \begin{Bmatrix} P_0 \\ P_1 \\ P'_0 \\ P'_1 \end{Bmatrix} \tag{6.37}$$

The matrix form of Equation 6.36 can be written as:

$$P(u) = [u^3 \ u^2 \ u \ 1] \begin{bmatrix} 0 & 0 & 0 & 0 \\ 6 & -6 & 3 & 3 \\ -6 & 6 & -4 & -2 \\ 0 & 0 & 1 & 0 \end{bmatrix} \begin{Bmatrix} P_0 \\ P_1 \\ P'_0 \\ P'_1 \end{Bmatrix} \tag{6.38}$$

The important characteristics of a cubic spline curve are as follows:

1. The order of the curve is 3.
2. The geometric information of a cubic spline curve consists of the set of data points and the two end tangent vectors.
3. The spline curve passes through the end points ($u = 0$ and $u = 1$).
4. The curve shape can be changed by changing its end points or tangent vectors.
5. If the two endpoints are fixed, the shape of the spline can be changed by changing either the magnitudes or the directions of the tangent vectors.

In design applications, cubic splines are not as popular as the Bezier and B-spline curves. There are two reasons for this. These are:

1. The curve cannot be modified locally, i.e., when a data point is moved, or an end slope is changed, the entire curve is affected as shown in Figure 6.15.
2. The order of the curve is always constant (cubic), regardless of the number of data points. An increase in the number of data points increases shape flexibility, However, this requires more data points, creating more splines that are joined together (only two data points and slopes are utilised for each spline).

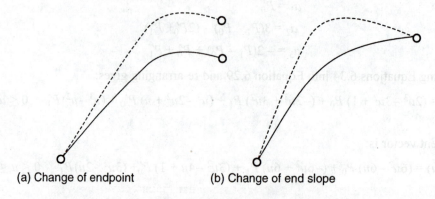

(a) Change of endpoint   (b) Change of end slope

Fig. 6.15 Control of spline curve.

Example 6.8 A parametric cubic curve passes through the points (0, 0), (2, 4), (4, 3), (5, –2) which are parameterised at $u = 0$, 1/4, 3/4 and 1, respectively. Determine the geometric coefficient matrix and the slope of the curve when $u = 0.5$.

Solution

$$\begin{Bmatrix} x_1 \\ x_2 \\ x_3 \\ x_4 \end{Bmatrix} = \begin{Bmatrix} 0 \\ 2 \\ 4 \\ 5 \end{Bmatrix} = \begin{bmatrix} 0 & 0 & 0 & 1 \\ 0.0156 & 0.0625 & 0.25 & 1 \\ 0.4218 & 0.5625 & 0.75 & 1 \\ 1 & 1 & 1 & 1 \end{bmatrix} \begin{bmatrix} 2 & -2 & 1 & 1 \\ -3 & 3 & -2 & -1 \\ 0 & 0 & 1 & 0 \\ 1 & 0 & 0 & 0 \end{bmatrix} \begin{Bmatrix} P_0 \\ P_1 \\ P_0' \\ P_1' \end{Bmatrix}$$

$$\begin{Bmatrix} y_1 \\ y_2 \\ y_3 \\ y_4 \end{Bmatrix} = \begin{Bmatrix} 0 \\ 4 \\ 3 \\ -2 \end{Bmatrix} = \begin{bmatrix} 0 & 0 & 0 & 1 \\ 0.0156 & 0.0625 & 0.25 & 1 \\ 0.4218 & 0.5625 & 0.75 & 1 \\ 1 & 1 & 1 & 1 \end{bmatrix} \begin{bmatrix} 2 & -2 & 1 & 1 \\ -3 & 3 & -2 & -1 \\ 0 & 0 & 1 & 0 \\ 1 & 0 & 0 & 0 \end{bmatrix} \begin{Bmatrix} P_0 \\ P_1 \\ P_0' \\ P_1' \end{Bmatrix}$$

$$\begin{Bmatrix} P_0(x,y) \\ P_1(x,y) \\ P_0'(x,y) \\ P_1'(x,y) \end{Bmatrix} = \begin{Bmatrix} (0,0) \\ (5,-2) \\ (10.33, 22) \\ (4.99, -26) \end{Bmatrix}$$

At $u = 0.5$:

$$P'(x) = [0.5^3 \ 0.5^2 \ 0.5 \ 1] \begin{bmatrix} 0 & 0 & 0 & 0 \\ 6 & -6 & 3 & 3 \\ -6 & 6 & -4 & -2 \\ 0 & 0 & 1 & 0 \end{bmatrix} \begin{Bmatrix} 0 \\ 5 \\ 10.33 \\ 4.99 \end{Bmatrix} = 3.67$$

$$P'(y) = [0.5^3 \ 0.5^2 \ 0.5 \ 1] \begin{bmatrix} 0 & 0 & 0 & 0 \\ 6 & -6 & 3 & 3 \\ -6 & 6 & -4 & -2 \\ 0 & 0 & 1 & 0 \end{bmatrix} \begin{Bmatrix} 0 \\ -2 \\ 22 \\ -26 \end{Bmatrix} = -2.0$$

$$\text{Slope} = \frac{p'(y)}{p'(y)} = \frac{-2.0}{3.67} = -0.545$$

6.7.2 Bezier Curve

A Bezier curve is defined by approximating a set of data points. Given $n + 1$ points (called control points) $P_0, P_1, P_2, ..., P_n$ in space, the Bezier curve defined by these control points is:

$$P(u) = \sum_{i=0}^{n} B_{n,i}(u) P_i \qquad 0 \le u \le 1 \tag{6.39}$$

where the coefficients are defined as follows:

$$B_{n,j}(u) = \frac{n!}{i!(n-i)!} u^i (1-u)^{n-1} \tag{6.40}$$

Therefore, the point that corresponds to u on the Bezier curve is the 'weighted' average of all control points, where the weights are the coefficients $B_{n,i}(u)$. The line segments $P_0 P_1, P_1 P_2, ..., P_{n-1} P_n$, called legs, joining in this order form a *characteristic polygon*. Functions $B_{n,i}(u)$, are referred to as the *Bezier basis functions* or *Bernstein polynomials*.

Note that the domain of u is [0, 1]. As a result, all basis functions are non-negative. In the above, since u and i can both be zero and so do $1 - u$ and $n - i$, we adopt the convention that 0^0 is 1.

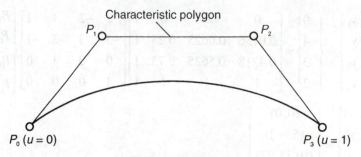

Fig. 6.16 Bezier curve.

Following are the important characteristics of a Bezier curve:

1. *The degree of a Bezier curve defined by n + 1 control points is n:* In each basis function, the exponent of u is $i + (n - i) = n$. Therefore, the degree of the curve is n.
2. *P(u) passes through P_0 and P_n:* This is shown in Figure 6.16. The curve passes though the first and the last control points.
3. *Non-negativity:* All basis functions are non-negative.
4. *Partition of unity:* The sum of the basis functions at a fixed u is 1. It is not difficult to verify that the basis functions are the coefficients in the binomial expansion of the expression $1 = [u + (1 - u)]^n$. Hence, their sum is one. Moreover, since they are non-negative, we conclude that the value of any basis function is in the range of 0 and 1.

   Since all basis functions are in the range of 0 and 1 and add to one, they can be considered as weights in the computation of a weighted average. More precisely, we could say "to compute $\mathbf{P}(u)$, one takes the weight $B_{n,i}(u)$ for control point $\mathbf{P}_i$ and sum them together."
5. *Convex hull property:* This means that the Bezier curve defined by the given $n + 1$ control points lies completely in the convex hull of the given control points. The convex hull of a set of points is the smallest convex set that contains all points. In Figure 6.17, the convex hull of the 11 control points is shown. Note that not all control points are on the boundary of the convex hull. For example, control points 3, 4, 5, 8 and 9 are in the interior. The curve, except for the first two end points, lies completely in the convex hull.

   This property is important because we are guaranteed that the generated curve will be in an understood and computable region and will not go outside of it.

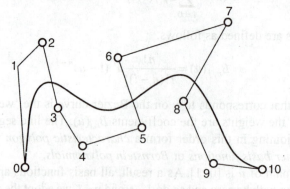

Fig. 6.17 Illustration of convex hull property.

6. *Variation diminishing property:*   If the curve is in a plane, this means that no straight line intersects a Bézier curve more times than it intersects the characteristics polygon. Take a look at Figure 6.18. Line 1 intersects the curve three times and the polyline seven times; line 2 intersects the curve and its polyline twice; the line 3-intersects the curve four times and the polyline seven times. You can draw other straight lines to verify this property. So, what is the meaning of this characteristic? It tells us that the complexity (i.e., turning and twisting) of the curve is no more complex than the characteristic polygon. In other words, the characteristic polygon twists and turns more frequently than the Bezier curve does, because an arbitrary line hits the control polyline more often than it hits the curve. Take a look at Figure 6.18, the characteristic polygon is more complex than the curve it defines.

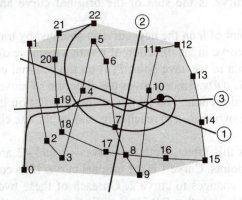

Fig. 6.18   Complexity of characteristic polygon.

7. *Affine invariance:*   If an affine transformation is applied to a Bezier curve, the result can be constructed from the affine images of its control points. This is a nice property. When we want to apply a geometric or even affine transformation to a Bezier curve, this property states that we can apply the transformation to control points, which is quite easy, and once the transformed control points are obtained the transformed Bezier curve is the one defined by these new points. Therefore, we do not have to transform the curve.

8. *Moving control points:*   Changing the position of a control point will change the shape of the defined Bezier curve. Suppose a control point P_k is moved to a new position $P_k + \mathbf{v}$, where vector **v** gives both the direction and length of this move. This is shown in Figure 6.19.

Fig. 6.19   Effect of control point.

Let the original Bezier curve be as follows:

$$P(u) = \sum_{i=0}^{n} B_{n,i}(u)P_i \qquad 0 \le u \le 1$$

Since the new Bezier curve is defined by P_0, P_1...., $P_k + \mathbf{v}$, ..., P_n, its equation $D(u)$ is:

$$Q(u) = \sum_{i=0}^{k-1} B_{n,i}(u)P_i + B_{n,k}(u)(P_k + v) + \sum_{i=k+1}^{n} B_{n,i}(u)P_i$$

$$= \sum_{i=0}^{n} B_{n,i}(u)P_i + B_{n,k}(u)\mathbf{v} \qquad (6.41)$$

$$= P(u) + B_{n,k}(u)\mathbf{v}$$

In the above, since only the kth term uses a different control point $P_k + \mathbf{v}$, after re-grouping, we know that the new curve is the sum of the original curve and an extra term $B_{n,k}(u)v$. This means:

The corresponding point of u on the new curve is obtained by translating the corresponding point of u on the original curve in the direction of v with a distance of $|B_{n,k}(u)\mathbf{v}|$.

More precisely, given a u, we have point $P(u)$ on the original curve and $Q(u)$ on the new curve and $Q(u) = P(u) + B_{n,k}(u)\mathbf{v}$. Since $\mathbf{v}$ gives the direction of movement, $Q(u)$ is the result of moving $P(u)$ in the same direction. The length of this translation is, of course, the length of vector $B_{n,k}(u)\mathbf{v}$. Therefore, when $B_{n,k}(u)$ reaches its maximum, the change from $P(u)$ to $Q(u)$ is the largest.

Figure 6.20 illustrates this effect. Both the curves −1 and −2 are Bezier curves of degree 8 defined by nine control points. Curve 1 is the original curve. If its control point 3 is moved to a new position, the curve 1 changes to curve 2. On each of these two curves there is the point corresponding to $u = 0.5$. It is clear that $P(0.5)$ moves in the same direction to $Q(0.5)$. The distance between $P(0.5)$ and $Q(0.5)$ is the length of vector $B_{8,3}(0.5)\mathbf{v} = 8!/(3!(8-3)!) \times 0.5^3(1-0.5)^{8-3}$ $\mathbf{v} = 0.22\mathbf{v}$. Hence, the distance is about 22 per cent of the distance between the original control point 3 and the new control point 3 as shown in the figure.

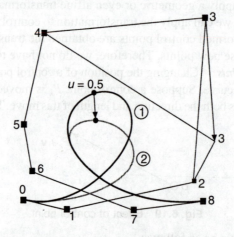

Fig. 6.20 Effect of translation.

We can obtain one more important conclusion from the above discussion. Since $B_{n,k}(u)$ is non-zero in the open interval $(0,1)$, $B_{n,k}(u)\mathbf{v}$ is not a zero vector in $(0, 1)$. This means that except for the two endpoints $P(0)$ and $P(1)$, all points on the original curve are moved to new locations. Therefore, we have:

Changing the position of a control point causes the shape of a Bezier curve to change globally.

9. *Bezier curves are tangent to their first and last legs:* Differentiating Equation (6.39) with respect to u, we get

$$\frac{d}{du} P(u) = P'(u) = \sum_{i=0}^{n-1} B_{n-1,i}(u) \{P_{i+1} - P_i\} \tag{6.42}$$

Letting $u = 0$ and $u = 1$ gives $P'(0) = n(P_1 - P_0)$ and $P'(1) = n(P_n - P_{n-1})$ The first means that the tangent vector at $u = 0$ is in the direction of $P_1 - P_0$ multiplied by n. Therefore, the first leg in the indicated direction is tangent to the Bezier curve. The second means that the tangent vector at $u = 1$ is in the direction of $P_n - P_{n-1}$ multiplied by n. Therefore, the last leg in the indicated direction is tangent to the Bezier curve. Figure 6.21 shows this property well.

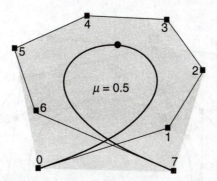

Fig. 6.21 Tangential property of Bezier curve.

6.7.3 Finding a Point on a Bezier Curve: De Casteljau's Algorithm

Following the construction of a Bezier curve, the next important task is to find the point $P(u)$ on the curve for a particular u. A simple way is to plug u into every basis function, compute the product of each basis function and its corresponding control point, and finally add them together. While this works fine, it is not numerically stable (i.e., could introduce numerical errors during the course of evaluating the Bernstein polynomials).

In what follows, we shall only write down the control point numbers, i.e. the control points are 00 for P_0, 01 for P_1, ..., $0i$ for P_i, ..., $0n$ for P_n. The 0s in these numbers indicate the initial or the 0-th iteration. Later on, it will be replaced with **1, 2, 3** and so on.

The fundamental concept of de Casteljau's algorithm is to choose a point **C** in line segment AB such that C divides the line segment AB in a ratio of $u:1 - u$ (i.e., the ratio of the distance between A and C and the distance between A and B is u). Let us find a way to determine point C.

$$A \qquad C \qquad\qquad B$$

The vector from *A* to *B* is **B** – **A**. Since *u* is a ratio in the range of 0 and 1, point *C* is located at $u(\mathbf{B} - \mathbf{A})$. Taking the position of A into consideration, point *C* is $A + u(\mathbf{B} - \mathbf{A}) = (1 - u)A + uB$. Therefore, given a *u*, $(1 - u)A + uB$ is the point *C* between *A* and *B* that divides *AB* in a ratio of $u:1 - u$.

The idea of de Casteljau's algorithm goes as follows:

Suppose we want to find $\mathbf{P}(u)$, where *u* is in [0, 1]. Starting with the first polyline, **00-01-02-03...–0n**, use the above formula to find a point **1i** on the leg (i.e. line segment) from **0i** to **0(i + 1)** that divides the line segment **0i** and **0(i + 1)** in a ratio of *u*: 1 – *u*. In this way, we will obtain *n* points **10, 11, 12, ..., 1(n – 1)**. They define a new polyline of **n** – 1 legs.

In Figure 6.22, *u* is 0.4. **10** is in the leg of **00** and **01**, **11** is in the leg of **01** and **02**, ..., and **14** is in the leg of **04** and **05**. All these new points are 10, 11, 12, 13 and 14.

The new points are numbered as **1i**'s. Apply the procedure to this new polyline and we shall get a second polyline of *n* –1 points **20, 21, ..., 2(n –2)** and *n* – 2 legs. Starting with this polyline, we can construct a third one of *n* – 2 points **30, 31, ..., 3(n – 3)** and *n* –3 legs. Repeating this process *n* times yields a single point **n0**. De Casteljau proved that this is the point $\mathbf{P}(u)$ on the curve that corresponds to *u*.

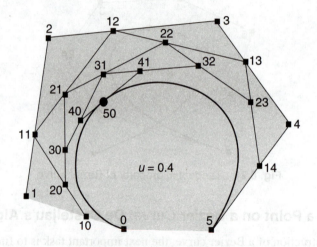

Fig. 6.22 Casteljau's algorithm.

Let us continue with Figure 6.22. Let **20** be the point in the leg of **10** and **11** that divides the line segment **10** and **11** in a ratio of *u*:1–*u*. Similarly, choose **21** on the leg of **11** and **12**, **22** on the leg of **12** and **13**, and **23** on the leg of **13** and **14**. This gives a third polyline defined by **20, 21, 22** and **23**. This third polyline has 4 points and 3 legs. Keep doing this and we shall obtain a new polyline of three points **30, 31** and **32**. From this fourth polyline, we have the fifth one of two points **40** and **41**. Do it once more, and we have **50**, the point $\mathbf{P}(0.4)$ on the curve.

This is the geometric interpretation of de Casteljau's algorithm.

6.7.4 Joining Two Bezier Curves with C^1-Continuity

A Bezier curve being tangent to its first and last legs provides us with a technique for joining two or more Bezier curves together for designing a desired shape. Let the first curve *P*(*u*) be defined by $m + 1$ control points $P_0, P_1, P_2, ..., P_m$. Let the second curve $Q(u)$ be defined by $n + 1$ control points $Q_0, Q_1, Q_2, ..., Q_n$. If we want to join these two Bezier curves together, then P_m must be equal to Q_0. This guarantees a C^0 continuous join.

Recall that the first curve is a tangent to its last leg and the second curve is a tangent to its first leg. Consequently, to achieve a smooth transition, $P_{m-1}, P_m = Q_0$, and Q_1 must be on the same line such that the directions from P_{m-1} to P_m and the direction from Q_0 to Q_1 are the same. This is shown below.

P_{m-1} $P_m = Q_0$ Q_1

While joining two Bezier curves in this way looks smooth, it is still a C^0 join and is not yet C^1. In order to achieve C^1 continuity, we have to make sure that the tangent vector at $u = 1$ of the first curve, $P'(1)$, and the tangent vector at $u = 0$ of the second curve, $Q'(0)$, are identical. That is, the following must hold:

$$P'(1) = m(P_m - P_{m-1}) = Q'(0) = n\,(Q_1 - Q_0) \qquad (6.43)$$

This relation states that to achieve C^1 continuity at the joining point, the ratio of the length of the last leg of the first curve (i.e., $|p_m - p_{m-1}|$) and the length of the first leg of the second curve (i.e., $|q_1 - q_0|$) must be n/m. Since the degrees m and n are fixed, we can adjust the positions of p_{m-1} or q_1 on the same line so that the above relation is satisfied.

Figure 6.23 has two Bézier curves. The characteristic polygon defines a Bezier curve of degree 4 while the Bezier curve of degree 5. Since the last leg of the first curve and the first leg of the second are not on the same line, the two curves are not joint smoothly. Figure 6.24 shows two Bezier curves that are tangent to a line at the joining point. However, they are not C^1 continuous. The left curve is of degree 4, while the right curve is of degree 7. But, the ratio of the last leg of the left curve and the first leg of the right curve seems near 1 rather than $7/4 = 1.75$. To achieve C^1 continuity, we should increase (resp., decrease) the length of the last (resp. first) leg of the left (resp., right)

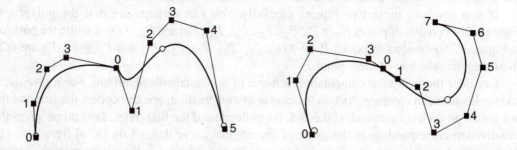

Fig. 6.23   Bezier curves.   **Fig. 6.24**   Tangential property

There is one more application of this tangency property. If we let the first and last control points are identical (i.e., $P_0 = P_n$) and P_1, P_0 and P_{n-1} collinear, the generated Bezier curve will be a closed one (Figure 6.25). To achieve C^1 continuous at P_0, we must have $P_1 - P_0 = P_n - P_{n-1}$ (i.e., the first and last legs have the same length and P_1, $P_0 = P_n$, P_{n-1} are collinear).

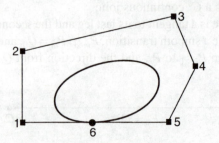

Fig. 6.25   Closed Bezier curve.

Note that though the above curve looks like an ellipse, it is not because this curve is of degree 6 and Bezier curves are polynomials, which cannot represent circles and ellipses.

6.7.5   Sub-dividing a Bezier Curve

The meaning of *sub-dividing* a curve is to cut a given Bezier curve at $P(u)$ for some u into two curve segments, each of which is still a Bezier curve. Since the resulting Bezier curves must have their own new control points, the original set of control points is discarded. Moreover, since the original Bezier curve of degree n is cut into two pieces, each of which is a sub-set of the original degree n Bezier curve, the resulting Bezier curves must be of degree n.

Given a set of $n + 1$ control points P_0, P_1, P_2, ..., P_n and a parameter value u in the range of 0 and 1, we want to find *two* sets of $n + 1$ control points Q_0, Q_1, Q_2, ..., Q_n and R_0, R_1, R_2, ..., R_n such that the Bezier curve defined by Q_i's (resp., R_i's) is the piece of the original Bezier curve on $[0, u]$ (resp., $[u, 1]$).

The algorithm is very simple. In fact, de Casteljau's algorithm for evaluating the point $P(u)$ on the curve has provided all necessary information. In Figure 6.26a, all intermediate steps of applying de Casteljau's algorithm for computing $P(u)$ are shown and Figure 6.26b shows the sub-divisions of the curve at $P(u)$ and their corresponding characteristic polygons.

If you compare these two figures carefully, you can perhaps see that the polygon in Figure 6.26a consists of points $P_{00} = P_0$, P_{10}, P_{20}, P_{30}, P_{40}, P_{50} and $P_{60} = P(u)$, while the polygon in Figure 6.26b consists of points $P_{60} = P(u)$, P_{51}, P_{42}, P_{33}, P_{24}, P_{15} and $P_{06} = P_6$. Figure 6.27 illustrates the selection of these points.

Consider the triangular computation scheme of de Casteljau's algorithm. For a given u, it takes n iterations to compute $P(u)$. In the course of computation, one can collect the first and the last points on each column and, at the end, the collection of the first (resp., last) points gives the sub-division corresponding to the piece of the original curve defined on $[0, u]$ (resp., $[u, 1]$). Thus, in the triangular scheme given in Figure 6.28, the top edge in the direction of the arrows and the lower edge in the reversed direction of the arrows provide the control points of the first and the second curve segments, respectively.

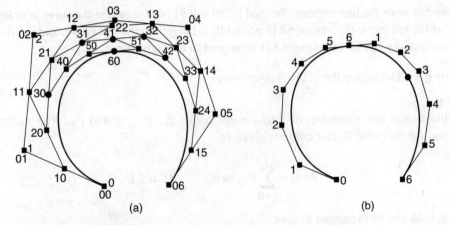

(a)

(b)

Fig. 6.26 Casteljau's algorithm for computing.

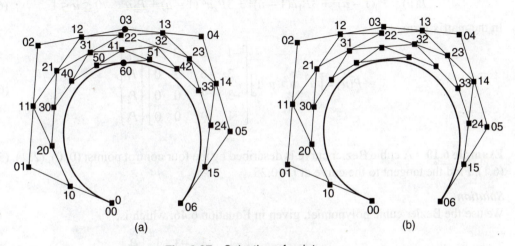

(a)

(b)

Fig. 6.27 Selection of points.

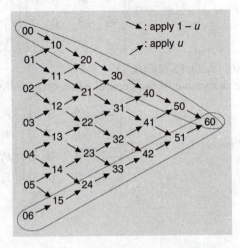

Fig. 6.28 Triangular scheme.

Note that since the line segment defined by **50** and **51** is a tangent to the curve at point **60**, the last leg of the left curve (i.e., point **50** to point **60**) is tangent to the left curve, and the first leg of the right curve (i.e., point **60** to point **51**) is tangent to the right curve.

Example 6.9   Determine the cubic Bezier curve.

Solution

The cubic Bezier curve consists of four control points P_0, P_1, P_2, and P_3. The mathematical expression for the cubic Bezier curve is given by:

$$P(u) = \sum_{i=0}^{3} B_{3,i}(u)P_i \qquad 0 \le u \le 1 \tag{6.44}$$

Equation 6.44 can be expanded to give:

$$P(u) = P_0(1-u)^3 + 3P_1u(1-u)^2 + 3P_2u^2(1-u) + P_3u^3 \qquad 0 \le u \le 1 \tag{6.45}$$

In the matrix form:

$$P(u) = \begin{bmatrix} u^3 & u^2 & u & 1 \end{bmatrix} \begin{bmatrix} -1 & 3 & -3 & 1 \\ 3 & -6 & 3 & 0 \\ -3 & 3 & 0 & 0 \\ 1 & 0 & 0 & 0 \end{bmatrix} \begin{Bmatrix} P_0 \\ P_1 \\ P_2 \\ P_3 \end{Bmatrix} \tag{6.46}$$

Example 6.10   A cubic Bezier curve is described by the four control points: (0, 0), (2, 1), (5, 2), (6,1). Find the tangent to the curve at $t = 0.25$.

Solution

We use the Bezier cubic polynomial, given in Equation 6.46, which is:

$$P(u) = \begin{bmatrix} u^3 & u^2 & u & 1 \end{bmatrix} \begin{bmatrix} -1 & 3 & -3 & 1 \\ 3 & -6 & 3 & 0 \\ -3 & 3 & 0 & 0 \\ 1 & 0 & 0 & 0 \end{bmatrix} \begin{Bmatrix} P_0 \\ P_1 \\ P_2 \\ P_3 \end{Bmatrix}$$

The control points are (0, 0), (2, 1), (5, 2), (6, 1).

The tangent is given by the derivative of the general equation as follows:

$$P'(u) = \begin{bmatrix} 3u^2 & 2u & 1 & 0 \end{bmatrix} \begin{bmatrix} -1 & 3 & -3 & 1 \\ 3 & -6 & 3 & 0 \\ -3 & 3 & 0 & 0 \\ 1 & 0 & 0 & 0 \end{bmatrix} \begin{Bmatrix} P_0 \\ P_1 \\ P_2 \\ P_3 \end{Bmatrix}$$

At $u = 0.25$, we get:

$$P'(u) = [3(0.25)^2 \quad 2(0.25) \quad 1 \quad 0] \begin{bmatrix} -1 & 3 & -3 & 1 \\ 3 & -6 & 3 & 0 \\ -3 & 3 & 0 & 0 \\ 1 & 0 & 0 & 0 \end{bmatrix} \begin{Bmatrix} P_0 \\ P_1 \\ P_2 \\ P_3 \end{Bmatrix} = (7.36, 2.91)$$

6.7.6 B-Spline Curve

In order to design a B-spline curve, we need a set of control points, a set of knots and a set of coefficients, one for each control point, so that all curve segments are joined together satisfying certain continuity condition. The computation of the coefficients is perhaps the most complex step because they must ensure certain continuity conditions. Given $(n + 1)$ control points $P_0, P_1, ..., P_n$ and a knot vector $U = \{u_0, u_1, ..., u_m\}$, the B-spline curve of degree k defined by these control points and knot vector U is:

$$P(u) = \sum_{i=0}^{n} N_{i,k}(u)P_i \qquad 0 \le u \le u_{\max} \tag{6.47}$$

where $N_{i,p}(u)$s are B-spline basis functions of degree k. The control points called deBoor points form the vertices of control polygon.

The basis functions are given by:

$$N_{i,0}(u) = \begin{cases} 1 & \text{if } u_i \le u \le u_{i+1} \\ 0 & \text{otherwise} \end{cases} \tag{6.48}$$

$$N_{i,k}(u) = \frac{u - u_i}{u_{i+k} - u_i} N_{i,k-1}(u) + \frac{u_{i+k+1} - u}{u_{i+k+1} - u_{i+1}} N_{i+1,k-1}(u) \tag{6.49}$$

The above is usually referred to as the ***Cox-de Boor recursion formula***, i.e., the basis function $N_{i,0}(u)$ is 1 if u is in the i-th knot span $[u_i, u_{i+1})$. For example, if we have four knots $u_0 = 0$, $u_1 = 1$, $u_2 = 2$ and $u_3 = 3$, knot spans 0, 1 and 2 are $[0, 1)$, $[1, 2)$, $[2, 3)$, and the basis functions of degree 0 are $N_{0,0}(u) = 1$ on $[0, 1)$ and 0 elsewhere, $N_{1,0}(u) = 1$ on $[1, 2)$ and 0 elsewhere, and $N_{2,0}(u) = 1$ on $[2, 3)$ and 0 elsewhere. This is shown in Figure 6.29.

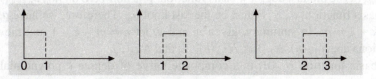

Fig. 6.29 The basis functions

In order to understand the way of computing $N_{i,p}(u)$ for k greater than 0, we use the triangular computation scheme. All knot spans are listed on the left (first) column and all degree zero basis functions on the second. This is shown in Figure 6.30.

For computing $N_{i,1}(u)$, $N_{i,0}(u)$ and $N_{i+1,0}(u)$ are required. Therefore, we can compute $N_{0,1}(u)$, $N_{1,1}(u)$, $N_{2,1}(u)$, $N_{3,1}(u)$ and so on. All these $N_{i,1}(u)$'s are written in the third column. Once all $N_{i,1}(u)$'s have been computed, we can compute $N_{i,2}(u)$'s and put them on the fourth column. This process continues until all required $N_{i,k}(u)$'s are computed.

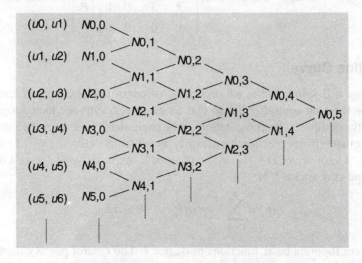

Fig. 6.30   Triangular scheme.

The B-spline functions have the following properties:

1. $N_{i,k}(u)$ is a degree k polynomial in u.
2. **Non-negativity:** For all i, k and u, N_i, $k(u)$ is non-negative.
3. **Local support:** $N_{i,k}(u)$ is a non-zero polynomial on (u_i, u_{i+k+1})
4. On any span $(u_i \ u_{i+1})$ at most $k + 1$ degree k basis functions are non-zero, namely: $N_{i-k,k}(u)$, $N_{i-k+1,k}(u)$, $N_{i-k+2,k}(u)$, ..., $N_{i,k}(U)$.
5. **Partition of unity:** The sum of all non-zero degree k basis functions on span (u_i, u_{i+1}) is unity. The previous property shows that $N_{i-k,k}(u)$, $N_{i-k+1,k}(u)$, $N_{i-k+2,k}(u)$,..., $N_{i,k}(u)$ are non-zero on (u_i, u_{i+1}). This one states that the sum of these $k + 1$ basis functions is 1.
6. If the number of knots is $m + 1$, the degree of the basis functions is k, and the number of degree k basis functions is $n + 1$, then $m = n + k + 1$:
   Let $N_{n,k}(u)$ be the last degree k basis function. It is non-zero on $[u_n, u_{n+k+1})$. Since it is the last basis function, u_{n+k+1} must be the last knot u_m. Therefore, we have $u_{n+k+1} = u_m$ and $n + k + 1 = m$. In summary, given m and k, let $n = m - k - 1$ and the degree k basis functions are $N_{0,k}(u)$, $N_{1,k}(u)$, $N_{2,k}(u)$, ..., and $N_{n,k}(u)$.
7. The basis function $N_{i,k}(u)$ is a composite curve of degree k polynomials with joining points at knots in (u_i, u_{i+k+1}).

The form of a B-spline curve is very similar to that of a Bezier curve. Unlike a Bezier curve, a B-spline curve involves more information, namely: a set of $n + 1$ control points, a knot vector of $m + 1$ knots, and a degree k. Note that n, m and k must satisfy $m = n + k + 1$. More precisely, if we want to define a B-spline curve of degree k with $n + 1$ control points, we have to supply $n + k + 2$ knots $u_0, u_1, ..., u_{n+k+1}$. On the other hand, if a knot vector of $m + 1$ knots and $n + 1$ control points are given, the degree of the B-spline curve is $k = m - n - 1$. The point on the curve that corresponds to a knot u_i, $P(u_i)$, is referred to as a *knot point*. Hence, the knot points divide a B-spline curve into curve segments, each of which is defined on a knot span. Although $N_{i,k}(u)$ looks like $B_{n,i}(u)$, the degree of a B-spline basis function is an input, while if the knot vector does not have any particular structure, the generated curve will not touch the first and last legs of the control polygon as shown in Figure 6.31a. Such B-spline curves are called *open* B-spline curves.

We may want to clamp the curve so that it is a tangent to the first and the last legs at the first and last control points, respectively, as a Bezier curve does. To do so, the first knot and the last knot must be of multiplicity $k + 1$. This will generate the so-called *clamped* B-spline curves. See Figure 6.31b.

By repeating some knots and control points, the generated curve can be a *closed* one. In this case, the start and the end of the generated curve join together, forming a closed loop as shown in Figure 6.31c.

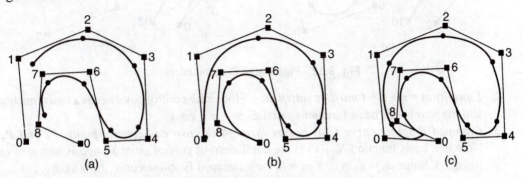

Fig. 6.31 Clamped B-spline curves.

The figures in Figures 6.31 have $n + 1$ control points ($n = 9$) and $k = 3$. Then, m must be 13 so that the knot vector has 14 knots. To have the clamped effect, the first $k + 1 = 4$ and the last four knots must be identical. The remaining $14 - (4 + 4) = 6$ knots can be anywhere in the domain. In fact, the curve is generated with knot vector $U = \{0, 0, 0, 0, 0.14, 0.28, 0.42, 0.57, 0.71, 0.85,$ $1, 1, 1, 1\}$. Note that except for the first four and last four knots, the middle ones are almost uniformly spaced. The figures also show the corresponding curve segment on each knot span. In fact, the little triangles are the knot points.

B-spline curves share many important properties with Bezier curves, because the former is a generalization of the later. Moreover, B-spline curves have more desired properties than Bezier curves. The list below shows some of the most important properties of B-spline curves.

In the following we shall assume that a B-spline curve $P(u)$ of degree k is defined by $n + 1$ control points and a knot vector $U = \{ u_0, u_1, ..., u_m \}$ with the first $k + 1$ and last $k + 1$ knots 'clamped' (i.e., $u_0 = u_1 = ... = u_p$ and $u_{m-k} = u_{m-k+1} = ... = u_m$).

1. **B-spline curve $P(u)$ is a piece-wise curve with each component being curve of degree k:** $P(u)$ can be viewed as the union of curve segments defined on each knot span. In Figure 6.31, where $n = 10$, $m = 14$ and $k = 3$, the first four knots and last four knots are clamped and the 7 internal knots are uniformly spaced. There are eight knot spans, each of which corresponds to a curve segment. In Figure 6.32a, these knot points are shown as triangles.

This nice property allows us to design complex shapes with lower degree polynomials. For example, Figure 6.32b shows a Bezier curve with the same set of control points. It still cannot follow the control polygon nicely even though its degree is 10.

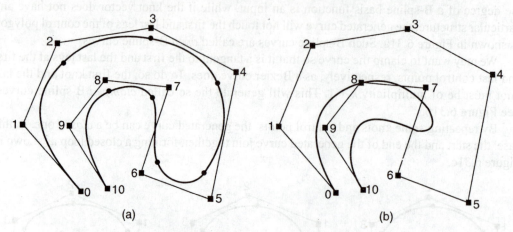

Fig. 6.32   Piece-wise B-spline curve.

2. *Equality m = n + k + 1 must be satisfied:*   Since each control point needs a basis function and the number of basis functions satisfies $m = n + k + 1$.

3. *Clamped B-spline curve C(u) passes through the two end control points P_0 and P_n:* Note that basis function $N_{0,k}(u)$ is the coefficient of control point P_0 and is non-zero on $[u_0, u_{k+1})$. Since $u_0 = u_1 = ... = u_k = 0$ for a clamped B-spline curve, $N_{0,0}(u)$, $N_{1,0}(u)$, ..., $N_{k-1,0}(u)$ are zero and only $N_{k,0}(u)$ is non-zero (recall from the triangular computation scheme). Consequently, if $u = 0$, then $N_{0,k}(0)$ is 1 and $P(0) = P_0$. A similar discussion can show $P(1) = P_n$.

4. **Strong Convex hull property:**   A B-spline curve is contained in the convex hull of its control polygon. More specifically, if u is in knot span $[u_i, u_{i+1})$, then $P(u)$ is in the convex hull of control points P_{i-k}, P_{i-k+1}, ..., P_i. If u is in knot span $[u_i, u_{i+1})$, there are only $k + 1$ basis functions (i.e., $N_{i,k}(u)$, ..., $N_{i-k+1,k}(u)$, $N_{i-k,k}(u)$) non-zero on this knot span. Since $N_{l,k}(u)$ is the coefficient of control point P_l, only $k + 1$ control points P_i, P_{i-1}, P_{i-2}, .., P_{i-k} have non-zero coefficients. Since on this knot span the basis functions are non-zero and sum to 1, their 'weighted' average, $P(u)$, must lie in the convex hull defined by control points P_i, P_{i-1}, P_{i-2}, .., P_{i-p}. The meaning of 'strong' is that while $P(u)$ still lies in the convex hull defined by *all* control points, it lies in a much smaller one.

The two B-spline curves shown in Figure 6.33 have eleven control points (i.e., $n = 10$), degree 3 (i.e., $k = 3$) and 15 knots ($m = 14$) with the first four and last four knots clamped. Therefore, the number of knot spans is equal to the number of curve segments. The knot vector is:

u_0	u_1	u_2	u_3	u_4	u_5	u_6	u_7	u_8	u_9	u_{10}	u_{11}	u_{12}	u_{13}	u_{14}
0	0	0	0	0.12	0.25	0.37	0.5	0.62	0.75	0.87	1	1	1	1

Figure 6.33a has u in knot span $(u_4, u_5) = (0.12, 0.25)$ and the corresponding point (i.e. $P(u)$) in the second curve segment. Therefore, there are $k + 1 = 4$ basis functions non-zero on this knot span (i.e., $N_{4,3}(u)$, $N_{3,3}(u)$, $N_{2,3}(u)$ and $N_{1,3}(u)$) and the corresponding control points are P_4, P_3, P_2 and P_1. The shaded area is the convex hull defined by these four points. It is clear that $P(u)$ lies in this convex hull.

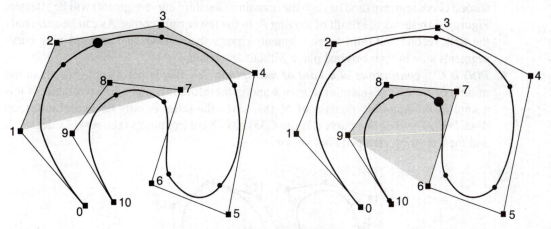

Fig. 6.33 Illustration of convex hull property.

The B-spline curve in the right figure is defined the same way. However, u is in $[u_9, u_{10}] = [0.75, 0.87)$ and the non-zero basis functions are $N_{9,3}(u)$, $N_{8,3}(u)$, $N_{7,3}(u)$ and $N_{6,3}(u)$. The corresponding control points are P_9, P_8, P_7 and P_6.

5. *Local modification scheme: Changing the position of control point P_i only affects the curve $P(u)$ on interval (u_i, u_{i+k+1})*: This follows from another important property of B-spline basis functions. Recall that $N_{i,k}(u)$ is non-zero on interval $[u_i, u_{i+k+1})$. If u is not in this interval, $N_{i,k}(u) P_i$ has no effect in computing $P(u)$ since $N_{i,k}(u)$ is zero. On the other hand, if u is in the indicated interval, $N_{i,k}(u)$ is non-zero. If P_i changes its position, $N_{i,k}(u)P_i$ is changed and consequently $P(u)$ is changed.

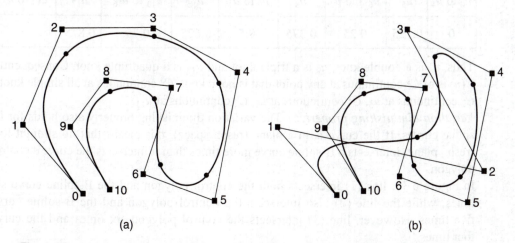

(a) (b)

Fig. 6.34 Some more examples of B-spline curves with same parameters of Figure 6.33.

The B-spline curves shown in Figure 6.34 are defined with the same parameters as in the previous convex hull example (Figure 6.33). We intend to move control point P_2. The coefficient of this control point is $N_{2,3}(u)$ and the interval on which this coefficient is non-zero is $(u_2, u_{2+3+1}) = [u_2, u_6] = (0, 0.37)$. Since $u_2 = u_3 = 0$, only three segments that correspond to (u_3, u_4) (the domain of the first curve segment), $[u_4, u_5)$ (the domain of the second curve segment) and $[u_5, u_6)$ (the domain of the third curve segment) will be affected. Figure 6.34b shows the result of moving P_2 to the lower right corner. As can be seem only the first, second and third curve segments change their shapes and all remaining curve segments stay in their original place without any change.

6. ***$P(u)$ is C^{k-1} continuous at a knot of multiplicity l:*** If u is not a knot, $P(u)$ is in the middle of a curve segment of degree k and is therefore infinitely differentiable. If u is a knot in the non-zero domain of $N_{i,k}(u)$, since the latter is only C^{k-1} continuous, so does $P(u)$. The B-spline curve (Figure 6.35) has 18 control points (i.e., $n = 17$), degree 4, and the following clamped knot vector.

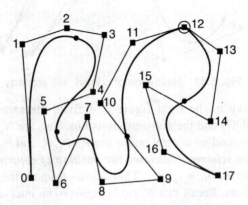

Fig. 6.35   Continuity of B-spline curve.

u_0 to u_4	u_5	u_6 and u_7	u_8	u_9 to u_{11}	u_{12}	u_{13} to u_{16}	u_{17}	u_{18} to u_{22}
0	0.125	0.25	0.375	0.5	0.625	0.75	0.875	1

Thus, u_6 is a double knot, u_9 is a triple knot and u_{13} is a quadruple knot. Consequently, $C(u)$ is of C^4 continuous at any point that is not a knot, C^3 continuous at all simple knots, C^2 continuous at u_6, C^1 continuous at u_9, C^0 continuous at u_{13}.

7. ***Variation diminishing property:*** The variation diminishing property also holds for B-spline curves. If the curve is in a plane (resp., space), this means that no straight line (resp., plane) intersects a B-spline curve more times than it intersects the curve's control polygon.

In Figure 6.36, line (1) intersects both the control polygon and the B-spline curve six times, while the line (2) also intersects the control polygon and the B-spline curve five times. However, line (3) intersects the control polygon six times and the curve four times.

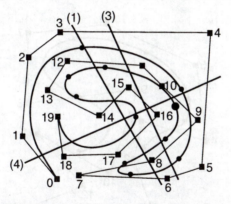

Fig. 6.36 Illustration of diminishing property.

8. *Bezier curves are special cases of B-spline curves:* If $n = k$ (i.e., the degree of a B-spline curve is equal to n, the number of control points minus 1), and there are $2(k + 1) = 2(n + 1)$ knots with $k + 1$ of them clamped at each end, this B-spline curve reduces to a Bezier curve.

9. *Affine invariance:* The affine invariance property also holds for B-spline curves. If an affine transformation is applied to a B-spline curve, the result can be constructed from the affine images of its control points. This is a nice property. When we want to apply a geometric or even affine transformation to a B-spline curve, this property states that we can apply the transformation to control points, which is quite easy, and once the transformed control points are obtained the transformed B-spline curve is the one defined by these new points. Therefore, we do not have to transform the curve.

6.7.7 B-Spline Open Curves

If the first and last knots do not have multiplicity $k + 1$, where k is the degree of a B-spline curve, the curve will not be a tangent to the first and last legs at the first and last control points, respectively. The curve is an open B-spline curve.

Consider a B-spline curve of degree 6 (i.e., $k = 6$) defined by 14 control points (i.e., $n = 13$). The number of knots is 21 (i.e., $m = n + k + 1 = 20$). If the knot vector is uniform, the knots are 0, 0.05, 0.10, 0.15, ..., 0.90, 0.95 and 1.0. The open curve is defined on $[u_k, u_{n-k}] = [u_6, u_{14}] = [0.3, 0.7]$ and is not tangent to the first and last legs. Figure 6.37 shows the curve. The values of u_i are given by:

$$u_j = \begin{cases} 0 & \text{if } j < k \\ j - k & \text{if } k \le j \le n \\ n - k + 1 & \text{if } j > n \end{cases} \tag{6.50}$$

where

$$0 \le j \le n + k + 1$$

and the range of u is:

$$0 < u < n - k + 1 \tag{6.51}$$

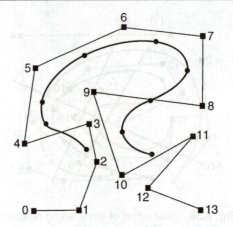

Fig. 6.37   Open curve.

For example, an open B-spline curve of degree 4 defined by nine control points (i.e., $n = 8$) and a uniform knot vector {0, 1/13, 2/13, 3/13, ..., 12/13, 1}. Describe the change between an open curve and a clamped one.

If we change the second knot 1/13 to 0 making 0 a double knot, the result is curve 1 in Figure 6.38.

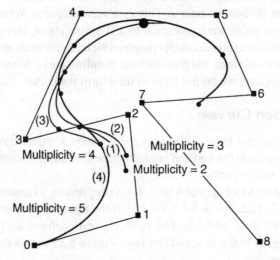

Fig. 6.38   Effect of changing knot.

In fact, this curve and the original one with 0 being a simple knot are almost identical. Now, if we change the third knot 2/13 to 0 making 0 a knot of multiplicity 3, the result is curve 2.

If the fourth knot 3/13 is change to 0 (multiplicity 4), the resulting curve is curve 3. As you can see, these three open curves are not very different from each other.

Now, let us make the fifth knot 4/13 to 0. Since 0 is now a knot of multiplicity 5 (i.e., $k + 1$), the curve not only passes through the first control point but also is tangent to the first leg of the control polygon (i.e., clamped). As you can see from curve 4, the shape of the curve changes drastically by pulling one end of it to the first control point. The same holds true if we make the last 5 knots to 1.

6.7.8   B-Spline Closed Curves

There are many ways to generate closed curves. The simple ones are either wrapping control points or wrapping knot vectors.

The values of u_i are given by:

$$u_j = j \qquad 0 \le j \le n + 1 \qquad\qquad (6.51)$$

and the range of u is:

$$0 \le u \le n + 1 \qquad\qquad (6.52)$$

Wrapping Control Points
Suppose we want to construct a closed B-spline curve $P(u)$ of degree k defined by $n + 1$ control points $P_0, P_1, ..., P_n$. The number of knots is $m + 1$, where $m = n + k + 1$. Here is the construction procedure:

1. Design a uniform knot sequence of $m + 1$ knots: $u_0 = 0$, $u_1 = 1/m$, $u_1 = 2/m$, ..., $u_m = 1$. Note that the domain of the curve is $[u_k, u_{n-k}]$.
2. Wrap the first p and last p control points. More precisely, let $P_0 = P_{n-p+1}$, $P_1 = P_{n-k+2}, ..., P_{k-2} = P_{n-1}$ and $P_{k-1} = P_n$. This is shown in Figure 6.39.

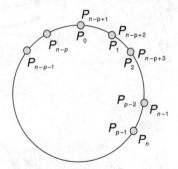

Fig. 6.39   Closed B-spline curve.

The constructed curve is C^{k-1} continuous at the joining point $C(u_p) = C(u_{n-k})$.

The following is an example. Figure 6.40a shows an open B-spline curve of degree 3 defined by 10 ($n = 9$) control points and a uniform knot vector. In the figure, control point pairs 0 and 7, 1 and 8, and 2 and 9 are placed close to each other to illustrate the construction. Figure 6.40b shows the result of making control points 0 and 7 identical. The shape of the curve does not change very much. Then, control points 1 and 8 are made identical as shown in Figure 6.40c. It is clear that the gap between the first and last points of the curve is closer. Finally, the curve becomes a closed one when control points 2 and 9 are made identical as shown in Figure 6.40d.

Wrapping Knots
Another way of constructing closed B-spline curves is by wrapping knots. Suppose we want to construct a closed B-spline curve $P(u)$ of degree k defined by $n + 1$ control points $P_0, P_1, ..., P_n$. The following is the construction procedure:

1. Add a new control point $P_{n+1} = P_0$. Therefore, the number of control points is $n + 2$.
2. Find an appropriate knot sequence of $n + 1$ knots $u_0, u_1, ..., u_n$. These knots are not necessarily uniform, an advantage over the method discussed above.
3. Add $k + 2$ knots and wrap around the first $k + 2$ knots: $u_{n+1} = u_0$, $u_{n+2} = u_1$, ..., $u_{n+k} = u_{k-1}$, $u_{n+k+1} = u_k$, $u_{n+k+2} = u_{k+1}$ as shown in Figure 6.41. In this way, we have $n + k + 2 = (n + 1) + k + 1$ knots.
4. The open B-spline curve $P(u)$ of degree k defined on the above constructed $n + 1$ control points and $n + k + 2$ knots is a closed curve with C^{k-1} continuity at the joining point $P(u_0) = P(u_{n+1})$. Note that the domain of this closed curve is $[u_0, u_{n+1}]$.

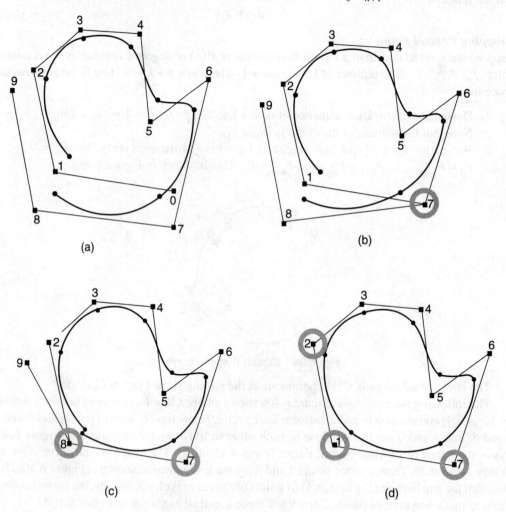

(a)

(b)

(c)

(d)

Fig. 6.40 Open B-spline curve.

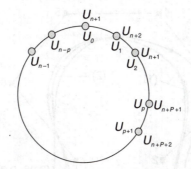

Fig. 6.41 Generations of closed curve by wraping knots.

6.7.9 Modifying Knots of B-Spline Curve

Since a B-spline curve is the composition of a number of curve segments, each of which is defined on a knot span, modifying the position of one or more knots will change the association between the curve segments and knot spans, and hence change the shape of the curve.

Figure 6.42 depicts the effect of modifying a single knot. It is a B-spline curve of degree 6 with 17 knots with the first seven and last seven clamped at the end points, while the internal knots are 0.25, 0.5 and 0.75. The initial curve is shown in Figure 6.42a. If knot 0.25 is moved to 0.1, the shape of the curve changes and the original P(0.25) moves downward to a new position. If knot 0.5 is moved to 0.1 so that knot 0.1 becomes a double knot (with multiplicity 2), the shape of the curve moves to the left; but P(0.1) is moved upward to a position near to the original point (i.e., the original P(0.25)). The result is shown in Figure 6.42b. Moreover, even though we have a double knot at 0.1 and another knot at 0.75 that unevenly sub-divide the domain [0,1] into three knot spans, the B-spline curve is more or less evenly sub-divided by their corresponding points.

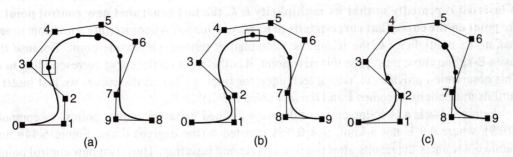

| (a) | (b) | (c) |

Fig. 6.42 Effect of modifying a single knot.

Figure 6.43 shows the change of shape of three curves, each of which is defined by 10 ($n = 9$) control points and is of degree 6. Their internal knot vectors are (0.25, 0.5, 0.75)—curve 1, (0.25, 0.25, 0.75)—curve 2, and (0.25, 0.25, 0.25)—curve 3.

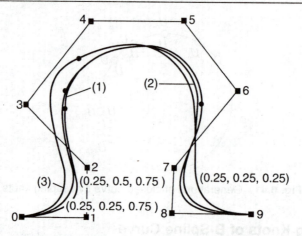

Fig. 6.43 Changing the shape of curves using knot vectors.

6.7.10   Finding a Point on a B-Spline Curve: De Casteljau's Algorithm

De Boor's algorithm is a generalisation of de Casteljau's algorithm. It provides a fast and numerically stable way for finding a point on a B-spline curve given a u in the domain. Recall from a property of multiple knots that increasing the multiplicity of an internal knot decreases the number of non-zero basis functions at this knot. In fact, if the multiplicity of this knot is l, there are at most $k - l + 1$ non-zero basis functions at this knot. Consequently, at a knot of multiplicity p, there will be only one non-zero basis function whose value at this knot is one because of the property of partition of unity. Let this knot be u_i. If u is u_i, since $N_{i,k}(u)$ is non-zero on $[u_i, u_{i+1})$, the point on the curve $P(u)$ is affected by *exactly one* control point P_i. More precisely, we actually have $P(u) = N_{i,k}(u) P_i = P_i$!

So, what is the point of this interesting or somewhat strange property? Simple: **if a knot u is inserted repeatedly so that its multiplicity is k, the last generated new control point is *the* point on the curve that corresponds to u.** Why is this so? After inserting u multiple times, making its multiplicity k, the triangular computation scheme yields one point. Because the given B-spline curve must pass this new point, it is the point on the curve corresponding to u. This observation provides us with a technique for finding $P(u)$ on the curve. We just insert u until its multiplicity becomes k and the *last* point is $P(u)$!

Figure 6.44a is a B-spline curve of degree 4 defined by seven control points. To compute $P(0.9)$, where 0.9 is not a knot, $u = 0.9$ is inserted 4 (the degree) times. Figure 6.44b and Figure 6.44c show the results after the first and second insertion. Thus, two new control points are added near the lower right corner. Note that the control polygon is closer to the curve than the original. The result of the third insertion is shown in Figure 6.44d. The fourth insertion yields the point on the curve (Figure 6.44e). Therefore, after four insertions, $P(0.9)$ is a control point.

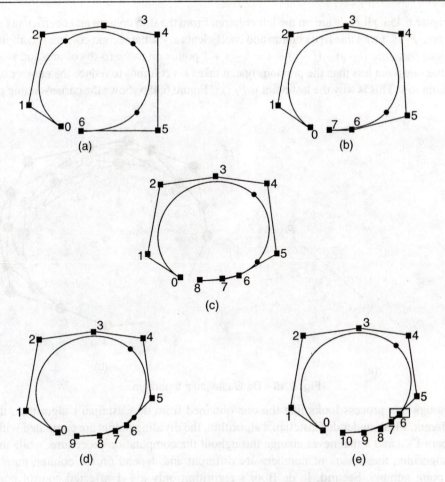

Fig. 6.44 Finding a control point on a B-spline curve.

Input: A value u

Output: The point on the curve, $P(u)$

If u lies in (u_l, u_{l+1}) and $u != u_l$, let $h = k$ (i.e., inserting u k times) and $s = 0$; If $u = u_l$ and u_l is a knot of multiplicity s, let $h = k - s$ (i.e., inserting u $k - s$ times); Copy the affected control points P_{l-s}, P_{l-s-1}, P_{l-s-2}, ..., P_{l-k+1} and P_{l-k} to a new array and rename them as $P_{l-s, 0}$, $P_{l-s-1, 0}$, $P_{l-s-2, 0}$, ..., $P_{l-k+1, 0}$;

for $r := 1$ to h do

        for $i := l - k + r$ to $l - s$ do

            begin

                Let $a_{i, r} = (u - u_i) / (u_{i+k-r+1} - u_i)$

                Let $P_{i, r} = (1 - a_{i, r}) P_{i-1, r-1} + a_{i, r} P_{i, r-1}$

            end

$P_{l-s, k-s}$ is the point $P(u)$.

In Figure 6.45a, all $P_{i,0}$'s are on the left column. From the 0-th column and coefficients $a_{i,1}$, one can compute $P_{i,1}$'s. From this first column and coefficients $a_{i,2}$'s, the second column is computed and so on. Since there are $(l-s) - (l-k) + 1 = k - s + 1$ points on the zero-th column and since each column has one point less than the previous one, it takes k-s columns to reduce the number of points on a column to 1. This is why the last point is $P_{l-s,l-s}$. Figure 6.45b shows the corner-cutting process.

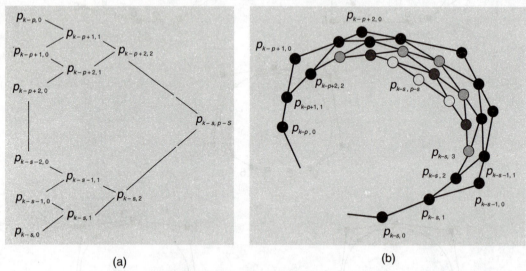

(a)   (b)

Fig. 6.45   De Casteljau's algorithm.

Although this process looks like the one obtained from de Casteljau's algorithm, they are very different. **First**, under de Casteljau's algorithm, the dividing points are computed with a pair of numbers 1 - u and u that never change throughout the computation procedure, while under de Boor's algorithm these pairs of numbers are different and depend on the column number and control point number. **Second**, in de Boor's algorithm only $k + 1$ affected control points are involved in the computation, while de Casteljau's algorithm uses *all* control points. Since control points P_{l-k} to P_l define a convex hull that contains the curve segment on knot span $[u_l, u_{l+1})$, the computation of de Boor's algorithm is performed *within* the corresponding convex hull.

Example 6.11   Find the equation of a cubic B-spline curve. Compare the same with the Bezier curve.

Solution

The cubic spline has $n = 3, k = 3$

$m = k + n + 1 = 3 + 3 + 1 = 7$

Number of knots = $m + 1 = 7 + 1 = 8$

The range of u is $0 \leq u \leq 3 - 3 + 1 = 0 \leq u \leq 1$

The knot vector is $[u_0 \quad u_1 \quad u_2 \quad u_3 \quad u_4 \quad u_5 \quad u_6 \quad u_7]^T$

$$u_j = \begin{cases} 0 & \text{if } j < k \\ j - k & \text{if } k \leq j \leq n \\ n - k + 1 & \text{if } j > n \end{cases}$$

The knot vector is $[0 \quad 0 \quad 0 \quad 0 \quad 1 \quad 1 \quad 1 \quad 1]^T$

$$N_{i,0}(u) = \begin{cases} 1 & \text{if } u_i \leq u \leq u_{i+1} \\ 0 & \text{otherwise} \end{cases}$$

$$N_{0,0}(u) = N_{1,0}(u) = N_{2,0}(u) = \begin{cases} 1 & \text{if } u = 0 \\ 0 & \text{otherwise} \end{cases}$$

$$N_{3,0}(u) = \begin{cases} 1 & \text{if } 0 \leq u \leq 1 \\ 0 & \text{otherwise} \end{cases}$$

$$N_{4,0}(u) = N_{5,0} = N_{6,0}(u) = N_{7,0}(u) = \begin{cases} 1 & \text{if } u = 0 \\ 0 & \text{otherwise} \end{cases}$$

$$N_{i,k}(u) = \frac{u - u_i}{u_{i+k} - u_i} N_{i,k-1}(u) + \frac{u_{i+k+1} - u}{u_{i+k+1} - u_{i+1}} N_{i+1,\,k-1}(u)$$

$$N_{0,1}(u) = \frac{u - u_0}{u_1 - u_0} N_{0,0}(u) + \frac{u_2 - u}{u_2 - u_1} N_{1,0}(u)$$

$$= \frac{u - 0}{0 - 0} N_{0,0}(u) + \frac{0 - u}{0 - 0} N_{1,0}(u) = 0$$

$$N_{1,1}(u) = \frac{u - u_1}{u_2 - u_1} N_{1,0}(u) + \frac{u_3 - u}{u_3 - u_2} N_{2,0}(u)$$

$$= \frac{u - 0}{0 - 0} N_{1,0}(u) + \frac{0 - u}{0 - 0} N_{2,0}(u) = 0$$

$$N_{2,1}(u) = \frac{u - u_2}{u_3 - u_2} N_{2,0}(u) + \frac{u_4 - u}{u_4 - u_3} N_{3,0}(u)$$

$$= \frac{u - 0}{0 - 0} N_{2,0}(u) + \frac{1 - u}{1 - 0} N_{3,0}(u) = (1 - u) N_{3,0}(u)$$

$$N_{3,1}(u) = \frac{u - u_3}{u_4 - u_3} N_{3,0}(u) + \frac{u_5 - u}{u_5 - u_4} N_{4,0}(u)$$

$$= \frac{u - 0}{1 - 0} N_{3,0}(u) + \frac{1 - u}{1 - 1} N_{4,0}(u) = u N_{3,0}(u)$$

$$N_{4,1}(u) = \frac{u - u_4}{u_5 - u_4} N_{4,0}(u) + \frac{u_6 - u}{u_6 - u_5} N_{5,0}(u)$$

$$= \frac{u - 1}{1 - 1} N_{4,0}(u) + \frac{1 - u}{1 - 1} N_{5,0}(u) = 0$$

$$N_{5,1}(u) = \frac{u - u_5}{u_6 - u_5} N_{5,0}(u) + \frac{u_7 - u}{u_7 - u_6} N_{6,0}(u)$$

$$= \frac{u - 1}{1 - 1} N_{5,0}(u) + \frac{1 - u}{1 - 1} N_{6,0}(u) = 0$$

$$N_{0,2}(u) = \frac{u - u_0}{u_2 - u_0} N_{0,1}(u) + \frac{u_3 - u}{u_3 - u_1} N_{1,1}(u)$$

$$= \frac{u - 0}{0 - 0} N_{0,1}(u) + \frac{0 - u}{0 - 0} N_{1,1}(u) = 0$$

$$N_{1,2}(u) = \frac{u - u_1}{u_3 - u_1} N_{1,1}(u) + \frac{u_4 - u}{u_4 - u_2} N_{2,1}(u)$$

$$= \frac{u - 0}{0 - 0} N_{1,1}(u) + \frac{1 - u}{1 - 0} N_{2,1}(u) = (1 - u) N_{2,1}(u) = (1 - u)^2 N_{3,0}(u)$$

$$N_{2,2}(u) = \frac{u - u_2}{u_4 - u_2} N_{2,1}(u) + \frac{u_5 - u}{u_5 - u_3} N_{3,1}(u)$$

$$= \frac{u - 0}{1 - 0} N_{2,1}(u) + \frac{1 - u}{1 - 0} N_{3,1}(u) = uN_{2,1}(u) + (1 - u) N_{3,1}(u) = 2u (1 - u) N_{3,0}(u)$$

$$N_{3,2}(u) = \frac{u - u_3}{u_5 - u_3} N_{3,1}(u) + \frac{u_6 - u}{u_6 - u_4} N_{4,1}(u)$$

$$= \frac{u - 0}{1 - 0} N_{3,1}(u) + \frac{1 - u}{1 - 1} N_{4,1}(u) = uN_{3,1}(u) = u^2 N_{3,0}(u)$$

$$N_{4,2}(u) = \frac{u - u_4}{u_6 - u_4} N_{4,1}(u) + \frac{u_7 - u}{u_7 - u_5} N_{5,1}(u)$$

$$= \frac{u - 0}{1 - 1} N_{4,1}(u) + \frac{1 - u}{1 - 1} N_{5,1}(u) = 0$$

$$N_{0,3}(u) = \frac{u - u_0}{u_3 - u_0} N_{0,2}(u) + \frac{u_4 - u}{u_4 - u_1} N_{1,2}(u)$$

$$= \frac{u - 0}{0 - 0} N_{0,2}(u) + \frac{1 - u}{1 - 0} N_{1,2}(u) = (1 - u) N_{1,2}(u) = (1 - u)^3 N_{3,0}(u)$$

$$N_{1,3}(u) = \frac{u - u_1}{u_4 - u_1} N_{1,2}(u) + \frac{u_5 - u}{u_5 - u_2} N_{2,2}(u)$$

$$= \frac{u - 0}{1 - 0} N_{1,2}(u) + \frac{1 - u}{1 - 0} N_{2,2}(u) = uN_{1,2}(u) + (1 - u)N_{2,2}(u) = 3u (1 - u)^2 N_{3,0}(u)$$

$$N_{2,3}(u) = \frac{u - u_2}{u_5 - u_2} N_{2,2}(u) + \frac{u_6 - u}{u_6 - u_3} N_{3,2}(u)$$

$$= \frac{u - 0}{1 - 0} N_{2,2}(u) + \frac{1 - u}{1 - 0} N_{3,2}(u) = u N_{2,2}(u) + (1 - u) N_{3,20}(u) = 3u^2 (1 - u) N_{3,0}(u)$$

$$N_{3,3}(u) = \frac{u - u_3}{u_6 - u_3} N_{3,2}(u) + \frac{u_7 - u}{u_7 - u_4} N_{4,2}(u)$$

$$= \frac{u - 0}{1 - 0} N_{3,2}(u) + \frac{1 - u}{1 - 1} N_{4,2}(u) = u N_{3,2}(u) = u^3 N_{3,0}(u)$$

$$P(u) = N_{0,3}(u) P_0 + N_{1,3}(u) P_1 + N_{2,3}(u) P_2 + N_{3,3}(u) P_3$$

$$= \left[(1 - u)^3 P_0 + 3u(1 - u)^2 P_1 + 3u^2 (1 - u) P_2 + u^3 P_3 \right] N_{3,0}(u)$$

$$= (1 - u)^3 P_0 + 3u (1 - u)^2 P_1 + 3u^2 (1 - u) P_2 + u^3 P_3 \qquad 0 \le u \le 1$$

This equation is the same as the one for the Bezier curve. Therefore, the cubic spline curve defined by four control points is identical to the cubic Bezier curve defined by the same points.

6.8 CURVE MANIPULATIONS

The effective use of wireframe entities depends on their manipulation to achieve the requirements of design and manufacturing. The important manipulations are:

1. Finding points on curves
2. Blending
3. Segmentation
4. Trimming
5. Intersection
6. Transformation

6.8.1 Finding Points on Curves

Points on curves are evaluated for different modelling requirements. A point on a curve can be found by its parametric value. A point on a Bezier curve and a B-spline curve can be generated by using De Casteljau's Algorithm and De Casteljau's Algorithm, respectively.

6.8.2 Blending

Blending of two curves implies the joining of two curves subjected to the satisfaction of continuity conditions. Blending is used to construct composite curves. The composite curves are widely used for engineering applications. Given two points $P_1(u')$, $0 \le u' \le a$ and $P_2(u'')$, $0 \le u'' \le b$ the conditions of continuity are determined at the joining point. The conditions of continuity are:

1. **C^0 continuity:**   The end point of the first curve and the start point of the second curve should be the same.

$$P_1(a) = P_2(0) \tag{6.54}$$

2. **C^1 continuity:**   Two curves should have common tangent at the point of joining.

$$P_1'(a) = P_2'(0) \tag{6.55}$$

3. **C^2 continuity:**   The curvature should be the same at the joining point. For the curvature to be continuous at the joining point, the following condition must be satisfied:

$$P_2''(0) = \frac{\alpha_2}{\alpha_1} P_1''(0) \tag{6.56}$$

where α_1, α_2 are constants.

Joining of two Bezier curves is explained in Section 6.6.4.

6.8.3   Segmentation

Segmentation is the process of sub-dividing the curve for some u into segments. The resulting curve segments will have their own new control points; the original set of control points is discarded. Mathematically, curve segmentation is a re-parameterisation of the curve.

Let us assume that a curve is defined over the range $u_0 \leq u \leq u_m$. To split the curve at a point defined $u = u_a$, the first and second segments are to be defined over the range and $u_a \leq u \leq u_m$, respectively. A new parameter is defined for each segment such that its range $0 \leq v \leq 1$. Figure 6.46 shows the segmentation of the curve.

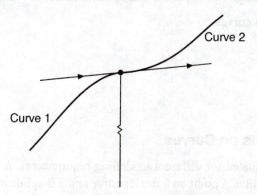

Fig. 6.46   Segmentation of a curve.

The re-parameterisation is as follows:

For the first segment:

$$u = u_0 + (u_a - u_0) v \tag{6.57}$$

For the second segment:

$$u = u_a + (u_m - u_a) v \tag{6.58}$$

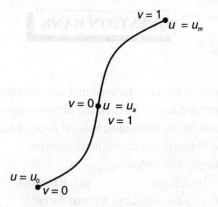

Fig. 6.47 Blending of two curves.

6.8.4 Trimming

Trimming is the process of truncating a curve as shown in Figure 6.48.

Trimming is mathematically equal to segmentation. The difference between trimming and segmentation is that the result of trimming is that only one segment of the curve is bounded by the trimming boundaries.

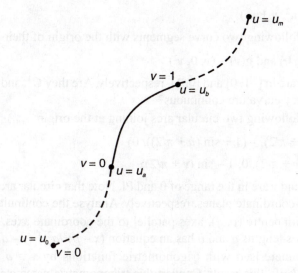

Fig. 6.48 Trimming.

6.8.5 Transformation

The transformation of a curve includes translation, rotation, scaling and reflection. The transformations are described in Chapter 4. In translation, every point on a curve translates exactly the same distance. In scaling transformation, the original coordinates of a curve are multiplied by the given scale factor. Rotation of a point through an angle θ about x or y or z is referred to as rotation about the origin. Reflection is also known as mirror.

QUESTION BANK

A. Descriptive Questions

1. Define points and lines in the two-dimensional coordinate system.
2. Define parallel and perpendicular lines in the dimensional coordinate system.
3. Define points and lines in the three-dimensional coordinate system.
4. Define vectors in the dimensional co-ordinate system.
5. Represent mathematically the following:
   (a) Circle   (b) Ellipse   (c) Parabola   (d) Hyperbola
6. Represent mathematically the conics in normal form.
7. Represent mathematically the conics in general form.
8. Represent mathematically the conics in matrix form.
9. Represent mathematically the quadratic surfaces in normal form.
10. Represent mathematically the quadratic surfaces in general form.
11. Represent mathematically the quadratic surfaces in matrix form.
12. Represent mathematically the torus.
13. Compute the curvature, normal vector or binormal vector of the following parabola:

    $f(u) = (u, 1 + u^2, u + u^2)$

14. Consider the following two curve segments with the origin of their joining point:

    $f(u) = (u, -u^2, 0)$ and $g(v) = (v, 0, v^2)$

    where u and v are in $[-1, 0]$ and $[0, 1]$, respectively, Are they C^1, and C^2 continuous at the origin? Are they curvature continuous?

15. Consider the following two circular arcs joining at the origin:

    $f(u) = (\cos(u + \pi/2), -(1 + \sin(u + \pi/2)), 0)$

    $g(v) = (-\cos(v + \pi/2), 0, 1 - \sin(v + \pi/2))$

    where both u and v are in the range of 0 and PI. Note that circular arcs $f(u)$ and $g(v)$ lie on the xy- and xz-coordinate planes, respectively. Analyse the continuity at the origin.

16. The ellipse with centre (p, q), axes parallel to the coordinate axes, and semi-major and semi-minor axis lengths a and b has an equation $(x - p)^2/a^2 + (y - q)^2/b^2 = 1$

    It can be parameterised with trigonometric functions by $x = a \cos(t) + p$ and $y = b \sin(t) + q$. Verify this result. Convert this trigonometric parameterisation to a rational one. Does your parameterisation contain circles as special cases?

17. Analyse the relationship between u and the two branches of the hyperbola parameterised with the following:

    $x = a(1 + u^2)/(2u)$
    $y = b(1 - u^2)/(2u)$

    Plotting several points that correspond to different u will be very helpful.

18. Given three control points on the *xy*-plane (–1, 0), (0, 1) and (2, 0), do the following:
    (a) Write down its Bezier curve equation.
    (b) Expand this equation to its equivalent conventional form.
    (c) Since there are three control points, there are three Bezier coefficients. Write down their equations and sketch their graphs.
    (d) Use your calculator to find enough number of points using the conventional parametric form and sketch the curve.
    (e) Find points on the curve that correspond to u = 0, 0.25, 0.5, 0.75 and 1 with the conventional form.
    (f) Use de Casteljau's algorithm to find points on the curve corresponding to u = 0, 0.25, 0.5, 0.75 and 1.
    (g) Sub-divide the Bezier curve at u = 0.4 and list the control points of the resulting curve segments.
    (f) Increase the degree of this curve to three and list the new set of control points. Then, increase the degree to four and list the new set of control points.

19. In the variation diminishing property, what happens if you have a line or a plane that passes through a control point or contains a line segment of the control polyline? Suggest a proper counting of intersection points and verify your claim with examples.

20. A Bezier curve of degree 2 defined by three control points P_0, P_1 and P_2 is a portion of a conic section. What type of conic section is it? Is it a portion of a parabola, a hyperbola or an ellipse? You can assume that the given control points are in the *xy*-coordinate plane.

21. Suppose Bezier curve $\mathbf{C}(u)$ (resp., $\mathbf{D}(u)$) of degree n is defined by control points P_0, P_1, ..., P_n (resp., O_0, Q_1, ..., Q_n). If the curves are identical (i.e., $C(u) = D(u)$ for every u in [0,1]), then the corresponding control points are also identical (i.e., $P_i = Q_i$ for all $0 <= i <= n$).

    Hint: First show that if $(1 – u)\mathbf{A} + u\mathbf{B}$ is a zero vector for every u in [0,1], then $\mathbf{A}$ and $\mathbf{B}$ are both zero vectors. Then, work the de Casteljau's algorithm backward to show that $\mathbf{P}_i – \mathbf{Q}_i$ is a zero vector for all $0 <= i <= n$.

22. Suppose Bezier curve $C(u)$ of degree n is defined by control points P_0, P_1, ..., P_n.
    (a) Prove the following:

$$B_{n,i}(u) - \sum_{j=i}^{n} (-1)^{j-1} C(n,i) \, C(n-i,\, j-i) \, u^{j}$$

    (b) Show that curve $C(u)$ can be rewritten in the following *matrix* form:

$$C(u) = [P_0, P_1, ..., P_n] \cdot \begin{bmatrix} m_{00} & m_{01} & \cdots & m_{0n} \\ m_{10} & m_{11} & \cdots & m_{1n} \\ \vdots & & \ddots & \vdots \\ m_{n0} & m_{n1} & \cdots & m_{nn} \end{bmatrix} \cdot \begin{bmatrix} u^0 \\ u^1 \\ \vdots \\ u^n \end{bmatrix}$$

where entry m_{ij} is defined as follows:

$$m_{ij} = \begin{cases} (-1)^{j-i} C(n, i) \, C(n-i, j-i) & \text{if } j \geq i \\ 0 & \text{otherwise} \end{cases}$$

23. Show that the maximum of $B_{n,i}(u)$ occurs at $u = i/n$ and that the maximum value is

$$\frac{n!}{i!(n-i)!} \frac{i^i (n-1)^{n-i}}{n^n}$$

24. Verify the following results with your calculus knowledge:
    The derivative of $B_{n,i}(u)$:

    $$\frac{d}{du} B_{n,i}(u) = B'_{n,i}(u) = n(B_{n-1,i-1}(u) - B_{n-1,i}(u))$$

    The derivative of Bezier curve $p(u)$:

    $$\frac{d}{du} C(u) = C'(u) = \sum_{i=0}^{n-1} B_{n-1,i}(u) \left\{ n(P_{i+1} - P_i) \right\}$$

25. The discussion of joining two Bezier curves with C^1-continuity assumes the domain of the curves is [0, 1]. Suppose the domain of the first curve is [0, s] and the domain of the second curve is [s, 1]. Redo the calculation. What is your conclusion? Is there any modification required?

26. Prove the following:

    $$D_i^k = \sum_{j=0}^{k} (-1)^{k-j} C(k, j) \, P_{i+j}$$

    where D_i^k, s are the k-th difference points and $C(k, j)$ is the binomial coefficient defined as follows:
    With this formula, we can express a higher derivative using the original control points rather than using finite difference points.

27. After sub-dividing a Bezier curve of degree p at s, we have two Bezier curves of degree p, one on interval [0, s] while the other on [s, 1]. Show that these two curves are of C^1 continuous at the joining point.

    Hint: Suppose the last two control points of the curve on [0, s] are P_{p-1} and P_p, and the first two control points of the curve on [s, 1] are Q_0 and Q_1. Then, we have P_{p-1}, $P_p = Q_0$ and Q_1 are on the same line, and the ratio of the distance from P_{p-1} to $P_p = Q_0$ and the distance from $P_p = Q_0$ to Q_1 is equal to s due to subdivision. Now, change the variables of both curves so that they have domain on [0,1].

28. Compute and plot all basis functions up to degree 2 for knot vector $U = \{ 0, 1, 2, 3, 4 \}$.

29. Compute and plot all basis functions up to degree 2 for knot vector $U = \{ 0, 1, 2, 3, 3, 3, 4, 5, 6 \}$.

30. Verify the following propositions with convincing arguments:

    $N_{i,p}(u)$ is a degree p polynomial.

    For all i, p and u, $N_{i,p}(u)$ is non-negative.

31. Given knot sequences $U_1 = \{0, 0, 1, 1\}$ and $U_2 = \{0, 0, 0, 1, 1, 1\}$, use hand calculation to verify that the B-spline basis functions on U_1 and U_2 are identical to the Bezier basis functions.

32. Show that a clamped B-spline curve passes through the first and last control points. More precisely, show that $C(0) = P_0$ and $C(1) = P_n$ hold.

33. In the discussion of forcing a B-spline to pass through a control point, we indicated that if we let $P_i = P_{i-1} = \ldots = P_{i-p+1}$, the convex hull collapses to a line segment $P_{i-p}P_i$ and the curve must pass through P_i. Why is this so?

34. In the discussion of forcing a B-spline to pass a control point, we indicated that a point on the curve that corresponds to a knot may become identical to the collapsed control point. If we let $P_i = P_{i-1} = \ldots = P_{i-p+1}$, will you be able to identify the knot u_k such that $P(u_k)$ becomes identical to P_i? Why? Elaborate your finding.

35. In the discussion of multiple knots, we mentioned that if a knot u_i has multiplicity $k-1$, where k is the degree of a B-spline curve, then $C(u_i)$ lies on a leg of the control polyline. Based on your understanding of multiple knots, answer the following questions:

    (a) Why does this proposition hold?

    (b) On which leg does $C(u_i)$ lie?

36. Consider a clamped cubic B-spline curve defined by seven control points $P_0, \ldots, P_6$ and knot vector $U = \{ 0, 0, 0, 0, 2/5, 3/5, 3/5, 1, 1, 1, 1 \}$. Find its derivative B-spline curve, its new control points and knot vector.

37. Modify the derivative computation method so that it works for open and closed B-spline curves.

38. Use B-spline curves of degree 2 and 3 and hand calculation to verify that de Boor's algorithms reduces to de Casteljau's algorithm.

39. Suppose we have a clamped B-spline curve of degree p defined by $n + 1$ control points and a knot vector of simple knots except for the first and last knots, which are of multiplicity $p + 1$. Derive a relation of the number of control points between the given B-spline curve and the number of control points of its Bézier curve segments.

B. Multiple Choice Questions

1. The number of lines required to represent a cube in a wireframe model is:

    (a) 8   (b) 6   (c) 12   (d) 16

2. Which of the following is not an analytical entity?

    (a) Line   (b) Circle   (c) Spline   (d) Parabola

3. Which of the following is not a synthetic entity?

    (a) Hyperbola   (b) Bezier curve   (c) B-spline curve   (d) Cubic spline curve

4. Which one of the following does not belong to the family of conics?

    (a) Parabola   (b) Ellipse   (c) Hyperbola   (d) Line

5. The number of tangents required to describe cubic splines is:

    (a) 2   (b) 1   (c) 3   (d) 4

6. The order of the cubic spline is the _____.

    (a) 2nd order   (b) 3rd order   (c) 1st order   (d) 4th order

7. The shape of the Bezier curve is controlled by:

    (a) Control points   (b) Knots   (c) End points   (d) All the above

8. The curve that follows a convex hull property is:

    (a) Cubic spline   (b) B-spline   (c) Bezier curve   (d) Both (b) and (c)

9. The degree of the Bezier curve with n control points is:

    (a) $n + 1$ (b) $n - 1$ (c) n (d) $2n$

10. The degree of the B-spline with varying knot vectors:

    (a) Increases with knot vectors   (b) Decreases with knot vectors

    (c) Remains constant   (d) None of the above

11. C^0 continuity refers to:

    (a) Common tangent   (b) Common point

    (c) Common curvature   (d) Common normal

12. C^1 continuity refers to:

    (a Common tangent   (b) Common point

    (c) Common curvature   (d) Common normal

13. C^2 continuity refers to:

    (a) Common tangent   (b) Common point

    (c) Common curvature   (d) Common normal

14. If the degree of a B-spline curve is equal to the number of control points minus 1, the resultant curve is a:

    (a) Cubic spline curve   (b) Bezier curve

    (c) Closed B-spline curve   (d) Closed Bezier curve

Chapter 7

Surface Modelling

188

OBJECTIVES

After reading this chapter, the reader will be able to understand the following concepts:

- ➲ Planes
- ➲ Vector planes
- ➲ Surface entities
- ➲ Surface representation methods
- ➲ Quadric surfaces in normal forms
- ➲ Quadric surfaces in general form
- ➲ Quadric surfaces in matrix form
- ➲ Parametric surfaces
- ➲ Parametric representation of analytic surfaces
- ➲ Parametric representation of synthetic surfaces
- ➲ Tensor product surfaces
- ➲ De Castelijau's algorithm for Bezier surfaces
- ➲ B-spline surface
- ➲ De Boor's algorithm for B-spline surfaces
- ➲ Blending surface
- ➲ Surface manipulations

7.1 INTRODUCTION

Wireframe models are unable to represent complex surfaces of objects like car, ship, airplane wing, castings, etc. Only a surface model can be used to represent the surface profile of these objects. Also, a surface model can be used for calculating mass properties, and interference between parts, for generating cross-sectioned views, finite element mesh, and NC tool paths for continuous path machining. Additionally, a surface model can be used for fitting experimental data, discretised solutions of differential equations, construction of pressure surface, construction of stress distribution, etc.

Surface creation on a CAD system usually requires wireframe entities: lines, curves, points, etc. All analytical and synthetic curves can be used to generate surfaces. In order to visualise surfaces on a graphic display, a mesh, say $m \times n$ in size is usually displayed; the mesh size, is controlled by the user. Most CAD systems provide options to set the mesh size.

A surface of an object is a more complete and less ambiguous representation than its wireframe model; it is an extension of a wireframe model with additional information. A wireframe model can be extracted from a surface model by deleting all surface entities (not the wireframe entities—point, lines, or curves). Databases of surface models are centralised and associative, and manipulation of surface entities in one view is automatically reflected in the other views. Surface models can be shaded and represented with hidden lines.

7.2 PLANES

A plane in space has an equation as follows:

$$Ax + By + Cz + D = 0 \tag{7.1}$$

It consists of four coefficients A, B, C and D where D is the constant term. Similar to the line case, the distance between the origin and the plane is given as:

$$\text{Distance} = \frac{|D|}{\sqrt{A^2 + B^2 + C^2}} \tag{7.2}$$

The normal vector of a plane is its gradient. The gradient of an equation $f(x, y, z) = 0$ is defined as follows:

$$\nabla(f) = \left(\frac{\partial f}{\partial x}, \frac{\partial f}{\partial y}, \frac{\partial f}{\partial z} \right) \tag{7.3}$$

For a plane, its normal vector is simply (A, B, C).

Unfortunately, a line in space cannot be represented with a single equation. However, it can be considered as the intersection of two planes. In order to simplify this discussion, we shall switch to the use of vectors, though this traditional notation is still very useful.

7.3 VECTOR PLANES

A plane, in its vector form, is specified by a based point B and its normal vector n. For an arbitrary point, or position vector, X on the plane, the direction vector from the base point B to X, $X - B$, must be perpendicular to the normal vector n. Therefore, we have $(X - B) \cdot n$ must be zero. From $(X - B) \cdot n = 0$, we have the equation of a plane specified with a base point and its normal vector:

$$X \cdot n - B \cdot n = 0 \qquad (7.4)$$

Given the vector notation of lines and planes, it is very easy to compute the intersection point of a line and a plane. Let the given line be $A + td$. Let the plane be defined with a base point B and its normal vector n. Then, this plane has equation $X \cdot n = B \cdot n$. If the line intersects the plane, there must be a value of t such that the corresponding point lies on the plane. that is, there must be a t such that the point corresponding to this t would satisfy the plane equation. Since a point on the line is $A + td$, plugging $A + td$ into the plane equation yields:

$$(A + td) \cdot n - B \cdot n = 0 \qquad (7.5)$$

Re-arranging the terms and solving for t yields:

$$t = (B - A) \cdot n / d \cdot n \qquad (7.6)$$

Therefore, plugging this t into the line equation yields the intersection point.

In Equation 7.6, if $d \cdot n$ is zero, t cannot be solved and consequently no intersection point exists. The meaning of $d \cdot n = 0$ is that d and n are perpendicular to each other. Since n is the normal vector of a plane and d is perpendicular to n, d must be parallel to the plane. If the line is parallel to the plane, no intersection point exists.

7.4 SURFACE ENTITIES

Surface entities are broadly classified into following types:

1. Analytic surfaces

   - Plane surface
   - Ruled surface
   - Surface of revolution
   - Tabulated cylinder

2. Synthetic surfaces

   - Hermite bi-cubic surface
   - Bezier surface
   - B-spline surface

7.5 SURFACE REPRESENTATION METHODS

Two types of surfaces are commonly used in modelling systems: parametric and implicit. Parametric surfaces are defined by a set of three functions, one for each coordinate, as follows:

$$f(u, v) = [x(u, v), y(u, v), z(u, v)] \qquad (7.7)$$

where parameters u and v are in the certain domain. For our purpose, we shall assume that both u and v are in the range of 0 and 1. Thus, (u, v) is a point in the square defined by $(0, 0)$, $(1, 0)$, $(0, 1)$ and $(1, 1)$ in the uv-coordinate plane.

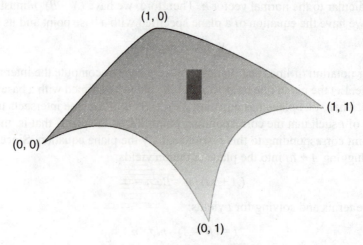

Fig. 7.1 Parametric surface.

Implicit surface is defined by a polynomial of three variables:

$$p(x, y, z) = 0 \qquad (7.8)$$

Surfaces, which have polynomial (implicit) forms are called algebraic surfaces. The highest degree of all terms is the degree of the algebraic surface. Therefore, spheres and all quadric surfaces are algebraic surfaces of degree two. The following equation shows a degree three algebraic surface whose implicit equation is:

$$8x^2 - xy^2 + xz^2 + y^2 + z^2 - 8 = 0 \qquad (7.9)$$

7.6 QUADRIC SURFACES IN NORMAL FORMS

Quadric surfaces consist of the following different types: ellipsoids, hyperboloids of one sheet, hyperboloids of two sheets, elliptic paraboloids, and hyperboloid paraboloids. These five quadric surfaces are normally referred to as rank four quadrics. The five quadric surfaces in their normal forms and their shapes are shown in Figure 7.2.

Ellipsoid $\dfrac{x^2}{a^2} + \dfrac{y^2}{b^2} + \dfrac{z^2}{c^2} = 1$

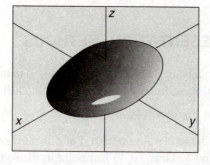

Hyperboloid of One sheet $\dfrac{x^2}{a^2} + \dfrac{y^2}{b^2} - \dfrac{z^2}{c^2} = 1$

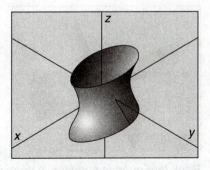

Hyperboloid of Two sheets $-\dfrac{x^2}{a^2} - \dfrac{y^2}{b^2} + \dfrac{z^2}{c^2} = 1$

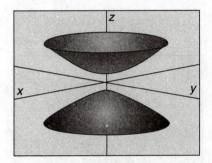

Elliptic Paraboloid $\dfrac{x^2}{a^2} + \dfrac{y^2}{b^2} = 2cz$

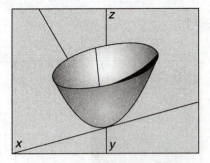

Hyperbolic Paraboloid $\dfrac{x^2}{a^2} - \dfrac{y^2}{b^2} = 2cz$

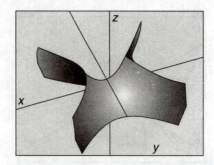

Fig. 7.2 Rank four quadric surfaces in normal forms.

There are two types of rank three quadrics: cones and cylinders. Cylinders have three sub-types: elliptic cylinders, hyperbolic cylinders and parabolic cylinders as shown in Figure 7.3.

Cone $\dfrac{x^2}{a^2} + \dfrac{y^2}{b^2} - \dfrac{z^2}{c^2} = 0$

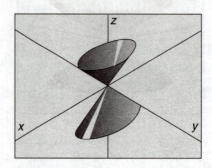

Elliptic Cylinder $\dfrac{x^2}{a^2} + \dfrac{y^2}{b^2} = 1$

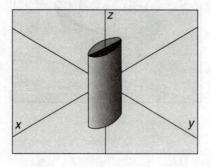

Hyperbolic Cylinder $\dfrac{x^2}{a^2} - \dfrac{y^2}{b^2} = 1$

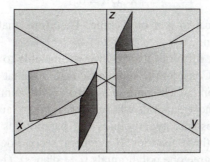

Parabolic Cylinder $x^2 = 4py$

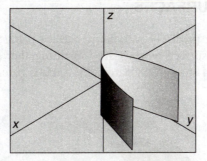

Fig. 7.3 Rank three quadric surfaces in normal forms.

7.7 QUADRIC SURFACES IN GENERAL FORM

The general form of quadric surfaces is the following:

$$Ax^2 + By^2 + Cz^2 + 2Dxy + 2Exz + 2Fyz + 2Gx + 2Hy + 2Iz + J = 0 \qquad (7.10)$$

It has ten coefficients, but, as mentioned in the discussion of conics, dividing the equation with one of its non-zero coefficients reduces the number of coefficients to nine. The coefficients for x^2, y^2 and z^2 and the constant term, all have a multiplier of 2.

7.8 QUADRIC SURFACES IN MATRIX FORM

The equation of a general quadric can also be put into matrix form as follows:

$$X^T = [x \quad y \quad z \quad 1], Q = \begin{bmatrix} A & D & E & G \\ D & B & F & H \\ E & F & C & I \\ G & H & I & J \end{bmatrix} \qquad (7.11)$$

where (x, y, z) are the coordinates of a point. This form translates the general second polynomial of a quadric to the following matrix form:

$$X^T Q x = 0 \tag{7.12}$$

Note that it is exactly identical to that of a conic. Therefore, matrices help bring conics and quadrics into an identical form.

After knowing the matrix form of quadrics, we will be able to discuss the meaning of rank four and rank three quadrics. Consider the symmetric matrix Q that contains the coefficients of a general second-degree polynomial. The rank of a matrix is the number of non-zero eigenvalues. Thus, rank four quadrics are those quadrics whose matrix Q is of rank four. It is easy to see (from their normal forms) that ellipsoids, hyperboloids and paraboloids are rank four quadrics, and cones and cylinders are rank three quadrics. If a general second-degree polynomial factors into the product of two distinct degree one polynomials (i.e., planes), Q will have rank two.

7.9 PARAMETRIC SURFACES

Parametric surfaces, or more precisely parametric surface patches, are not used individually. Normally, many parametric surface patches are joined together side-by-side to form a more complicated shape. Figure 7.4 shows four parametric surface patches joined together to form a larger surface area.

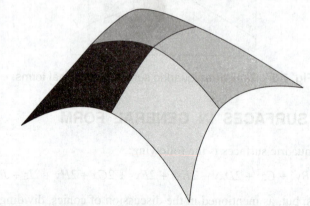

Fig. 7.4   Parametric surface patches.

In order to compute the tangent and normal vector at a point (u, v) in the domain, we need the partial derivatives. Suppose the parametric surface is defined as follows:

$$f(u, v) = [x(u, v), y(u, v), z(u, v)] \tag{7.13}$$

where parameters u and v are in certain domain.

The partial derivatives with respect to u and v are the tangent vectors at $f(u, v)$:

$$\frac{\partial f}{\partial u} = \left(\frac{\partial x}{\partial u}, \frac{\partial y}{\partial u}, \frac{\partial z}{\partial u} \right) \text{ and } \frac{\partial f}{\partial v} = \left(\frac{\partial x}{\partial v}, \frac{\partial y}{\partial v}, \frac{\partial z}{\partial v} \right) \tag{7.14}$$

In the above, the left one is the tangent vector in the u-direction while the right one is the tangent vector in the v-direction. The normal vector at $f(u, v)$, $n(u, v)$ is the cross-product of these partial derivatives detained by using the right-handed rule:

$$n = \dfrac{\dfrac{\partial f}{\partial u} \times \dfrac{\partial f}{\partial v}}{\dfrac{\partial f}{\partial u} \times \dfrac{\partial f}{\partial v}}$$

(7.15)

A parametric surface patch can be considered as a union of (infinite number) of curves. There are many ways to form these unions of curves; but the simplest one is the so-called 'isoparametric curves'. Given a parametric surface $f(u, v)$, if u is fixed to a value, say 0.1, and let v vary, this generates a curve on the surface whose u coordinate is a constant. This is the isoparametric curve in the v direction with $u = 0.1$. Similarly, fixing v to a value and letting u vary, we obtain an isoparametric curve whose v direction is a constant. Therefore, let u be fixed at $0, 0.1, 0.1, ..., 0.9$ and 1, we shall have 11 isoparametric curves $f(0, v), f(0.1, v), f(0.2, v), ..., f(0.9, v)$ and $f(1, v)$. These curves sweep out the surface if we let u change from 0 to 1 continuously. Similarly, the isoparametric curves generated by varying v cover the surface. Figure 7.5 shows a few isoparametric curves in both directions.

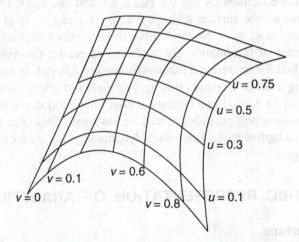

Fig. 7.5 Parametric surface patch generated by the union of isoparametric curves.

These isoparametric curves can help render the desired surface. In many applications, a parametric surface is 'triangulated' (or polygonised) into triangles or polygons. Then, these triangles and polygons can be rendered very efficiently with existing graphics programming libraries such as OpenGL and PHIGS PLUS.

Instead of triangulating the surface, it would be easier to triangulate the domain of (u, v). We can sub-divide the u-direction into m segments with $u_0 = 0, u_1, ..., u_i, ..., u_m = 1$ and sub-divide the v-direction into n segments with $v_0 = 0, v_1, ..., v_j, ..., u_n = 1$. The domain is sub-divided into $m \times n$ rectangles, each of which can be further sub-divided into two triangles.

Suppose u_i and u_{i+1} are two consecutive division points in the u-direction and v_j and v_{j+1} in the v-direction as shown in Figure 7.6. We have a rectangle in the domain with vertices (u_i, v_j), (u_{i+1}, v_j), (u_{i+1}, v_{j+1}) and (u_i, v_{j+1}). We have two ways to obtain the triangles because this rectangle has two diagonals. Let us follow the figure shown above. The first triangle is defined by (u_i, v_j), (u_{i+1}, v_j), and (u_i, v_{j+1}) while the second triangle is defined by (u_{i+1}, v_j), (u_{i+1}, v_{j+1}), and (u_i, v_{j+1}).

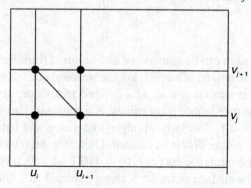

Fig. 7.6   Triangulation of the domain.

Consider the triangle defined by (u_i, v_j), (u_{i+1}, v_j), and (u_i, v_{j+1}). These three points are mapped to three points on the surface $f(u_i, v_j)$, $f(u_{i+1}, v_j)$, and $f(u_i, v_{j+1})$ with normal vectors $n(u_i, v_j)$, $n(u_{i+1}, v_j)$, and $n(u_i, v_{j+1})$. Now, we have three vertices each of which has a normal vector. These six pieces of information are sufficient to render the triangle smoothly. As a result, we have a method for rendering a parametric surface. Or, put in another way, we have a method for generating a set of triangles that approximate the given parametric surface. This approximation may not be a good one because it could have too many triangles and some of these triangles may be in wrong positions or may be too small. This situation, however, can be improved by using an adaptive technique, which dynamically adjusts the sizes, the number and the positions of triangles.

7.10   PARAMETRIC REPRESENTATION OF ANALYTIC SURFACES

7.10.1   Plane Surface

This is the simplest surface, and requires three non-coincidental points to define an infinite plane. The plane surface (Figure 7.7) can be used to generate cross-sectional views by intersecting a surface or solid model with it. Consider three points defined by P_0, P_1 and P_2 as shown in Figure 7.8. The position vector of any point P on the plane can be written as:

$$P(u, v) = P_0 + u(P_1 - P_0) + v(P_2 - P_0) \qquad 0 \le u \le 1, 0 \le v \le 1 \qquad (7.16)$$

The tangent vectors at point P are:

$$P_u(u, v) = (P_1 - P_0), \qquad P_u(u, v) = (P_2 - P_0) \qquad 0 \le u \le 1, 0 < v \le 1 \qquad (7.17)$$

The surface normal is:

$$\hat{n}(u, v) = \frac{(P_1 - P_0) \times (P_2 - P_0)}{(P_1 - P_0) \times (P_2 - P_0)} \qquad 0 \le u \le 1, 0 \le v \le 1 \tag{7.18}$$

which is constant for any point on the plane.

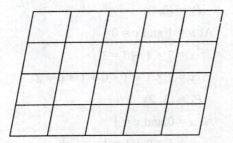

Fig. 7.7   Plane surface.

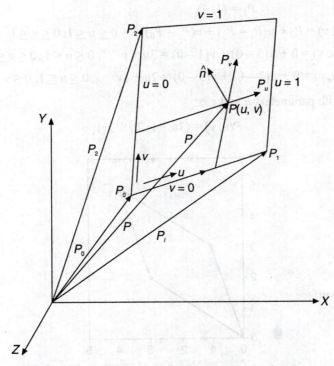

Fig. 7.8   Parametric representation of plane surface.

Example 7.1   Generate the surface having four sides with parameters u and v if $x = 3u + v$ and $y = 2u + 3v + uv$ with boundaries specified as follows:

$$u = 0; \quad 0 \le v \le 1 \qquad v = 0; \quad 0 \le u \le 1$$
$$u = 1; \quad 0 < v \le 1 \qquad v = 1; \quad 0 \le u \le 1$$

Solution

At $u = 0$ and $v = 0$

$x = 3 \times 0 + 0 = 0$

$y = 2 \times 0 + 3 \times 0 + 0 \times 0 = 0$

$P_0 = (0, 0)$

At $u = 1$ and $v = 0$

$x = 3 \times 1 + 0 = 3$

$y = 2 \times 1 + 3 \times 0 + 1 \times 0 = 2$

$P_1 = (3, 2)$

At $u = 0$ and $v = 1$

$x = 3 \times 0 + 1 = 1$

$y = 2 \times 0 + 3 \times 1 + 0 \times 1 = 3$

$P_1 = (1, 3)$

$P(u, v) = P_0 + u(P_1 - P_0) + v(P_2 - P_0)$ $0 \leq u \leq 1, 0 \leq v \leq 1$

$P_x(u, v) = 0 + u(3 - 0) + v(1 - 0) = 3u + v$ $0 \leq u \leq 1, 0 \leq v \leq 1$

$P_y(u, v) = 0 + u(2 - 0) + v(3 - 0) = 2u + 3v$ $0 \leq u \leq 1, 0 \leq v \leq 1$

The surface with parameters u and v is:

$$P(u, v) = (3u + v, 2u + 3v)$$

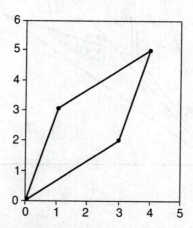

Fig. 7.9   Surface with four sides.

7.10.2   Ruled (Lofted) Surface

This is a linear surface. It interpolates linearly between two boundary curves that define the surface (Figure 7.10). Boundary curves can be in the form of any wireframe entity. The surface is ideal to represent surfaces that do not have any twists or kinks.

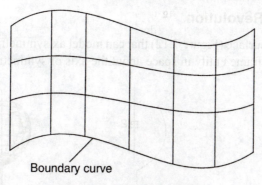

Boundary curve

Fig. 7.10 Ruled surface.

Consider that two boundary surfaces are $Q(u)$ and $R(u)$ as shown in Figure 7.11. Consider the ruling joining two points Ri and Qi. The mathematical equation of the ruling is:

$$P(u_i, v) = Q_i + v\,(R_i - Q_i) \tag{7.19}$$

where v is the parameter along the ruling.

The parametric equation for the ruled surface is

$$P(u, v) = Q(u) + v[R(u) - Q(u)] \qquad 0 \le u \le 1,\, 0 < v \le 1 \tag{7.20}$$

The vertical and horizontal rulings are generated by Equation 7.20 by holding u and v values in the v-direction and u-direction, respectively.

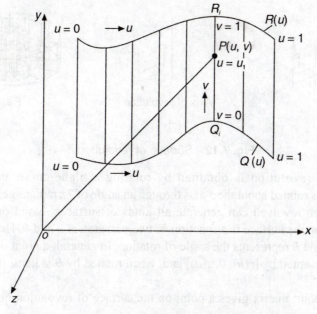

Fig. 7.11 Parametric representation of ruled surface.

7.10.3 Surface of Revolution

This is an axisymmetric surface (Figure 7.12) that can model axisymmetric objects. It is generated by rotating a planar wireframe entity in space about the axis of symmetry of a given angle.

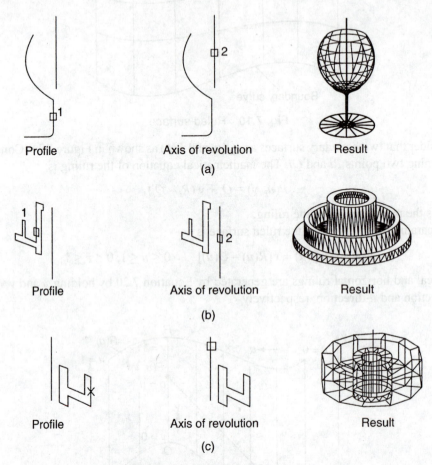

Profile   Axis of revolution   Result

(a)

Profile   Axis of revolution   Result

(b)

Profile   Axis of revolution   Result

(c)

Fig. 7.12 Surface of revolution.

The surface of revolution is obtained by rotating a plane-curve around an axis. In Figure 7.13, line AB is rotated about the z-axis through an angle of 2π radians generating a cylinder. A line or curve when revolved can generate all kinds of surfaces, based on the condition of rotation. Any point on the surface is a function of two parameters u and θ. Here, u describes the entity to be rotated and θ represents the angle of rotation. In general, a point on line AB (lying in the xz-plane) is represented by $[r(u), 0, z(u)]$ and, when rotated by θ radians, it becomes $[r(u)\cos(\theta, r(u)\sin(\theta, z(u)]$.

In general, the point matrix gives a point on the surface of revolution obtained by rotation around the z-axis:

$$P(u, v) = r(u)\cos\theta + r(u)\sin\theta + z(u)\hat{n}_3 \qquad 0 \le u \le 1, 0 \le \theta \le 2\pi \qquad (7.21)$$

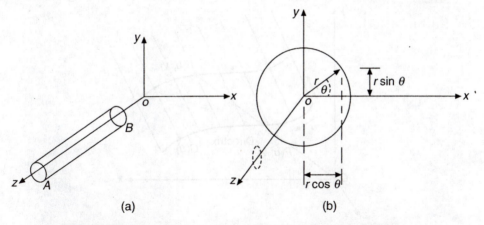

Fig. 7.13 Parametric representation of surface of revolution.

7.10.4 Tabulated Cylinder

This is a surface generated by translating a planar curve (directrix) at a given distance along a specified direction (Figure 7.14). The plane of the curve is perpendicular to the axis of the generated cylinder.

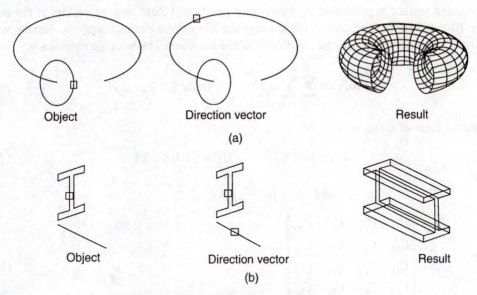

Object   Direction vector   Result

(a)

Object   Direction vector   Result

(b)

Fig. 7.14 Tabulated cylinder.

The position vector of any point $P(u, v)$ on the surface is:

$$P(u, v) = G(u) + v\hat{n} \qquad 0 \le u \le 1, 0 \le v \le 1 \qquad (7.22)$$

where $\hat{n}$ is the unit vector along the v-direction.

The cylinder length v is the input in the form of lower and upper limits where the difference between them gives the length.

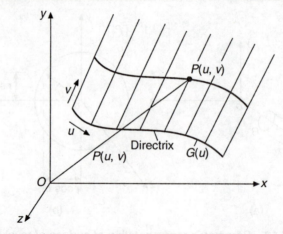

Fig. 7.15 Parametric representation of tabulated cylinder.

7.11 PARAMETRIC REPRESENTATION OF SYNTHETIC SURFACES

7.11.1 Hermite Bi-cubic Surface

The bi-cubic surface is generated by four corner points and eight tangent vectors at the corner points. Bi-cubic surfaces (Figure 7.16) are very useful in finite element analysis. Sixteen vector conditions are required to find the coefficient of the equation. The bi-cubic equation is:

$$P(u, v) = \sum_{i=0}^{3} \sum_{j=0}^{3} a_{ij} u^i v^j \qquad 0 \le u \le 1, 0 \le v \le 1 \tag{7.23}$$

The matrix form of Equation 7.23 is:

$$P(u, v) = UCV^T \qquad 0 \le u \le 1, 0 \le v \le 1 \tag{7.24}$$

where

$$U = [u^3 \ u^2 \ u \ 1] \quad \text{and} \quad V = [v^3 \ v^2 \ v \ 1]$$

$$C = \begin{bmatrix} C_{33} & C_{32} & C_{31} & C_{30} \\ C_{23} & C_{22} & C_{21} & C_{20} \\ C_{13} & C_{12} & C_{11} & C_{10} \\ C_{03} & C_{02} & C_{01} & C_{00} \end{bmatrix} \tag{7.25}$$

$$p(u, v) = UMBM^T V^T \tag{7.26}$$

$$B = \left[\begin{array}{cc|cc} P_{00} & P_{01} & P_{v00} & P_{v01} \\ P_{10} & P_{11} & P_{v10} & P_{v11} \\ \hline P_{u00} & P_{u01} & P_{uv00} & P_{uv01} \\ P_{u10} & P_{u11} & P_{uv10} & P_{uv11} \end{array} \right] \quad \text{and} \quad M = \begin{bmatrix} 2 & -2 & 2 & 1 \\ -3 & 3 & -2 & -1 \\ 0 & 0 & 1 & 0 \\ 1 & 0 & 0 & 0 \end{bmatrix} \tag{7.27}$$

$$B = \begin{bmatrix} [P] & [P_v] \\ [P_u] & [P_{uv}] \end{bmatrix} \tag{7.28}$$

where $[P]$, $[P_u]$, $[P_v]$ and $[P_{uv}]$ are the sub-matrices of the corner points, corner u-tangent vectors, corner v-tangent vectors and corner twist, respectively.

The normal vector at N_{00} is:

$$N_{00} = P_{u00} \times P_{v00} \tag{7.29}$$

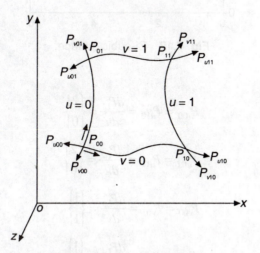

Fig. 7.16 Bi-cubic surface.

Example 7.2 Given the four corners $P_0(1, 1)$, $P_1(3, 1)$, $P_2(3, 3)$, and $P_3(4, 2)$, find the equation of the bi-cubic surface.

Solution

To generate a bi-cubic surface, 16 boundary conditions are required. Only four corner points are given. We use four edges connecting the four corners to evaluate eight tangent vectors at corners and four twist vectors at corners.

$$P_{L1}(u) = P_1 + u(P_2 - P_1) = \begin{Bmatrix} 1 \\ 1 \end{Bmatrix} + u \begin{Bmatrix} 2 \\ 0 \end{Bmatrix}$$

$$P_{L2}(u) = P_3 + u(P_4 - P_3) = \begin{Bmatrix} 2 \\ 2 \end{Bmatrix} + u \begin{Bmatrix} 2 \\ 0 \end{Bmatrix}$$

$$P_{L3}(u) = P_1 + v(P_3 - P_1) = \begin{Bmatrix} 1 \\ 1 \end{Bmatrix} + v \begin{Bmatrix} 1 \\ 1 \end{Bmatrix}$$

$$P_{L4}(u) = P_2 + v(P_4 - P_2) = \begin{Bmatrix} 3 \\ 1 \end{Bmatrix} + v \begin{Bmatrix} 1 \\ 1 \end{Bmatrix}$$

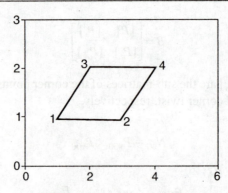

Fig. 7.17 Bi-cubic surface.

The tangent vectors are:

$$P_{u00} = P_{u10} = \frac{dP_{L1}}{du} = \begin{Bmatrix} 2 \\ 0 \end{Bmatrix}$$

$$P_{u01} = P_{u11} = \frac{dP_{L2}}{du} = \begin{Bmatrix} 2 \\ 0 \end{Bmatrix}$$

$$P_{v00} = P_{v01} = \frac{dP_{L3}}{dv} = \begin{Bmatrix} 1 \\ 1 \end{Bmatrix}$$

$$P_{v10} = P_{v11} = \frac{dP_{L4}}{dv} = \begin{Bmatrix} 1 \\ 1 \end{Bmatrix}$$

The twist vectors are:

$$\frac{d^2 P_{L1}}{du^2} = \frac{d^2 P_{L2}}{du^2} = \frac{d^2 P_{L3}}{dv^2} = \frac{d^2 P_{L4}}{dv^2} = \begin{Bmatrix} 0 \\ 0 \end{Bmatrix}$$

$$P_{00} = \begin{Bmatrix} 1 \\ 1 \end{Bmatrix}, P_{10} = \begin{Bmatrix} 3 \\ 1 \end{Bmatrix}, P_{01} = \begin{Bmatrix} 2 \\ 2 \end{Bmatrix}, \text{ and } P_{11} = \begin{Bmatrix} 4 \\ 2 \end{Bmatrix}$$

$$B_x = \begin{bmatrix} 1 & 2 & 1 & 1 \\ 3 & 4 & 1 & 1 \\ 2 & 2 & 0 & 0 \\ 2 & 2 & 0 & 0 \end{bmatrix}, \quad B_y = \begin{bmatrix} 1 & 2 & 1 & 1 \\ 1 & 2 & 1 & 1 \\ 0 & 0 & 0 & 0 \\ 0 & 0 & 0 & 0 \end{bmatrix}$$

Substituting these values into Equation 7.26, we get:

$$x(u, v) = UMB_x M^T V^T$$
$$x(u, v) = -2v^3 + 3v^2 + 2u + 1 \qquad 0 \le u \le 1, 0 \le v \le 1$$
$$y(u, v) = UMB_y M^T V^T$$
$$y(u, v) = 2v^2 - 3v^2 + 1 \qquad 0 \le u \le 1, 0 \le v \le 1$$

7.11.2 Bezier Surface

This is a synthetic surface similar to the Bezier curve and is obtained by the transformation of a Bezier curve. It permits twists and kinks in the surface. The surface does not pass through all the data points. A Bezier surface is defined by a two-dimensional set of control points $P_{i,j}$, where i is in the range of 0 and m, and j is in the range of 0 and n. Thus, in this case, we have $m + 1$ rows and $n + 1$ columns of control points and the control point on the ith row and jth column is denoted by $P_{i,j}$. Note that we have $(m + 1)(n + 1)$ control points in total.

The following is the equation of a Bezier surface defined by $m + 1$ rows and $n + 1$ columns of control points:

$$P(u, v) = \sum_{i=0}^{m} \sum_{j=0}^{n} B_{m,i}(u) B_{n,j}(v) P_{ij} \tag{7.30}$$

where $B_{m,i}(u)$ and $B_{n,j}(v)$ are the ith and jth Bezier basis functions in the u- and v-directions, respectively.

Recall from the discussion of Bezier curves, these basis functions are defined as follows:

$$\left. \begin{aligned} B_{m,i}(u) &= \frac{m!}{i!(m-i)!} u'(1-u)^{m-i} \\ B_{m,j}(v) &= \frac{n!}{j!(n-i)!} v'(1-v)^{n-j} \end{aligned} \right\} \tag{7.31}$$

Since $B_{m,i}(u)$ and $B_{n,j}(v)$ are degree m and degree n functions, we shall say that this is a Bezier surface of degree (m, n). The set of control points is usually referred to as the Bezier net or control net. Note that parameters u and v are in the range of 0 and 1, and hence a Bezier surface maps the unit square to a rectangular surface patch.

Figure 7.18 shows a Bezier surface defined by three rows and three columns (i.e., nine) control points and hence is a Bezier surface of degree $(2, 2)$.

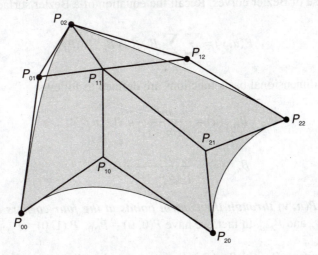

Fig. 7.18 Bezier surface defined by nine control points.

Basis Functions

The basis functions of a Bezier surface are the coefficients of control points. From the definition, it is clear that these two-dimensional basis functions are the product of two one-dimensional Bezier basis functions and consequently, the basis functions for a Bezier surface are parametric surfaces of two variables u and v defined on the unit square. Figure 7.19 shows the basis functions for control points $P_{0,0}$ (left) and $P_{1,1}$ (right), respectively. For control point $P_{0,0}$, its basis function is the product of two one-dimensional Bezier basis functions $B_{2,0}(u)$ in the u-direction and $B_{2,0}(v)$ in the v-direction. In Figure 7.19a, both $B_{2,0}(u)$ and $B_{2,0}(v)$ are shown along with their product (shown in wireframe). Figure 7.19b shows the basis function for $P_{1,1}$, which is the product of $B_{2,1}(u)$ in the u-direction and $B_{2,1}(v)$ in the v-direction.

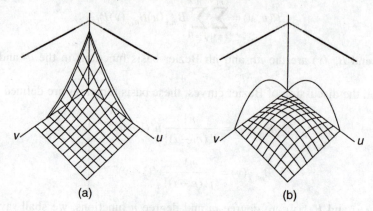

(a)   (b)

Fig. 7.19 Basis functions.

Important Properties of Bezier Surfaces

Several important properties of Bezier surfaces are listed here. These properties can be proved easily by applying the same techniques used for Bezier curves. Please compare these important properties with those of Bezier curves. Recall the equation of a Bezier surface:

$$P(u, v) = \sum_{i=0}^{m} \sum_{j=0}^{n} B_{m,i}(u)\, B_{n,j}(v) P_{ij} \tag{7.32}$$

where the two one-dimensional basis functions are defined as follows:

$$B_{m,i}(u) = \frac{m!}{i!(m-i)!} u^i (1-u)^{m-i}$$

$$B_{n,j}(v) = \frac{n!}{j!(n-j)!} v^i (1-v)^{n-j} \tag{7.33}$$

1. **Passing of P(u, v) through the control points at the four corners of the control net:** $P_{0,0}$, $P_{m,0}, P_{0,n}$ and $P_{m,n}$. In fact, we have $P(0, 0) = P_{0,0}$. $P(1, 0) = P_{m,0}$, $P(0, 1) = P_{0,n}$ and $P(1, 1) = P_{m,n}$.
2. **Non-negativity:** $B_{m,i}(u)\, B_{n,j}(v)$ is non-negative for all m, n, i, j and u and v in the range of 0 and 1. This is obvious.

3. **Partition of unity:** The sum of all $B_{m,i}(u) B_{n,j}(v)$ is 1 for all u and v in the range of 0 and 1. More precisely, this means that for any pair of u and v in the range of 0 and 1, the following holds:

$$\sum_{i=0}^{m} \sum_{j=0}^{n} B_{m,i}(u) B_{n,j}(v) = 1 \qquad (7.34)$$

4. **Convex hull property:** A Bezier surface $P(u, v)$ lies in the convex hull defined by its control net. Since $P(u, v)$ is the linear combination of all its control points with positive coefficients whose sum is 1 (partition of unity), the surface lies in the convex hull of its control points.

5. **Affine invariance:** This means that to apply an affine transformation to a Bezier surface, one can apply the transformation to all control points and the surface defined by the transformed control points is identical to the one obtained by applying the same transformation to the surface's equation.

6. **Variation diminishing property:** No such thing exists for surfaces.

7.11.3 Isoparametric Curves on a Bezier Surface

A parametric surface is defined as:

$$f(u, v) = [x(u, v), y(u, v), z(u, v)] \qquad (7.35)$$

An isoparametric curve for $u = a$ is a curve defined as $f(a, v)$. Note that this function has only one variable v and, therefore, represents a curve in the v-direction. Similarly, an isoparametric curve in the u-direction for a fixed $v = b$ is $f(u, b)$.

Isoparametric curves on a Bezier surface, in fact, on any tensor product surface, have a very simple structure. In the equation of a Bezier surface, the basis function $B_{m,i}(u)$ only depends on the index i and can be taken out of the summation in j. Thus, the equation has the following form:

$$P(u, v) = \sum_{i=0}^{m} B_{m,i}(u) \left(\sum_{j=0}^{n} B_{n,j}(v) P_{ij} \right) \qquad (7.36)$$

The expression in the parenthesis involves basis functions $B_{n,j}(v)$ and control points $P_{i,j}$. Note that the basis functions do not depend on i; but the control points do. Therefore, we can define a new function $q_i(v)$ to reflect this fact:

$$q_i(v) = \left(\sum_{j=0}^{n} B_{n,j}(v) P_{ij} \right) \qquad (7.37)$$

Obviously, each $q_i(v)$ is a Bezier curve defined by control points $P_{i0}, P_{i1}, ... P_{in}$ (i.e., the i-th row of control points). As a result, we have $m + 1$ new points $q_0(v), q_1(v), ..., q_m(v)$. Since v is fixed and can be considered as a constant, points $q_0(v), q_1(v), ..., q_m(v)$ will not change positions as u changes. Consequently, the surface equation becomes:

$$P(u, v) = \sum_{i=0}^{m} B_{m,i}(u) q_i(v) \qquad (7.38)$$

Since v is fixed, $P(u, v)$ is actually a single variable parametric equation in u and hence represents a curve on the surface. This is a Bezier curve in u defined by $m + 1$ control points $q_0(v)$, $q_1(v)$, ..., $q_m(v)$.

Therefore, we conclude that any isoparametric curve with v fixed is a Bezier curve defined by a set of control points that can be computed from the equation of the surface. Interchanging the roles of u and v, we will have the same conclusion for isoparametric curves in the v direction. Figure 7.20 represents isoparametric curves on a Bezier surface in both directions.

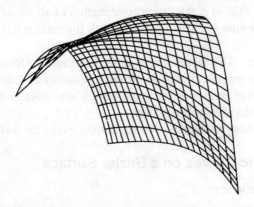

Fig. 7.20 Isoparametric curves on a Bezier surface.

7.11.4 Boundary Curves of a Bezier Surface

There are four special isoparametric curves $P(0, v)$, $P(1, v)$, $P(u, 0)$ and $P(u, 1)$. These are the boundary curves because they map the boundary of the unit square (i.e., the domain of the surface) to the surface. Setting u to 0 and 1 and setting v to 0 and 1 yields the following equations of the boundary curves:

$$P(0, v) = \sum_{j=0}^{n} B_{n,j}(v) P_{0j}$$

$$P(1, v) = \sum_{j=0}^{n} B_{n,j}(v) P_{mj}$$

$$\text{(7.39)}$$

$$P(u, 0) = \sum_{i=0}^{m} B_{n,j}(v) P_{i0}$$

$$P(u, 1) = \sum_{i=0}^{m} B_{n,j}(v) P_{in}$$

Therefore, the boundary curve corresponding to $u = 0$ and $u = 1$ are Bezier curves defined by the 0-th row and the m-th row of the given control points. Similarly, the boundary curve corresponding to $v = 0$ and $v = 1$ are Bezier curves defined by the 0-th column and the n-th column of the given control points.

7.11.5 The *u*-Direction and *v*-Direction of Bezier Surfaces

We know that the number of control points are organised into $m + 1$ rows and $n + 1$ columns. What is the relationship between rows and columns and the *u*-direction and *v*-direction? Recall that the *v*-direction is the curve with u fixed to a constant. In this case, the definition can be rewritten as follows:

$$P(u, v) = \sum_{i=0}^{m} B_{m,i}(u) \left(\sum_{j=0}^{n} B_{n,j}(v) P_{ij} \right) \tag{7.40}$$

Therefore, as v changes, the expression in the parenthesis defines a Bezier curve with control points $P_{i0}, P_{i1}, ..., P_{in}$. These are exactly the control points on row i. Therefore, the *v*-direction curve runs horizontally and by a similar argument, we know that the *u*-direction curve runs vertically. As examples, boundary curves $P(0, v)$ and $P(1, v)$ are in the *v*-direction and are defined by row 0 and row n, respectively, and boundary curves $P(u, 0)$ and $P(u, 1)$ are in the *u*-direction and are defined by column 0 and column m, respectively.

7.12 TENSOR PRODUCT SURFACES

The tensor product technique constructs surfaces by 'multiplying' two curves. Given two Bezier curves, the tensor product method constructs a surface by multiplying the basis functions of the first curve with the basis functions of the second, and uses the results as the basis functions for a set of two-dimensional control points. Surfaces generated in this way are called 'tensor product surfaces'.

If we arrange the control points into a matrix of $m + 1$ rows and $n + 1$ columns:

$$\begin{bmatrix} P_{0,0} & P_{0,1} & \cdots & P_{0,n} \\ P_{1,0} & P_{1,1} & \cdots & P_{1,n} \\ \cdot & \cdot & \cdots & \cdot \\ \cdot & \cdot & \cdots & \cdot \\ P_{m,0} & P_{m,1} & \cdots & P_{m,n} \end{bmatrix} \tag{7.41}$$

and the basis functions of the *v*-direction Bezier curve into a column matrix of $n + 1$ rows:

$$\begin{Bmatrix} B_{n,0}(v) \\ B_{n,1}(v) \\ \cdot \\ \cdot \\ B_{n,n}(v) \end{Bmatrix} \tag{7.42}$$

then the result of the parenthesis can be rewritten as a matrix product:

$$\begin{bmatrix} P_{0,0} & P_{0,1} & \cdots & P_{0,n} \\ P_{1,0} & P_{1,1} & \cdots & P_{1,n} \\ \cdot & \cdot & \cdots & \cdot \\ \cdot & \cdot & \cdots & \cdot \\ P_{m,0} & P_{m,1} & \cdots & P_{m,n} \end{bmatrix} \times \begin{Bmatrix} B_{n,0}(v) \\ B_{n,1}(v) \\ \cdot \\ \cdot \\ B_{n,n}(v) \end{Bmatrix} \quad (7.43)$$

In this matrix form, the result is a column matrix of $m + 1$ entries. If we further make the basis functions of the u-direction Bezier curve into a row matrix of $m + 1$ entries:

$$[B_{m,0}(u) \quad B_{m,1}(u) \quad \cdots \quad B_{m,m}(u)] \quad (7.44)$$

The equation of a Bezier curve becomes the product of three matrices as follows:

$$P(u, v) = [B_{m,0}(u) \quad B_{m,1}(u) \quad \cdots \quad B_{m,m}(u)] \times \begin{bmatrix} P_{0,0} & P_{0,1} & \cdots & P_{0,n} \\ P_{1,0} & P_{1,1} & \cdots & P_{1,n} \\ \cdot & \cdot & \cdots & \cdot \\ \cdot & \cdot & \cdots & \cdot \\ P_{m,0} & P_{m,1} & \cdots & P_{m,n} \end{bmatrix} \times \begin{Bmatrix} B_{n,0}(v) \\ B_{n,1}(v) \\ \cdot \\ \cdot \\ B_{n,n}(v) \end{Bmatrix} \quad (7.45)$$

Therefore, we have successfully converted the definition of a Bezier surface into a product form. Since the entities of the control points matrix are matrices (i.e., each control point can be considered as a vector and hence a matrix), this is the tensor product form in mathematics. As a result, Bezier surfaces are tensor product surfaces.

7.13 DE CASTELJAU'S ALGORITHM FOR BEZIER SURFACES

De Casteljau's algorithm can be extended to handle Bezier surfaces. More precisely, de Casteljau's algorithm can be applied several times to find the corresponding point on a Bezier surface $P(u, v)$ given (u, v). This algorithm is based on the concept of isoparametric curves.

Recall that the equation of a Bezier surface:

$$P(u, v) = \sum_{i=0}^{m} \sum_{j=0}^{n} B_{m,j}(u) B_{n,j}(v) P_{ij} \quad (7.46)$$

can be rewritten as the following:

$$P(u, v) = \sum_{i=0}^{m} B_{m,i}(u) \left(\sum_{j=0}^{n} B_{n,j}(v) P_{ij} \right) \quad (7.47)$$

For $i = 0, 1, ..., m$ define $q_i(v)$ as follows:

$$q_i(v) = \left(\sum_{j=0}^{n} B_{n,j}(v) P_{ij} \right) \quad (7.48)$$

For a fixed v, we have $m + 1$ points $q_0(v)$, $q_1(v)$, ..., $q_m(v)$ Each $q_i(v)$ is a point on the Bezier curve defined by control points P_{i0}, P_{i1},...P_{in}. Plugging these back into the surface equation yields:

$$P(u, v) = \sum_{i=0}^{m} B_{m,i}(u)\, q_i(v) \qquad (7.49)$$

This means that $P(u, v)$ is a point of the Bezier curve defined by $m + 1$ control points $q_0(v)$, $q_1(v)$,..., $q_m(v)$. Thus, we have the following conclusion:

To find a point $P(u, v)$ on a Bezier surface, we can find $m + 1$ points $q_0(v)$, $q_1(v)$,..., $q_m(v)$ and then from these points find $P(u, v)$.

This conclusion gives us a simple way for computing $P(u, v)$ given (u, v). Since each $qi(v)$ is a point on the Bezier curve defined by the i-th row of control points: P_{i0}, P_{i1}, ..., P_{in} therefore, for the i-th row and a given v, we can apply de Casteljau's algorithm for the Bezier curve to compute $qi(v)$. After $m + 1$ applications of de Casteljau's algorithm (i.e., one for each row), we shall have $q_0(v)$, $q_1(v)$,..., $q_m(v)$ in hand. Then, applying de Casteljau's algorithm to these $m + 1$ control points again with u yields the final point $P(u, v)$ on the surface.

Figure 7.21 illustrates this concept. The given surface is a degree $(2, 2)$ Bezier surface defined by a 3×3 control net. Suppose $u = 2/3$ and $v = 1/3$. To determine $q_0(1/3)$, we take the 0-th row of control points P_{00}, P_{01} and P_{02}, and apply de Casteljau's algorithm to this Bezier curve with $v = 1/3$. We repeat this for the first row and the second row with $v = 1/3$. This yields three intermediate control points $q_0(1/3)$, $q_1(1/3)$ and $q_2(1/3)$. Finally, we apply de Casteljau's algorithm to these three new control points with $u = 2/3$. The result is $P(2/3, 1/3)$ which is marked $P(u, v)$ in Figure 7.21.

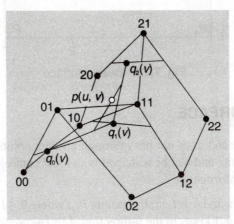

Fig. 7.21 De Casteljau's algorithm for Bezier surface.

Finally, the following summarises this algorithm:

Input: A $m + 1$ rows and $n + 1$ columns of control points and (u, v).

Output: Point on surface $P(u, v)$

Algorithm:

    for i: = 0 to m do

begin

Apply de Casteljau's algorithm to the *i*-th row of control points with *v*;

Let the point obtained be $q_i(v)$;

end

Apply de Casteljau's algorithm to $q_0(v), q_1(v),..., q_m$ with *u*;

The point obtained is $P(u, v)$;

Example 7.3 Find the equation of the Bezier surface shown in Figure 7.22.

Solution

We generate 2×2 surface. Applying Equation 7.30 gives:

$P(u, v) = P_{00} B_{0,1}(u) B_{0,1}(v) + P_{01} B_{0,1}(u) B_{1,1}(v) P_{10} B_{1,1}(u) B_{0,1}(v) + P_{11}(u) B_{0,1}(v) + P_{11} B_{1,1}(u)$
$B_{1,1}(v) B_{0,1}(u) = 1 - u; B_{0,1}(v) = 1 - v; B_{1,1}(u) = u; B_{1,1}(v) = v$

These two equations produce the following surface equation:

$$P(u, v) = \begin{Bmatrix} x(u, v) \\ y(u, v) \end{Bmatrix} = u \begin{Bmatrix} 3 \\ 0 \end{Bmatrix} + v \begin{Bmatrix} 0 \\ 2 \end{Bmatrix}$$

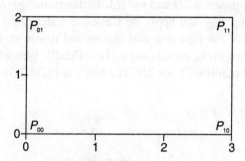

Fig. 7.22 Bezier surface.

7.14 B-SPLINE SURFACE

This is a synthetic surface and does not pass through all data points. The surface is capable of giving very smooth contours, and can be reshaped with local controls.

Given the following information:

1. A set of $m + 1$ rows and $n + 1$ control points $P_{i,j}$, where $0 \leq i \leq m$ and $0 \leq i \leq n$;
2. A knot vector of $h + 1$ knots in the *u*-direction, $U = [u_0, u_1,..., u_h]$;
3. A knot vector of $k + 1$ knots in the *v*-direction, $V = [v_0, v_1,..., v_k]$;
4. The degree *p* in the *u*-direction; and
5. The degree *q* in the *v*-direction;
6. The B-spline surface is defined by this information as follows:

$$P(u, v) = \sum_{i=0}^{m} \sum_{j=0}^{n} N_{i,p}(u) N_{j,q}(v) P_{i,j} \qquad (7.50)$$

where $N_{i,p}(u)$ and $N_{j,q}(v)$ are the B-spline basis functions of degree p and q, respectively. Note that the fundamental identities, one for each direction, must hold: $h = m + p + 1$ and $k = n + q + 1$. Therefore, a B-spline surface is another example of tensor product surfaces. As in Bezier surfaces, the set of control points is usually referred to as the control net and the range of u and v is 0 and 1. Hence, a B-spline surface maps the unit square to a rectangular surface patch. Figure 7.23 shows a B-spline surface defined by six rows and six columns of control points.

The knot vector and the degree in the u-direction are:

$$U = \{0, 0, 0, 0.25, 0.5, 0.75, 1, 1, 1\} \text{ and } 2.$$

The knot vector and the degree in the v-direction are:

$$V = \{0, 0, 0, 0, 0.33, 0.66, 1, 1, 1, 1\} \text{ and } 3.$$

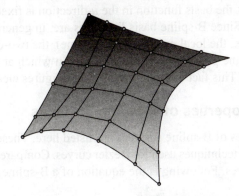

Fig. 7.23 A B-spline surface.

7.14.1 Basis Functions

The coefficient of control point $P_{i,j}$ is the product of two one-dimensional B-spline basis functions, one in the u-direction, $N_{i,p}(u)$, and the other in the v-direction, $N_{j,q}(v)$. All these products are two-dimensional B-spline functions. Figure 7.24 shows the basis functions of control points $P2,0$, $P2,1$, $P2,2$, $P2,3$, $P2,4$ and $P2,5$.

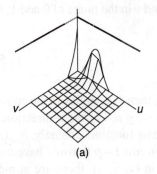
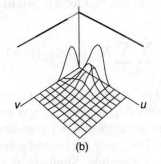
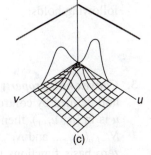

| (a) | (b) | (c) |

Fig. 7.24 (*Cont.*)

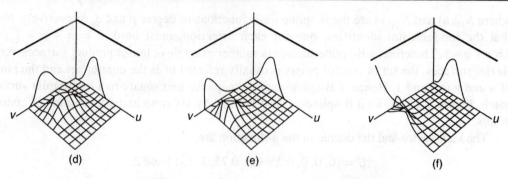

Fig. 7.24   Basis functions of a B-spline surface.

The two-dimensional basis functions are shown as wireframe surfaces. Since the control points are on the same row, the basis function in the u-direction is fixed while the basis functions in the v-direction change. Since B-spline basis functions are, in general, non-zero only on a few consecutive knot spans (i.e., the local modification scheme), the two-dimensional B-spline basis functions are non-zero on the product of two-knot spans on which at least one one-dimensional basis function is non-zero. This fact is shown in the above figures clearly.

7.14.2   Important Properties of B-Spline Surfaces

Several important properties of B-spline surfaces are listed here. These properties can be proved easily by applying the same techniques used for Bezier curves. Compare these important properties with those of B-spline curves. Following is the equation of a B-spline surface:

$$P(u, v) = \sum_{i=0}^{m} \sum_{j=0}^{n} N_{i,p}(u)\, N_{i,q}(v)\, P_{i,j} \tag{7.51}$$

where the degrees in the u- and v-directions are p and q, respectively, and there are $m + 1$ rows and $n + 1$ columns of control points.

1. **Non-negativity:** $N_{i,p}(u)\, N_{j,q}(v)$ is non-negative for all p, q, i, j and u and v in the range of 0 and 1. This is obvious.

2. **Partition of unity:**   The sum of all $N_{i,p}(u)\, N_{j,q}(v)$ is 1 for all u and v in the range of 0 and 1. More precisely, this means that for any pair of u and v in the range of 0 and 1, the following holds:

$$\sum_{i=0}^{m} \sum_{j=0}^{n} N_{i,p}(u)\, N_{j,q}(v) = 1 \tag{7.52}$$

3. **Convex hull property:**   If (u, v) is in $[u_i, u_{i+1}] \times (v_j, v_{j+1})$, then $P(u, v)$ lies in the convex hull defined by control points $P_{h,k}$, where $0 \leq i \leq m$ and $0 \leq i \leq n$. For the u-direction, if u is in $[u_i, u_{i+1})$, then there are at most $p + 1$ non-zero basis functions, namely, $N_{i,p}(u)$, $N_{i-1,p}(u)$, ..., and $N_{i-p,p}(u)$. Thus, only the control points on row $i - p$ to row i have non-zero basis functions in the u-direction. Similarly, if v is in $[v_j, v_{j+1})$, there are at most $q + 1$ non-zero basis functions on this knot span, namely $N_{j,q}(v)$, $N_{j-1,\,q}(v)$, ..., and

$N_{j-q,\,q}(v)$. Thus, only the control points on column $j - q$ to column j have non-zero basis functions in the v-direction. Combining these two facts together, only the control points in the range of row $i - p$ to row i and column $j - q$ to q have non-zero basis functions. Since these basis functions are non-negative and their sum is one (i.e., the partition of unity property), $P(u, v)$ lies in the convex hull defined by these control points.

4. *Local modification scheme:* $N_{i,p}(u)\, N_{j,q}(v)$ **is zero if (u, v) is outside of the rectangle** $[u_i, u_{i+1}) \times (v_j, v_{j+1})$.

   From the local modification scheme property, we know that in the u-direction $N_{i,p}(u)$ is non-zero on $[u_i, u_{i+p+1})$ and zero elsewhere. The local modification scheme property of B-spline surfaces follows directly from the curve case. If control point $P_{3,2}$ is moved to a new location, the surfaces illustrated in Figure 7.25 show that only the neighbouring area on the surface of the moved control point changes shape and elsewhere it remains unchanged.

5. *Affine invariance:* This means that to apply an affine transformation to a B-spline surface, one can apply the transformation to all control points and the surface defined by the transformed control points is identical to the one obtained by applying the same transformation to the surface equation.

6. *Variation diminishing property:* No such thing exists for surfaces.

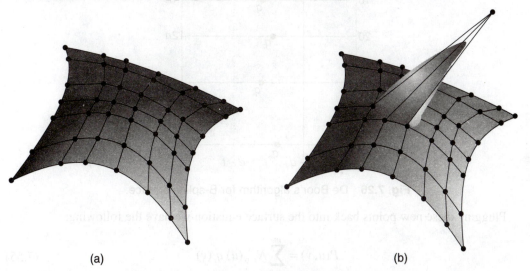

(a) (b)

Fig. 7.25 Illustration of local modification scheme.

7.15 DE BOOR'S ALGORITHM FOR B-SPLINE SURFACES

With the local modification property, de Boor's algorithm looks very similar to de Casteljau's algorithm. If the equation of a B-spline surface is:

$$P(u, v) = \sum_{i=0}^{m} \sum_{j=0}^{n} N_{i,p}(u)\,(N_{j,q}(v)\,P_{i,j}) \qquad (7.53)$$

then for a fixed i, the curve in the parenthesis is simply a B-spline curve defined by the control points on row i.

To simplify our discussion, let $q_i(v)$ be defined as follows:

$$q_i(v) = \sum_{j=0}^{n} [N_{j,q}(v)\, P_{i,j}] \tag{7.54}$$

Therefore, $q_i(v)$ is a point corresponding to v on the B-spline curve defined by the control points of row i. If v is in knot span (v_d, v_{d+1}), then only $q + 1$ control points on row i are involved in the computation of $q_i(v)$, where q is the degree of $N_{j,q}(v)$. These control points are $P_{i,d}, P_{i,d-1}, ...,$ $P_{i,d-q}$, if v is not equal to v_d. Otherwise, if v is equal to v_d, a knot of multiplicity t, then the involved control points are $P_{i,d-t}, P_{i,d-t-1}, ..., P_{i,d-q}$. Therefore, using the control points from column $d - q$ to column $d - t$, where t is zero if v is not a knot, we can apply de Boor's algorithm to each row to obtain $m + 1$ new points $q_0(v), q1(v), ..., q_m(v)$. This is shown in Figure 7.26.

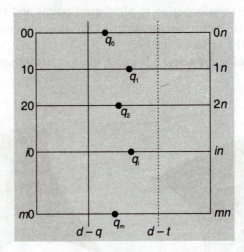

Fig. 7.26 De Boor's algorithm for B-spline surface.

Plugging these new points back into the surface equation we have the following:

$$P(u, v) = \sum_{i=0}^{m} N_{i,p}(u)\, q_i(v) \tag{7.55}$$

Therefore, $P(u, v)$ is a point on the B-spline curve defined by $q_0(v), q_1(v), ..., q_m(v)$. As a result, to find $P(u, v)$, what we need to do is to find the point on this curve that corresponds to u. Hence, de Boor's algorithm can be used again for this purpose.

Let u be in knot span $[u_c, u_{c+1})$. From the local modification property, only $p + 1$ control points will participate in the computation, where p is the degree of the B-spline curve. Thus, if u is not equal to u_c, the involved points are $q_c(v), q_{c-1}(v), ..., q_{c-p}(v)$. Otherwise, if u is equal to u_c, a knot of multiplicity s, the involved points are $q_{c-s}(v), q_{c-s-1}(v), ..., q_{c-p}(v)$. Based on this observation, even though each row of control points can produce a $q_i(v)$, not all of them are needed. In fact, only $p +1$ rows are needed. This is illustrated in Figure 7.27.

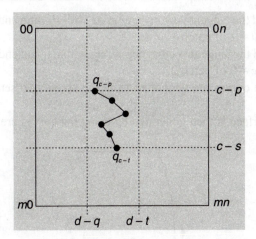

Fig. 7.27 De Boor's algorithm for B-spline surface with local modification property.

In summary, given u in $[u_c, u_{c+1})$ and v in $[v_d, v_{d+1})$, $P(u, v)$, for row i in the range of $c - p$ and $c - s$, applying de Boor's algorithm to control points $p_{i, d-q}$, $p_{i, d-q+1}$, ..., $p_{i, d-t}$ yields a new point $q_i(v)$. Then, if we apply de Boor's algorithm to $q_{c-p}(v)$, $q_{c-p+1}(v)$, ..., $q_{c-s}(v)$, the result is $P(u, v)$.

Finally, the following summarises this algorithm:

Input: A set of $m + 1$ rows and $n + 1$ columns of control points, knot vectors in the u- and v-directions and (u, v);

Output: Point on the surface $P(u, v)$

Algorithm:

```
Let u be in [u_c, u_{c+1});
Let v be in [v_d, v_{d+1});
If u is not equal to u_c, let s be zero; otherwise, let s be the
multiplicity of u_c;
If v is not equal to v_d, let t be zero; otherwise, let t be the multiplicity
of v_d;
for i: = c - p to c - s do
      begin
            Apply de Boor's algorithm to control points p_{i, d-q},
            p_{i, d-q+1}, ..., p_{i, d-t} with respect to v;
            Let the result be q_{i}(v);
      end
Apply de Boor's algorithm to points q_{c-p}(v), q_{c-p+1}(v), ..., q_{c-s}(v) with
respect to u; The point obtained is P(u, v).
```

7.16 BLENDING SURFACE

Blending surface connects two non-adjacent surfaces or patches. The blending surface should satisfy at least C^0 and C^1 continuities. Figure 7.28 shows a blending surface joining two patches. A bi-cubic surface is suitable to join bi-cubic Bezier or B-spline surfaces. The procedure of generation blending surface is as follows:

1. A set of point and the tangent vectors beginning with P_{00} and ending with P_{10} are generated along the curve $v = 1$ of patch 1.
2. A set of point and the tangent vectors beginning with P_{01} and ending with P_{11} are generated along the curve $v = 0$ of patch 2.
3. The cubic spline curves are generated from the above two sets generated in Step 1 and Step 2.
4. The blending surface is then generated by using the curves created in Step 3.

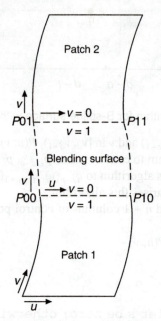

Fig. 7.28 Blending surface.

7.17 SURFACE MANIPULATIONS

The important surface manipulations are:

- Evaluating points and curves on surfaces
- Segmentation
- Intersection

7.17.1 Evaluating Points and Curves on Surfaces

Points and curves are useful geometric entities for finite element analysis. The points on the surface are determined by substituting values for u and v in the respective surface equation. The curves are generated by solving two non-linear polynomials in u and v simultaneously. The three polynomials are evaluated in u and v for each coordinate (i.e., x, y and z).

7.17.2 Segmentation

Segmentation is re-parameterisation of a surface while keeping the degree of its polynomial in u and v unchanged. The segmentation procedure is the same as that of a curve. The only difference is that the segmentation is extended in u- and v-directions.

For example, a surface is defined over the range $0 \leq u \leq 1$ and $0 \leq v \leq 1$. It is required to divide the surface at point $P_1(u_1, v_1)$. The segmentation is illustrated in Figure 7.29.

The re-parameterisation for sub-surface 1 is defined as follows:

$$u' = u_0 + u(u_1 - u_0)$$ (7.56)

$$v' = v_0 + v(v_1 - v_0)$$

Similarly, re-parameterisation can be carried out for the remaining three sub-surfaces also.

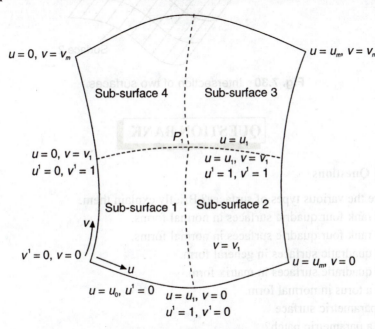

Fig. 7.29 Segmentation.

7.17.3 Intersection

The intersection of two surfaces is a curve. The intersection involves finding the points representing the two intersecting surfaces at the curve of intersection. The procedure is complex and non-linear in nature. Iterative methods are applied to find the points of intersecting curve. A typical intersection of two surfaces is shown in Figure 7.30.

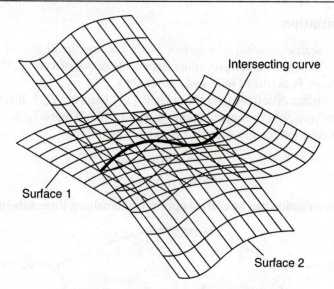

Fig. 7.30 Intersection of two surfaces.

QUESTION BANK

A. Descriptive Questions

1. What are the various types of surfaces? Briefly explain them.
2. Explain rank four quadric surfaces in normal forms.
3. Explain rank four quadric surfaces in normal forms.
4. Explain quadratic surfaces in general form.
5. Explain quadratic surfaces in matrix form.
6. Explain a torus in normal form.
7. Define parametric surface.
8. What is a parametric patch?
9. Explain triangularisation of the domain.
10. What is a Bezier surface? Explain.
11. Explain the basis functions of a Bezier surface.
12. What are the properties of Bezier surfaces?
13. Explain the isoparametric curves of a Bezier surface.
14. Explain the boundary curves of a Bezier surface.
15. Explain the u-direction and v-direction of a Bezier surface.
16. What is tensor product Bezier surface? Explain.
17. Explain De Casteljau's algorithm for Bezier surfaces with an example.
18. What is a B-spline surface? Explain.
19. Explain the basis functions of a B-spline surface.

20. What are the properties of B-spline surfaces?
21. What are clamped, closed and open B-spline surfaces? Explain.
22. Explain De Boor's algorithm for B-spline surfaces with an example.

B. Multiple Choice Questions

1. The number of non-coincidental points required to define the simplest surface are:
   (a) 4   (b) 3   (c) 2   (d) 5

2. The bi-cubic surface is generated by _____ corner points and _____ tangent vectors at the corner points.
   (a) 4 and 8   (b) 2 and 4   (c) 3 and 6   (d) 3 and 4

3. To generate a bi-cubic surface, _____ boundary conditions are required.
   (a) 8   (b) 12   (c) 16   (d) 18

4. The Bezier surface is defined by $m + 1$ _____ of control points.
   (a) $m + 1$ rows and $n + 1$ columns   (b) $m - 1$ rows and $n - 1$ columns
   (c) $m + 1$ rows and $n - 1$ columns   (d) m rows and n columns

5. The convex hull property is satisfied by the following surface:
   (a) Bezier   (b) B-spline   (c) NURBS   (d) All the above

6. The tensor product technique constructs surfaces by _____ two curves.
   (a) Adding   (b) Subtraction   (c) Multiplying   (d) Dividing

Chapter **8**

Solid Modelling

After reading this chapter, the reader will be able to understand the following concepts:

- ⊃ Application of solid models
- ⊃ Modelling considerations of solids
- ⊃ Wireframe models and their ambiguity
- ⊃ Geometry and topology
- ⊃ Solid modelling schemes
- ⊃ Boundary representation
- ⊃ Wing-edge data structure for boundary representation
- ⊃ The Euler-Poincare formula for boundary representation
- ⊃ How to count genus correctly?
- ⊃ Euler operators: The make group of Euler operators and the kill group of Euler operators
- ⊃ Constructive solid geometry
- ⊃ CSG primitives
- ⊃ Boolean operators
- ⊃ CSG expressions
- ⊃ Interior, exterior and closure
- ⊃ Regularised Boolean operators
- ⊃ Sweeping: Linear sweep and non-linear sweep
- ⊃ Solid manipulators: Displaying, segmentation, trimming, transformation and editing

8.1   INTRODUCTION

Most geometric objects that we see everyday are solids, that is, they are geometric objects with an interior. Solid models are known to be complete, valid and unambiguous objects. Solids can be very simple like a cube or very complex like a turbine blade. Typical examples of solid modelling are shown in Figure 8.1.

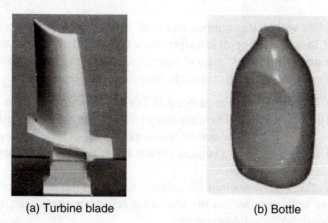

(a) Turbine blade   (b) Bottle

Fig. 8.1   Typical examples of solid modelling.

8.2   APPLICATION OF SOLID MODELS

In mechanical engineering, a solid model is used for the following applications:

1. **Graphics:**   Generating drawings, surface and solid models.
2. **Design:**   Mass property calculation, interference analysis, finite element analysis, kinematics and mechanism analysis, animation, etc.
3. **Manufacturing:**   Tool path generation and verification, process planning, dimension inspection, tolerance and surface finish.
4. **Assembly:**   Application to robotics and flexible manufacturing: Assembly planning, vision algorithm, kinematics and dynamics driven by solid models.

8.3   MODELLING CONSIDERATIONS OF SOLIDS

In order to be processed by computers, solids must have some representations that can describe the geometry and characteristics completely. In fact, a good representation should address the following issues:

1. **Domain:**   While no representation can describe all possible solids, a representation should be able to represent a useful set of geometric objects.
2. **Unambiguity:**   When you see a representation of a solid, you will know what is being represented without any doubt. An unambiguous representation is usually referred to as a **complete** one.

3. *Uniqueness:* That is, there is only one way to represent a particular solid. If a representation is unique, then it is easy to determine if two solids are identical since one can just compare their representations.
4. *Accuracy:* A representation is said to be **accurate** if no approximation is required.
5. **Validness:** This means that a representation should not create any invalid or impossible solids. More precisely, a representation will not represent an object that does not correspond to a solid.
6. *Closure:* Solids will be transformed and used with other operations such as union and intersection. **Closure** means that transforming a valid solid always yields a valid solid.
7. *Compactness and efficiency:* A good representation should be compact enough to save space and allow for efficient algorithms to determine the desired physical characteristics.

These issues may be contradictory to each other. For efficiency purposes, a curvilinear solid may be approximated by a polyhedron. There are many efficient and robust algorithms for handling polyhedra; however, accuracy may not be maintained in the process of approximation. For example, given two curvilinear solids that are at a tangent to each other, this tangency may disappear after conversion of the solid to a polyhedron.

In summary, designing representations for solids is a difficult job and compromises are often necessary. This course will only discuss the following representations: wireframes, boundary representations and constructive solid geometry.

8.4 WIREFRAME MODELS

The wireframe model as shown in Figure 8.2 is perhaps the oldest way of representing solids. A wireframe model consists of two tables, the *vertex* table and the *edge* table. Each entry of the vertex table records a vertex and its coordinate values, while each entry of the edge table has two components giving the two incident vertices of that edge. A wireframe model does not have face information. for example, representation of a cube defined by eight vertices and 12 edges (Table 8.1). Figure 8.3 shows all eight vertices and twelve edges.

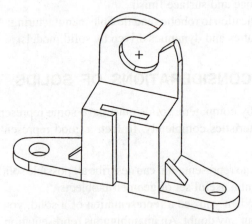

Fig. 8.2 A wireframe model.

Table 8.1 Vertex and Edge Tables of a Cube

Vertex Table				Edge Table		
Vertex #	x	y	z	Edge #	Start Vertex	End Vertex
1	1	1	1	1	1	2
2	1	−1	1	2	2	3
3	−1	−1	1	3	3	4
4	−1	1	1	4	4	1
5	1	1	−1	5	5	6
6	1	−1	−1	6	6	7
7	−1	−1	−1	7	7	8
8	−1	1	−1	8	8	5
				9	1	5
				10	2	6
				11	3	7
				12	4	8

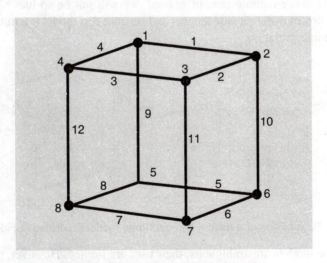

Fig. 8.3 Vertices and edges of a cube.

8.4.1 Wireframe Models are Ambiguous

While wireframe uses the simplest data structures, it is ambiguous. Figure 8.4 illustrates an example that consists of 16 vertices and 32 edges. We know that it represents a solid and each of the quadrilaterals (some of them are squares) defines a face of the solid.

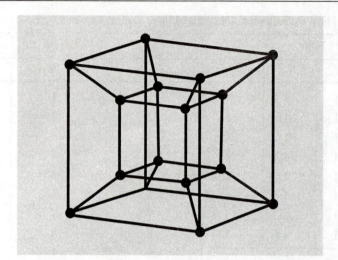

Fig. 8.4   A wireframe model consisting of 16 vertices and 32 edges.

The inner cube represents a hole; but we cannot tell the direction of the opening of the cube. As shown in Figure 8.5, there are three possibilities for this opening. While the other two can be obtained by rotating the remaining one, in general, we will not be so lucky because the outer boundary may be a box of different side lengths and because this model is part of a big one which does not allow free interpretation.

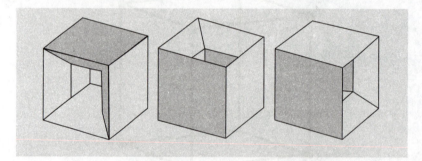

Fig. 8.5   Possibilities of a hole in the wireframe model illustrated in Figure 8.4.

Since wireframe models are ambiguous, their uses are limited. However, wireframe models are popular, because they are efficient (i.e., only vertices and edges are displayed and processed) when they work. For example, wireframe models can be used for a preview purpose. Rendering a complex model or an animation sequence could be very time-consuming if all objects are to be rendered. If wireframe models (usually including its face information) are available, one can easily obtain a general feeling of the final result without waiting for minutes or even hours before spotting a design flaw.

Note that the edges in a wireframe model do not have to be line segments. They can be curve segments and in this case, the edge table will be more complicated since in addition to the two endpoints, a description of the joining curve segment (e.g., equation) is required.

8.5 GEOMETRY AND TOPOLOGY

A solid model of an object consists of both the topological and geometrical data of the object. The completeness and unambiguity of a solid model are attributed to the fact that its database stores both its geometry and its topology.

The geometry of an object defines the actual dimensions of its entities. The topology of an object defines the connectivity and associativity of the entities. Figure 8.6 illustrates the difference between geometry and topology.

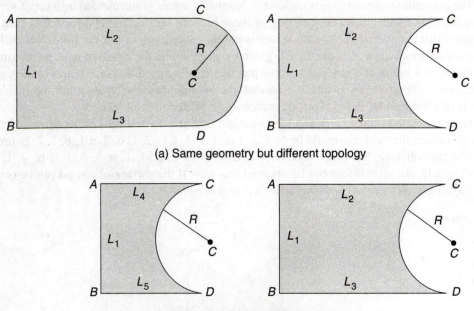

(a) Same geometry but different topology

(b) Same topology but different geometry

Fig. 8.6 Difference between geometry and topology.

The geometry is defined by length of edges, angles between the edges, radius and location of enter. The topology is defined by the connectivity of edges.

8.6 SOLID MODELLING SCHEME

A solid model can be generated by the following schemes:

1. Boundary Representation (B-Rep)
2. Constructive Solid Geometry (CSG)
3. Sweeping

8.7 BOUNDARY REPRESENTATION

Boundary Representation, or B-rep for short, can be considered as an extension of the wireframe model. The merit of a B-rep is that a solid is bounded by its surface and has its *interior* and *exterior*. The surface of a solid consists of a set of well-organised faces, each of which is a piece of some surface (e.g., a surface patch). Faces may share vertices and edges that are curve segments. Therefore, a B-rep is an extension of the wireframe model arrived at by adding face information to the latter.

There are two types of information in a B-rep: *topological* and *geometric*. Topological information provides the relationships among vertices, edges and faces similar to that used in a wireframe model. In addition to connectivity, topological information also includes orientation of edges and faces. *Geometric* information usually includes equations of the edges and faces.

The orientation of each face is important. Normally, a face is surrounded by a set of vertices. Using the right-handed rule, the ordering of these vertices for describing a particular face must guarantee that the normal vector of that face is pointing to the exterior of the solid. Normally, the order is counter-clockwise. If that face is given by an equation, the equation must be rewritten so that the normal vector at every point on the part that is being used as a face points to the exterior of the solid. Therefore, by inspecting normal vectors one can immediately tell the inside and outside of a solid under B-rep. This orientation must be done for all faces.

Figure 8.7 shows three faces and their outward pointing normal vectors. In order to describe the top surface, the vertices should be 6, 7, 2, 1 or 7, 2, 1, 6 or 2, 1, 6, 7 or 1, 6, 7, 2. In order to describe the left face, the order should be 1, 2, 3, 4 or 2, 3, 4, 1 or 3, 4, 1, 2 or 4, 1, 2, 3. Unfortunately, not all surfaces can be oriented this way. If the surface of a solid can be oriented this way, it is called orientable; otherwise, it is non-orientable.

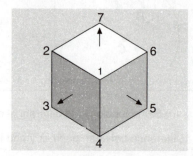

Fig. 8.7   Boundary representation.

Figure 8.8 shows the well-known Mobius band which is one-sided and non-orientable.

Fig. 8.8   Non-orientable boundary representation.

8.8 WINGED-EDGE DATA STRUCTURE FOR BOUNDARY REPRESENTATION

Perhaps the oldest data structure for a B-rep is Baumgart's *winged-edge* data structure. It is quite different from that of a wireframe model, because the winged-edge data structure uses edges to keep track of almost everything. ***In what follows, we shall assume that there are no holes in each face*** and later extend it to cope with holes. Moreover, we shall assume that edges and faces are line segments and polygons. Topologically, one can always stretch curvilinear edges and faces so that they become flat without changing the relationships among them.

Figure 8.9 shows a polyhedron with vertices, edges and faces indicated with upper cases, lower cases and digits, respectively. Let us take a look at edge $a = XY$. This edge has two incident vertices X and Y, and two incident faces 1 and 2. A face is a polygon surrounded by edges. For example, face 1 has its edges a, c and b, and face 2 has its edges a, e and d. Note that the ordering is clockwise if viewed from outside of the solid. If the direction of the edge is from X to Y, faces 1 and 2 are on the right and left side of edge a, respectively. In order to capture the ordering of edges correctly, we need four more pieces of information. Since edge a is traversed once while traversing face 1 and traversed a second time while traversing face 2, it is used twice in different directions. For example, when traversing the edges of face 1, the predecessor and successor of edge a are edge b and edge c, and when traversing the edges of face 2, the predecessor and successor of edge a are edge d and edge e. Note that though there are four edges incident to vertex X, only three of them are used when finding faces incident to edge a. Therefore, for each edge, the following information is important:

1. Vertices of this edge,
2. Its *left* and *right* faces,
3. The predecessor and successor of this edge when traversing its left face, and
4. The predecessor and successor of this edge when traversing its right face.

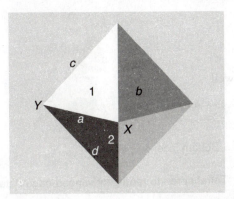

Fig. 8.9 Polyhedron to represent winged-edge data structure.

The edge table: Each entry in the edge table contains the information mentioned earlier, i.e., edge name, start vertex and end vertex, left face and right face, the predecessor and successor edges when traversing its left face, and the predecessor and successor edges when traversing its right face. Note that *clockwise* ordering (viewing from outside of the polyhedron) is used for traverse. Note also that the *direction* of edge *a* is from *X* to *Y*. If the direction is changed from *Y* to *X*, all entries but the first one in the following table must be changed accordingly.

Table 8.2 The edge table of polyhedron

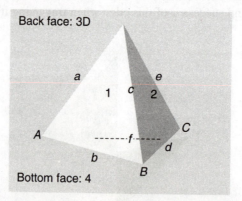

Edge	Vertices		Faces		Left Traverse		Right Traverse	
Name	Start	End	Left	Right	Pred.	Succ.	Pred.	Succ.
a	X	Y	1	2	b	d	e	c

The edge table shows the information for the entry of edge *a*. The four edges *b, c, d* and *e* are the wings of edge *a* and hence edge *a* is 'winged.'

Figure 8.10 is a tetrahedron with four vertices, *A, B, C* and *D*, six edges *a, b, c, d, e* and *f*, and four faces 1, 2, 3 (back) and 4 (bottom). Its edge table is given in Table 8.3.

Fig. 8.10 Tetrahedron to represent winged-edge data structure.

Vertex and face tables: The winged-edge data structure requires two more tables, the *vertex table* and the *face table*. These two are very simple. The vertex table has one entry for each vertex, which contains an edge that is incident to this vertex. The face table has one entry for each face, which contains an edge that is one of this face's boundary edges. Therefore, we have the Table 8.4. Note that since there are multiple choices of edges, you may come up with different tables.

Table 7.3 The edge table of tetrahedron

Edge	Vertices		Faces		Left Traverse		Right Traverse	
Name	Start	End	Left	Right	Pred	Succ	Pred	Succ
a	A	D	3	1	e	f	b	c
b	A	B	1	4	c	a	f	d
c	B	D	1	2	a	b	d	e
d	B	C	2	4	e	c	b	f
e	C	D	2	3	c	d	f	a
f	A	C	4	3	d	b	a	e

Table 7.4 The vertex and face tables of tetrahedron

Vertex Name	Incident Edge		Face Name	Incident Edge
A	a		1	a
B	b		2	c
C	d		3	a
D	e		4	b

With this data structure, one can easily answer the question: which vertices, edges, faces are adjacent to each face, edge, or vertex. There are nine such adjacency relations. For example, is vertex X adjacent to face 5? Are faces 3 and 5 adjacent to each other? The winged-edge data structure can answer these queries very efficiently and some of them may even be answered in constant time. However, it may take longer to answer other adjacency queries. Note also that once the numbers of vertices, edges and faces are known, the sizes of all three tables are fixed and will not change.

8.9 WHAT IF FACES HAVE HOLES?

If some faces of a solid have holes, the above form of the winged-edge data structure does not work. These holes may penetrate the solid (the left box of Figure 8.11) or just like a pothole (the right box of Figure 8.11).

Fig. 8.11 Solid with holes.

There are two ways for resolving this problem. These are:

- **Method 1:** For a face with inner loops, the outer boundary is ordered clockwise, while its inner loops, if any, are ordered counter-clockwise.

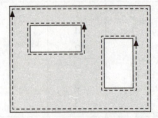

Fig. 8.12 Method 1 for resolving the representation of holes.

- **Method 2:** Another simple method is that of adding an *auxiliary* edge between each inner loop and the outer loop as shown in Figure 8.13. This auxiliary edge will have the same face for its left and right faces. In this way, a face with holes becomes a single loop which can be represented with the winged-edge data structure. When a loop is being traversed, auxiliary edges can be identified easily since its left and right faces are the same.

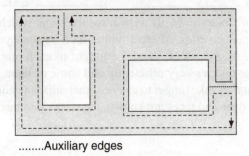

........Auxiliary edges

Fig. 8.13 Method 2 for resolving the representation of holes.

8.10 THE EULER–POINCARE FORMULA

The Euler–Poincare formula describes the relationship of the number of vertices, the number of edges and the number of faces of a manifold. It has been generalised to include potholes and holes that penetrate the solid. In order to state the Euler–Poincare formula, we need the following definitions:

- V: the number of vertices
- E: the number of edges
- F: the number of faces
- G: the number of holes that penetrate the solid, usually referred to as *genus* in topology
- S: the number of *shells*. A shell is an internal void of a solid. A shell is bounded by a 2-manifold surface, which can have its own genus value. Note that the solid itself is counted as a shell. Therefore, the value for S is at least 1.
- L: the number of loops, all outer and inner loops of faces are counted.

Then, the Euler–Poincare formula is as follows:

$$V - E + F - (L - F) - 2(S - G) = 0 \qquad (8.1)$$

Part of the information recorded in a B-rep is topological (i.e., adjacency relations). Invalid solids may be generated if the representation is not carefully constructed. One way of checking this topological invalidity is to use the Euler–Poincare formula. If its value is not zero, we are sure something must be wrong in the representation. However, this is only a *one-side* test. More precisely, a zero value of the Euler–Poincare formula does not mean that the solid is valid.

Illustration 8.1 A cube has eight vertices ($V = 8$), 12 edges ($E = 12$) and six faces ($F = 6$), no holes and one shell ($S = 1$); but $L = F$ since each face has only one outer loop. Therefore, we have:

$$V - E + F - (L - F) - 2(S - G) = 8 - 12 + 6 - (6 - 6) - 2(1 - 0) = 0$$

Illustration 8.2 The solid (Figure 8.14) has 16 vertices, 24 edges, 11 faces, no holes, 1 shell and 12 loops (11 faces + one inner loop on the top face). Therefore:

$$V - E + F - (L - F) - 2(S - G) = 16 - 24 + 11 - (12 - 11) - 2(1 - 0) = 0$$

Fig. 8.14 Visual of Illustration 8.2.

Illustration 8.3 The solid (Figure 8.15) has 16 vertices, 24 edges, 10 faces, 1 hole (i.e., genus is 1), 1 shell and 12 loops (10 faces + 2 inner loops on top and bottom faces). Therefore:

$$V - E + F - (L - F) - 2(S - G) = 16 - 24 + 10 - (12 - 10) - 2(1 - 1) = 0$$

Fig. 8.15 Visual of Illustration 8.3.

Illustration 8.4 The solid (Figure 8.16) has a penetrating hole and an internal cubic chamber as shown by the right cut-away figure. It has 24 vertices, 12*3 (cubes) = 36 edges, 6*3 (cubes) −2 (top and bottom openings) = 16 faces, 1 hole (i.e., genus is 1), 2 shells and 18 loops (16 faces + 2 inner loops on top and bottom faces). Therefore:

$$V - E + F - (L - F) - 2(S - G) = 24 - 36 + 16 - (18 - 16) - 2(2 - 1) = 0$$

Fig. 8.16 Visual of Illustration 8.4.

Illustration 8.5 The solid (Figure 8.17) has two penetrating holes and no internal chamber as shown by the right cut-away figure. It has 24 vertices, 36 edges, 14 faces, 2 hole (i.e., genus is 2), 1 shell and 18 loops (14 faces + 4). Therefore:

$$V - E + F - (L - F) - 2(S - G) = 24 - 36 + 14 - (18 - 14) - 2(1 - 2) = 0$$

Fig. 8.17 Visual of Illustration 8.5.

Illustration 8.6 Figure 8.18 has a box and an additional sheet which is simply a rectangle. This object has 10 vertices, 15 edges, 7 faces, 1 shell and no hole. Its loop number is equal to the number of faces. The value of the Euler–Poincare formula is zero as shown below.

$$V - E + F - (L - F) - 2(S - G) = 10 - 15 + 7 - (7 - 7) - 2(1 - 0) = 0$$

but this is not a valid solid! Therefore, if the value of the Euler–Poincare formula is non-zero, the representation is definitely not a valid solid. However, the value of the Euler–Poincare formula being zero does not guarantee that the representation would yield a valid solid.

Fig. 8.18 Visual of Illustration 8.6.

8.11 HOW TO COUNT GENUS CORRECTLY?

It is not always easy to count genus G correctly. For example, suppose we have a sphere punched by three tunnels as shown in Figure 8.19. The left object shows the outside look. The right one shows the inside by cutting half of the sphere off. What is the genus value G? We know that the genus value counts the number of penetrating holes. But, in this example, it is somewhat ambiguous. In fact, by combining any two centre-going tunnels we will have three penetrating holes. However, this is incorrect!

Fig. 8.19 Illustration to count genus.

The Euler–Poincare formula describes the topological property amount vertices, edges, faces, loops, shells and genus. Any topological transformation applied to the model will not alter this relationship. Intuitively, applying topological transformations means that we can twist, stretch and squash the model but we cannot cut some parts off nor glue some parts together. Let us apply some intuitive topological transformations to this model for computing the genus. We can push the 'walls' surrounding the three tunnels so that the interior of the model becomes a thin shell. This is shown in Figure 8.20.

Stretch the top hole so that it is large enough (left of Figure 8.21). Then, collapse the top portion to flatten the model. This is shown in the model (right of Figure 8.21). How many penetrating holes are there? Two! Therefore, G is 2.

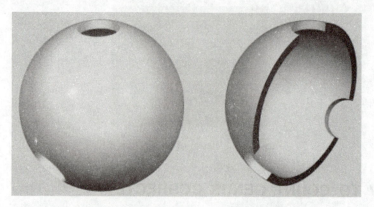

Fig. 8.20   Applying topological transformations to count genus.

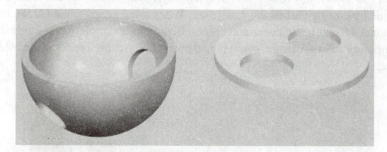

Fig. 8.21   Counting of genus.

Sometimes, penetrating holes may appear in an unlikely situation. Consider the following model (Figure 8.22), which is obtained by taking out a torus and tube from the interior of a sphere. What is the genus of this model? It does not look like there is a penetrating hole. So, is genus equal to 0? In fact, $G = 1$! Figure it out yourself. Do some twisting, stretching and squashing.

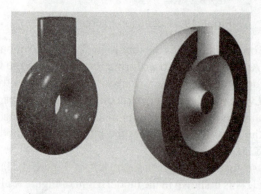

Fig. 8.22   Counting of genus by taking out torus and tube from the interior of a sphere.

8.12 EULER OPERATORS

Once a polyhedron model is available, one might want to edit it by adding or deleting vertices, edges and faces to create a new polyhedron. These operations are called *Euler Operators*. However, it has been shown that in the process of editing a polyhedron with Euler operators, some intermediate results may not be valid solids at all.

Recall from the discussion of the Euler–Poincare formula that the following holds for all polyhedra:

$$V - E + F - (L - F) - 2(S - G) = 0$$

where V, E, F, L, S and G are the numbers of vertices, edges, faces, loops, shells and genus, respectively. Based on this relation, some Euler operators have been selected for editing a polyhedron so that the Euler–Poincare formula is always satisfied. The two groups of such operators are:

- The Make group and
- The Kill group.

Operators start with M and K are operators of the Make and Kill groups, respectively.

Euler operators are written as $Mxyz$ and $Kxyz$ for operations in the Make and Kill groups, respectively, where x, y and z are elements of the model (e.g., a vertex, edge, face, loop, shell and genus). For example, MEV means adding an edge and a vertex while KEV means deleting an edge and a vertex.

It has been proved by Mantyla in 1984 that Euler operators form a complete set of modelling primitives for manifold solids. More precisely, every topologically valid polyhedron can be constructed from an initial polyhedron by a finite sequence of Euler operators. Therefore, Euler operators are powerful operations.

8.12.1 The Make Group of Euler Operators

The Make group consists of four operators for adding some elements into the existing model and creating a new one, and a Make-Kill operator for adding and deleting some elements at the same time.

Table 8.5 shows the change of values of V, E, F, L, S and G. Note that adding a face produces a loop, the outer loop of that face. Therefore, when F is increased, L should also be increased. This new loop and the new face will cancel each other in the sub-expression $L - F$. Please verify that none of these operators would cause the Euler–Poincaré formula to fail.

Table 8.5   Make group of Euler operators

Operator Name	Meaning	V	E	F	L	S	G
MEV	Make an edge and a vertex	+1	+1				
MFE	Make a face and an edge		+1	+1	+1		
MSFV	Make a shell, a face and a vertex	+1		+1	+1	+1	
MSG	Make a shell and a hole					+1	+1
MEKL	Make an edge and kill a loop		+1		−1		

Table 8.6 illustrates the method of using Euler operators to construct a tetrahedron. Vertices, edges and faces are in red, blue and green; the only shell is in transparent gray. The first step uses

MSFV to obtain a shell with a face and a vertex. The next three steps use MEVs, each of which adds an edge and a vertex. The last three steps use MFE, each of which adds a face and an edge. Thus, in seven steps or seven Euler operators, a tetrahedron is constructed.

Table 8.6   Euler operators to construct a tetrahedron

Operator Name	Meaning	V	E	F	L	S	G	Result
MSFV	Make a shell, a face and a vertex	+1		+1	+1	+1		
MEV	Make an edge and a vertex	+1	+1					
MEV	Make an edge and a vertex	+1	+1					
MEV	Make an edge and a vertex	+1	+1					
MFE	Make a face and an edge			+1	+1		+1	
MFE	Make a face and an edge			+1	+1		+1	
MFE	Make a face and an edge			+1	+1		+1	

MSG simply makes a shell with a hole. After this, one can add vertices, edges, faces, loops. There must be loops, because the new hole penetrates at least one face.

MEKL makes an edge and at the same time kills a loop. A commonly used MEKL is addition of an edge connecting the outer loop and the inner loop of a face. In this case, the number of edges E is increased by 1 and the number of loops L is decreased by 1 since that loop is killed. Figure 8.23 (left) shows two loops of the top face while the right one shows the new edge added after performing a MEKL. Thus, the inner and outer are 'joined' together with the new edge becoming a single face.

Fig. 8.23   Illustration of MEKL Euler operator.

8.12.2   The Kill Group of Euler Operators

The Kill group just performs the opposite of what the Make group does. In fact, replacing the M and K in all Make operators with K and M, respectively, would get the operators of the Kill group. The Kill group operators are listed in Table 8.7.

Table 8.7   Kill group of Euler operators

Operator Name	Meaning	V	E	F	L	S	G
KEV	Kill an edge and a vertex	−1	−1				
KFE	Kill a face and an edge		−1	−1	−1		
KSFV	Kill a shell, a face and a vertex	−1		−1	−1	−1	
KSG	Kill a shell and a hole					−1	−1
KEML	Kill an edge and make a loop		−1		+1		

With these operators, one can start with a tetrahedron and reduce it to nothing. Since these operators are the opposites of the Make operators.

8.13   CONSTRUCTIVE SOLID GEOMETRY

Constructive Solid Geometry, or *CSG* for short, is yet another way of representing solids. A CSG solid is constructed from a few **primitives** (block, wedge, sphere, cylinder, cone and torus) with **Boolean** operators (union, intersection and subtraction). Thus, a CSG solid can be written as a set of equations.

Data structures of the CSG representation are based on the concept of trees. The data of the solid model is stored in its database in a tree called *CSG tree*. A CSG tree is defined as an inverted, ordered binary tree whose leaf nodes are primitives (or other solids) and whose interior nodes are regularised set operations. Inverted means that the tree is upside down; its root is on the top. Ordered means that each tree node has a left and branches. Binary means that each node has two branches. Figure 8.24 shows a CSG tree. The CSG tree is shown with its full details (i.e., primitives, Boolean operations), including arrows.

The total number of nodes in a CSG tree of a given solid is directly to the number of primitives that the solid is decomposed into. The number of primitives decides automatically the number of Boolean operations required to construct the solid. If a solid has n primitives, then there are $(n-1)$ Boolean operations for a total of $(2n-1)$ nodes in its CSG tree. The balanced distribution of these nodes in the tree is a desired characteristic.

$$n_l + n_r = 2n - 2 \qquad (8.2)$$

where n_l and n_r are the number of nodes of the left and right sub-tress, respectively.

A perfect tree results only if the number of primitives is even. The following relation applies to a perfect tree:

$$n_l = n_r = n - 1 \qquad (8.3)$$

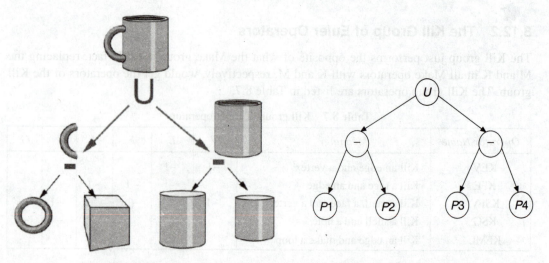

Fig. 8.24 The CSG tree (*P1*, *P2*, *P3* and *P4* are primitives).

8.13.1 CSG Primitives

The standard CSG primitives (Figure 8.25) consist of the block (i.e., cube), wedge (i.e., triangular prism), sphere, cylinder, cone and torus. These six primitives are in some *normal* or *generic* form and must be *instantiated* by the user to be used in the design. Moreover, the instantiated primitive may require transformations such as scaling, translation and rotation to be positioned at the desired place.

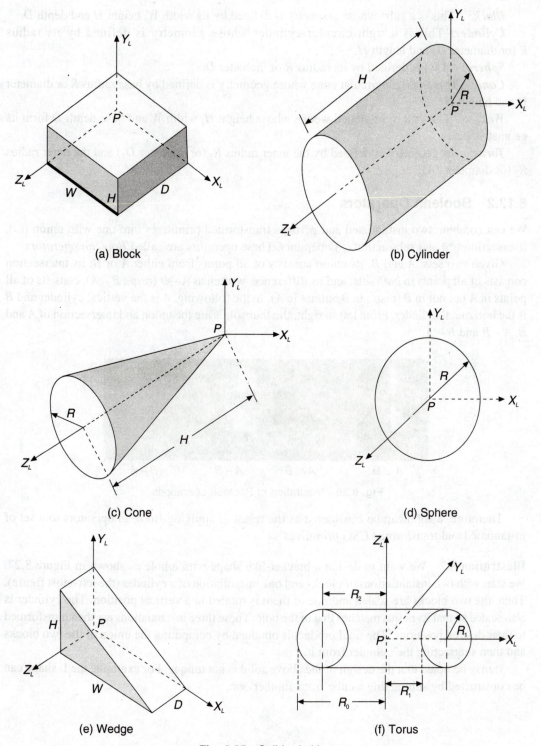

Fig. 8.25   Solid primitives.

Block: This is a cube whose geometry is defined by its width W, height H and depth D.

Cylinder: This is a right circular cylinder whose geometry is defined by its radius R (or diameter D) and length H.

Sphere: This is defined by its radius R or diameter D.

Cone: This is a right circular cone whose geometry is defined by base radius R or diameter D and height H.

Wedge: This is a right-angled wedge whose height H, width W and base depth D form its geometric data.

Torus: Its geometry is defined by the inner radius R_1 (or diameter D_1) and the outer radius R_2 (or diameter D_2).

8.13.2 Boolean Operators

We can combine two instantiated and perhaps transformed primitives into one with union ($\cup$), intersection ($\cap$) and subtraction ($-$) operators. These operators are called *Boolean operators*.

Given two sets, A and B, its union consists of all points from either A or B; its intersection consists of all points in *both* sets; and its difference, written as $A - B$ (resp., $B - A$), consists of all points in A but not in B (resp., in B but not in A). In the following, A is the vertical cylinder and B is the horizontal cylinder. From left to right, the four solids are the union and intersection of A and B, $A - B$ and $B - A$.

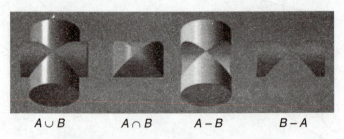

$A \cup B$ $A \cap B$ $A - B$ $B - A$

Fig. 8.26 Illustration of Boolean operations.

Therefore, a solid can be considered as the result of applying Boolean operators to a set of instantiated and transformed CSG primitives.

Illustration 8.7   We want to design a bracket-like shape with a hole as shown in Figure 8.27. We start with two instantiations of blocks and one instantiation of a cylinder (the left-most figure). Then, the two blocks are scaled and one of them is rotated to a vertical position. The cylinder is also scaled so that its radius matches that of the hole. These three instantiations are then transformed to their desired positions. The final product is obtained by computing the union of the two blocks and then subtracting the cylinder from it.

It may be noted that the design of the above solid is not unique. For example, the L shape can be constructed by subtracting a cube from another one.

(a) Initial size of primitives

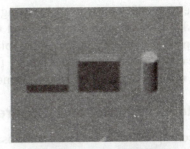
(b) Scaled size of primitives

(c) Transformed to the desired position

(d) Performing Boolean operations

Fig. 8.27 Bracket-like shapes.

8.13.3 CSG Expressions

The design procedure of the above bracket can be written as an expression:

$$\textbf{diff(union(trans(Block1), trans(Block2)), trans(Cylinder))} \tag{8.4}$$

where **union**(A, B) and **diff**(A, B) are the union and difference of A and B, and **trans**( ) indicates appropriate transformations. Or, if we use ∩, ∪ and – for set union, intersection and difference, the above function calls can be rewritten as a set expression as follows:

$$\textbf{(trans(Block1)} \cup \textbf{trans(Block2)) – trans(Cylinder)} \tag{8.5}$$

Expression (8.5) can be converted into a CSG tree as shown in Figure 8.28.

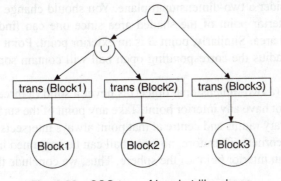

Fig. 8.28 CSG tree of bracket-like shape.

In fact, every solid constructed by using the CSG technique has a corresponding CSG expression which, in turn, has an associated CSG tree. The expression of the CSG tree is a representation of the final design. The same solid may have different CSG expressions/trees. For example, one might punch a hole from **Block1** first and then compute the union of this result with **Block2**. As a result, CSG representations are not unique.

8.13.4   Interior, Exterior and Closure

We need the concept of interior, exterior and closure to fully appreciate the discussion of regularised Boolean operators. Intuitively, the interior of a solid consists of all points lying inside the solid; the closure consists of all interior points and all points on the solid's surface; and the exterior of a solid is the set of all points that do not belong to the closure.

Consider a sphere, $x^2 + y^2 + z^2 = 1$. Its interior is the set of all points that satisfy $x^2 + y^2 + z^2 < 1$, while its closure is $x^2 + y^2 + z^2 \leq 1$. Therefore, the closure is the union of the interior and the boundary (its surface $x^2 + y^2 + z^2 = 1$). Obviously, its exterior is $x^2 + y^2 + z^2 > 1$.

A solid is a three-dimensional object and so are its interior and exterior. However, its boundary is a two-dimensional surface.

Consider the open ball with centre (a, b, c) and radius r consists of all points that satisfy the following relation:

$$(x - a)^2 + (y - b)^2 + (z - c)^2 < r^2 \tag{8.6}$$

A point P is an *interior point* of a solid S if there exists a radius r such that the open ball with centre P and radius r is contained in the solid S. The set of all interior points of solid S is the *interior* of S, written as **int(S)**. On the basis of this definition, the interior of an open ball is seen to be the open ball itself.

On the other hand, a point Q is an *exterior point* of a solid S if there exists a radius r such that the open ball with centre Q and radius r does not intersect S. The set of all exterior points of solid S is the *exterior* of solid S, written as **ext(S)**.

The points that are not in the interior nor in the exterior of a solid S constitute the *boundary* of solid S, written as **b(S)**. Therefore, the union of interior, exterior and boundary of a solid is the whole space.

The *closure* of a solid S is defined to be the union of S's interior and boundary, written as **closure(S)**. Or, equivalently, the closure of solid S contains all points that are not in the exterior of S.

Illustration 8.8   Consider a two-dimensional plane. You should change all open balls to open disks. Point A is an interior point of the shaded area since one can find an open disk that is contained in the shaded area. Similarly, point B is an exterior point. Point C is a boundary point because whatever the radius the corresponding open ball will contain some interior points and some exterior points.

Note that a surface (a two-dimensional object) is never a solid (a three-dimensional object). In fact, a surface does not have any interior point. Take any point of the surface (see Figure 8.30), the open ball with arbitrary radius and centre at that point always intersects the sphere in an open disk (in the lower right corner). Therefore, no open ball can be contained in the sphere, and, as a result, that point is not an interior point of the sphere. Thus, we conclude that a surface does not have any interior point.

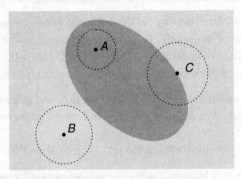

Fig. 8.29 Illustration of interior exterior and boundary point in a two-dimensional plane.

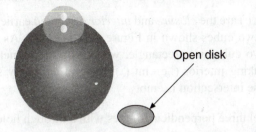

Open disk

Fig. 8.30 Illustration of "Surface does not have any interior point".

8.13.5 Regularised Boolean Operators

We certainly expect that the union, intersection and difference of two solids is a solid. Unfortunately, in many cases, this is not always true. In the following figure, two cubes touch each other and their intersection is a rectangle shown on the right. A rectangle is not a three-dimensional object and hence not a solid!

Fig. 8.31 Illustration of "The intersection of two objects is not always a solid".

In order to eliminate these lower dimensional branches, the three set operations are regularised as follows. The regularisation procedure is very simple. It involves the following steps:

- Compute the result as usual and lower dimensional components may be generated.
- Compute the interior of the result. This step removes all lower dimensional components. An example has been shown on page 276. The result is a solid without its boundary.
- Compute the closure of the result obtained in the above step. This adds the boundary back.

Let $\cup$, $\cap$ and – be the *regularised* set union, intersection and subtraction operators. Let A and B be two solids. Then, $A \cup B$, $A \cap B$ and $A - B$ can be defined mathematically on the basis of the above procedure:

$$A \cup B = \text{closure}(\text{int}(\text{the set union of } A \text{ and } B)$$

$$A \cap B = \text{closure}(\text{int}(\text{the set intersection of } A \text{ and } B)$$

$$A - B = \text{closure}(\text{int}(\text{the set difference of } A \text{ and } B)$$

where closure ( ) and int ( ) are the *closure* and *interior* discussed earlier. Based on this definition, the intersection of the two cubes shown in Figure 8.31 is empty. As mentioned earlier, the set intersection of these two cubes is a rectangle, which is a two-dimensional object and has no interior. Hence, after taking interior (i.e., int ( )), we get an empty set, whose closure is also empty. Consequently, the intersection is empty.

Illustration 8.9   Model three perpendicular pipes with a through hole at the centre of the pipes as shown in Figure 8.32.

An immediate reaction is that let us subtract a smaller cylinder from a larger one, yielding a pipe which is shown in Figure 8.33. Then, take two more instances of this pipe, each of which is rotated at an appropriate angle; compute the union of these three pipes; and the result is shown in Figure 8.34.

Fig. 8.32   Three pipes with a through hole.   **Fig. 8.33**   Subtraction of small cylinder from big cylinder

But, the result is not quite right, because the inner junction of the pipes is blocked as seen in Figure 8.34 (right). A correct solution is to design two instances of three perpendicular cylinders, one larger and the other smaller. Then, subtracting the smaller from the larger yields the designed result as shown in Figure 8.35.

Fig. 8.34 Union of three hollow pipes resulting no through hole.

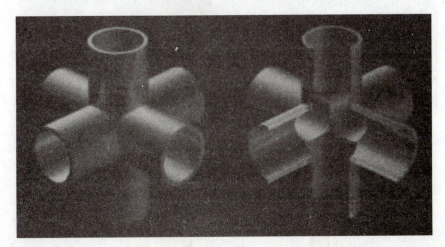

Fig. 8.35 Union of large pipes and subtraction of small pipes from large pipes give through hole.

8.14 SWEEPING

A cross-section or profile is created and the same is swept along a direction to create a solid. This method is useful for creating 2½-dimension models. The profiles can be any analytic and synthetic two-dimensional contours. The 2½ models include both solids of uniform thickness in a given direction to create axisymmetric solids. There are three types of sweeps. These are:

- Linear sweep
- Non-linear sweep
- Hybrid sweep

8.14.1 Linear Sweep

In linear sweep, the sweeping path is a linear (for extrusion solids) or circular (for axisymmetric solids) vector described by a parametric linear equation.

Thus, the linear sweep is divided into the following two types:

- Translational sweep
- Rotational sweep

In translational sweep, a planar two-dimensional profile is moved in a perpendicular direction called 'directrix' as shown in Figure 8.36.

In rotational sweep, a planar two-dimensional profile is rotated about an axis of rotation at a given angle as shown in Figure 8.37.

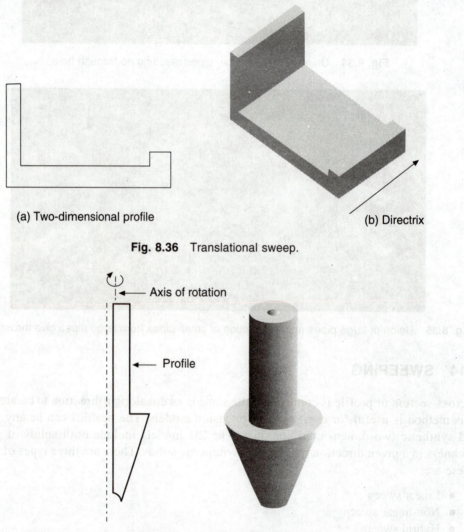

(a) Two-dimensional profile   (b) Directrix

Fig. 8.36   Translational sweep.

Axis of rotation

Profile

Fig. 8.37   Rotational sweep.

8.14.2 Non-linear Sweep

Non-linear sweep is similar to linear sweep but with the directrix being a curve instead of straight line as shown in Figure 8.38.

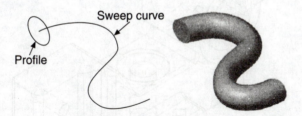

Fig. 8.38 Non-linear sweep.

8.15 SOLID MANIPULATIONS

Solid manipulation involves manipulating both its geometry and topology to ensure that the resulting solids are valid. The solid manipulations are:

1. Displaying
2. Segmentation
3. Trimming
4. Transformation
5. Editing

8.15.1 Displaying

Displaying of a solid is done in the following two ways:

- Wire display
- Shaded image

The wire display requires the boundary representation of the solid in which vertices and edges are used to generate the wireframe model of the solid. (Figure 8.39)

Displaying solids as shaded images provides realistic visual information to the users. Shading can be performed directly from CSG by ray-tracing algorithms or Z-buffer algorithms. (Figure 8.40)

8.15.2 Segmentation

Segmentation is a procedure of splitting the solid into two or four valid sub-solids depending on where it is to be split by a plane or a point, respectively. Each resulting sub-solid has its own geometry and topology.

8.15.3 Trimming

In a trimming operation, the solid to be trimmed is intersected with the trimming surfaces, followed by the removal of solid portions outside the trimming surfaces. During trimming, the solid is divided into three sub-solids, two of which are removed.

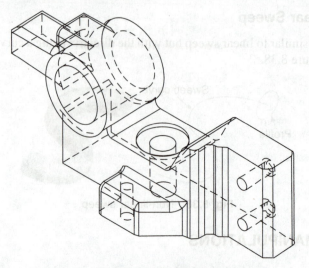

Fig. 8. 39 Wire display.

Fig. 8.40 Shaded image.

8.15.4 Transformation

The transformations include translation, rotation or scaling. The transformations are used while constructing a solid. When constructing a solid, its primitives are scaled, positioned, and oriented properly before applying Boolean operations using the transformations.

8.15.4 Editing

Editing of a solid implies changing of its existing geometrical and topological information. An efficient means of solid editing is to employ its CSG tree.

QUESTION BANK

A. Descriptive Questions

1. What are the applications of solid models?
2. Discuss the modelling considerations of solid models.
3. Explain the vertex and edge tables of wireframe models.
4. Wireframe models are ambiguous. Justify the statement.
5. Define geometry and topology with simple examples.
6. Differentiate between geometry and topology.
7. What are the various methods of representation of solids?
8. Explain the boundary representation method of solid modelling with an example.
9. Describe winged-edge data structure for boundary representation.
10. Explain the importance of vertex, edge and face tables in the boundary representation of solid modelling.
11. What if faces have holes? Explain different methods to resolve this problem.
12. Describe the Euler–Poincare formula for the boundary representation of solid modelling with an example.
13. How can we create genus of Euler–Poincare formula correctly? Illustrate the same with examples.
14. What are Euler operators? Explain them.
15. Explain constructive solid geometry for the representation of solids.
16. What are CSG primitives? Define them schematically.
17. What are Boolean operators? Explain their importance in the construction of CSG solid models with illustrative examples.
18. What are CSG trees? Explain their importance in the construction of CSG solid models.
19. What are CSG expressions? Explain their importance in the construction of CSG solid models.
20. Define interior, exterior and closure of CSG solid models. Explain their importance with examples.
21. Explain the method of regularising Boolean operators.
22. Explain the importance of regularising the Boolean operators with an example.
23. What is sweeping? Explain different methods of solid modelling using sweeping.
24. What are the various types of solid manipulation techniques? Explain them.
25. How can you use a cylinder primitive to generate a sphere?
26. How can you generate a sphere by using sweeping solid modelling technique?
27. Construct a CSG tree and CSG expressions for a solid model as shown in Figure 8.41.

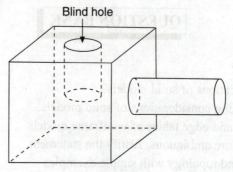

Fig. 8.41

28. Verify the Euler–Poincare equation for the solids shown in Figure 8.42.

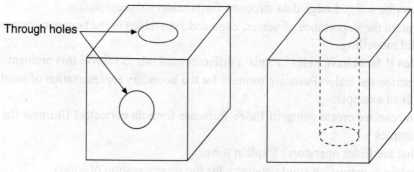

Fig. 8.42

29. Find the winged-edge data structure of a cube.
30. Find the winged-edge data structure of the solid shown in Figure 8.43.

Fig. 8.43

31. Find the winged-edge data structure of the following solid as shown in Figure 8.44.

Fig. 8.44

32. Verify the Euler–Poincare formula with the following polyhedra shown in Figure 8.45. List the number of vertices, edges, faces, loops, shells and holes.

Fig. 8.45

33. Use Euler operators to construct the following polyhedra: (1) a cube, (2) a cube with pothole shown in Figure 8.43 and (3) a cube with a penetrating hole shown in Figure 8.44.

34. Construct CSG tree and CSG expressions for the solid model shown in Figure 8.46.

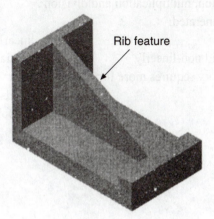

Rib feature

Fig. 8.46

B. Multiple Choice Questions

1. Wireframe models consist of two tables, namely:
   (a) Vertex and edge
   (b) Edge and surface
   (c) Vertex and surface
   (d) None of the above

2. Cube is represented by:
   (a) 12 vertices and 8 edges
   (b) 8 vertices and 8 edges
   (c) 12 vertices and 12 edges
   (d) 8 vertices and 12 edges

3. Solid models can be generated by:
   (a) B-rep
   (b) CSG
   (c) Sweeping
   (d) All of the above

4. Topology refers to:
   (a) Information of lines
   (b) Connectivity and associativity of entities
   (c) Information of surfaces
   (d) Angles between edges

5. Boundary representation is the extension of:
   (a) Wireframe models
   (b) CSG models
   (c) Surface models
   (d) All of the above

6. A polyhydral object that does not have holes and whose face is bounded by a single set of connected edges is called a:
   (a) Simply polyhydral
   (b) Polyhydral with holes
   (c) Complex polyhydral
   (d) None of the above

7. The Euler–Poincare formula is:
   (a) $V + E - F - (L - F) + 2(S - G) = 0$
   (b) $V - E + F - (L - F) - 2(S - G) = 0$
   (c) $V - E - F - (L - F) - 2(S - G) = 0$
   (d) $V - E - F + (L - F) - 2(S - G) = 0$

8. The Boolean operators are:
   (a) Union, subtraction and intersection
   (b) Union, subtraction, multiplication and division
   (c) Union, subtraction and multiplication
   (d) Union, subtraction, multiplication and division

9. Sweeping can be generated:
   (a) Linearly
   (b) Non-linearly
   (c) Both linearly and non-linearly
   (d) Exponentially

10. The computer memory requires more for:
    (a) B-rep
    (b) CSG solids
    (c) Sweep solids
    (d) All the above

Chapter 9

Computer-aided Drafting

OBJECTIVES

After reading this chapter, the reader will be able to understand the following concepts:

- ➲ Drafting set-up: Units, angle, angle measure and angle direction, area, co-ordinate system, limits, grid, and linetype and lineweight
- ➲ Drawing structure
- ➲ Basic geometric commands: Point, line, polyline, arc, circle, ellipse, spline, rectangle, polygon, donut, block, table and text
- ➲ Layers
- ➲ Display control commands: Zoom, pan, window, aerial view, and viewport
- ➲ Editing a drawing: copy, mirror, offset, array, move, rotate, scale, sketch, trim, chamfer, and fillet
- ➲ Dimensioning
- ➲ Geometric tolerances

9.1 INTRODUCTION

Drafting serves as a tool to document a design and communicate it to the design and manufacturing departments. The generation of engineering drawings has changed over the years. The CAD system can generate drawings easily and efficiently. AutoCAD is a widely popular drafting CAD software. There are other software packages, namely Pro-E, Unigraphics, Catia, I-deas, Solidworks, etc.

In this chapter, the basic commands employed in AutoCAD are discussed.

9.2   DRAFTING SET-UP

The drafting set-up includes planning for the following:

1. Units
2. Angle, angle measure, and angle direction
3. Area
4. Coordinate system
5. Limits
6. Grid
7. Snap
8. Linetype and lineweight

You can change units, angle, angle measure, and angle direction using the UNITS command, and you can change area using the LIMITS command.

9.2.1   Units

It indicates the unit format and precision. The unit format is the format in which you enter and in which AutoCAD displays coordinates and measurements. Several formats are available in AutoCAD. Two of them, Engineering and Architectural, have a specific base unit (inches) assigned to them. You can select from other measurement styles that can represent any convenient unit of measurement.

You can also control the precision (the number of decimal places displayed in all measurements) by using the Advanced Set-up wizard or the UNITS command. The default precision used by Quick Set-up is four (0.0000). The various measurement styles are:

- *Decimal:*   Displays measurements in decimal notation.
- *Engineering:*   Displays measurements in feet and decimal inches.
- *Architectural:*   Displays measurements in feet, inches, and fractional inches.
- *Fractional:*   Displays measurements in mixed-number (integer and fractional) notation.
- *Scientific:*   Displays measurements in scientific notation (numbers expressed in the form of the product of a decimal number between 0 and 10 and a power of 10).

9.2.2   Angle, Angle Measure and Angle Direction

Angle option indicates the format in which you enter angles. These are:

- *Decimal Degrees:*   Displays partial degrees as decimals.
- *Deg/Min/Sec:*   Displays partial degrees as minutes and seconds.
- *Grads:*   Displays angles as grads.
- *Radians:*   Displays angles as radians.
- *Surveyor:*   Displays angles in surveyor's units.

Angle measure indicates the direction of the 0 angle for the entry of angles. When you enter an angle value in AutoCAD, AutoCAD measures the angle either counter-clockwise or clockwise from the compass direction. You can control the counter-clockwise/clockwise direction on the Angle Direction page.

- *East:* Specifies the compass direction east as the 0 angle.
- *North:* Specifies the compass direction north as the 0 angle.
- *West:* Specifies the compass direction west as the 0 angle.
- *South:* Specifies the compass direction south as the 0 angle.
- *Other:* Specifies a direction other than east, north, west, or south. Enter a specific compass angle to treat as the 0 angle.

Angle direction indicates the direction from the 0 angle in which you enter and in which AutoCAD displays positive angle values, counter-clockwise or clockwise.

9.2.3 Area

This indicates the width and length in full-scale units of what you plan to draw. This setting limits the area of the drawing covered by grid dots when the grid is turned on. When limits checking are turned on with the LIMITS command, this setting also restricts the coordinates you can enter to within the rectangular area. You can change the drawing area and turn limits checking on and off with the LIMITS command.

9.2.4 Coordinate System

A Cartesian coordinate system has three axes, X, Y, and Z (Figure 9.1). When you enter coordinate values, you indicate a point's distance (in units) and its direction (+ or −) along the X, Y, and Z-axes relative to the coordinate system origin (0, 0, 0).

In 2D, you specify points on the XY plane, also called the construction plane. The construction plane is similar to a flat sheet of grid paper. The X value of a Cartesian coordinate specifies horizontal distance, and the Y value specifies vertical distance. The origin point (0, 0) indicates where the two axes intersect.

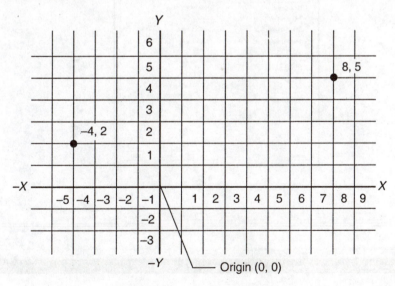

Fig. 9.1 A coordinate system.

Absolute coordinate values are based on the origin (0, 0), where the *X*- and *Y*-axes intersect. Use absolute coordinates when you know the precise *X* and *Y* values of the point. For example, 3, 4 specifies a point 3 units along the *X* axis and 4 units along the *Y* axis from the origin.

Relative coordinates are based on the last point entered. Use relative coordinates when you know the location of a point in relation to the previous point. To specify relative coordinates, precede the coordinate values with an @ sign. For example, @3, 4 specifies a point 3 units along the *X*-axis and 4 units along the *Y*-axis from the last point specified.

9.2.5 Limits

Limits establish the size of the drawing and the associated drawing guides such as grid, snap, rulers, etc. It is necessary to specify the limits of the drawing. The lower limit is the left bottom corner and the upper limit is the right top corner. The limits can be in English or metric units.

9.2.6 Grid

This represents an area covered with regularly spaced dots to aid drawing. The spacing between grid dots is adjustable. Grid dots are not plotted. The user-defined rectangular boundary of the drawing area is covered by dots when the grid is turned on (Figure 9.2).

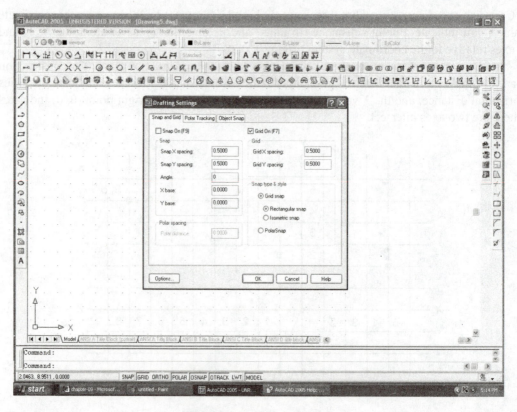

Fig. 9.2 Drafting settings.

9.2.7 Snap

Snap grid is the invisible grid that locks the pointer into alignment with the grid points according to the spacing set by Snap. Snap grid does not necessarily correspond to the visible grid, which is controlled separately by GRID. Snap mode is used for locking a pointing device into alignment with an invisible rectangular grid. When the Snap mode is on, the screen cross-hairs and all input coordinates are snapped to the nearest point on the grid. The snap resolution defines the spacing of this grid (Figure 9.3).

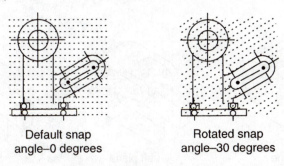

Default snap
angle–0 degrees

Rotated snap
angle–30 degrees

Fig. 9.3   Effect of snap angle.

Object snaps constrain point specification to exact locations, such as a midpoint or an intersection, on existing objects. Using object snaps is a quick way to locate an exact position on an object without having to know the coordinate or draw construction lines. For example, you can use an object snap to draw a line to the centre of a circle or to the midpoint of a polyline segment. You can specify an object snap whenever you are prompted for a point.

By setting the Isometric Snap/Grid (Figure 9.4), you can easily align objects along one of three isometric planes; however, though the isometric drawing appears to be three-dimensional, it is actually a two-dimensional representation. Therefore, you cannot expect to extract three-dimensional distances and areas, display objects from different viewpoints, or remove hidden lines automatically.

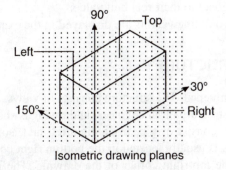

Isometric drawing planes

Fig. 9.4   Isometric snap/grid.

If the snap angle is 0, the axes of the isometric planes are 30 degrees, 90 degrees and 150 degrees. Once you set the snap style to Isometric, you can work on any of three planes, each with an associated pair of axes:

1. *Left:* Aligns snap and grid along 90- and 150-degree axes.
2. *Top:* Aligns snap and grid along 30- and 150-degree axes.
3. *Right:* Aligns snap and grid along 30- and 90-degree axes.

Choosing one of the three isometric planes causes Ortho and the cross-hairs to be aligned along the corresponding isometric axes. For example, when Ortho is on, the points you specify align along the simulated plane you are drawing on. Therefore, you can draw the top plane, switch to the left plane to draw another side, and switch to the right plane to complete the drawing (Figure 9.5).

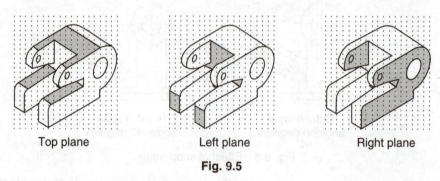

| Top plane | Left plane | Right plane |

Fig. 9.5

9.2.8 Linetype and Lineweight

These indicate how a line or type of curve is displayed. For example, a continuous line has a different linetype than a dashed line. It is also called line font. A linetype consists of a repeating pattern of dashes, dots, and blank spaces displayed in a line or a curve. You assign linetypes to objects either by layer or by specifying the linetype explicitly, independent of layers.

Lineweight is a width value that can be assigned to all graphical objects except fonts and raster images. Lineweights are displayed differently in model space than in a paper space layout.

- In model space, a 0-value lineweight is displayed as one pixel, and other lineweights use a pixel width proportional to their real unit value.
- In a paper space layout, lineweights are displayed in the exact plotting width.

9.3 DRAWING STRUCTURE

The drawing structure is universal. The structure consists of views, a title block, bill of material, and labels and notes. The structure of an engineering drawing is shown in Figure 9.6.

The views, in general, consist of top, front, right/left and isometric views. Each displays dimensions. The title block is usually located in the bottom right corner of the drawing. The bill of material is located in the top right corner of the drawing. The labels and notes provide the additional information required to understand the drawing.

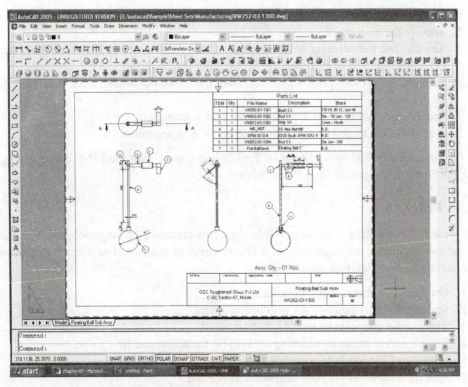

Fig. 9.6 Structure of an engineering drawing.

9.4 BASIC GEOMETRIC COMMANDS

The basic geometric commands are:

1. Point
2. Line
3. Polyline
4. Arc
5. Circle
6. Spline
7. Ellipse
8. Rectangle
9. Polygon
10. Donut
11. Block
12. Table
13. Text

9.4.1 Point

Points can act as nodes to which you can snap objects. You can specify a full three-dimensional location for a point.

9.4.2 Line

AutoCAD draws a line segment and continues to prompt for points. You can draw a continuing series of line segments, but each line segment is a separate object. Press ENTER to end the command. The steps for drawing a line are as follows:

1. On the Draw menu, click Line.
2. Specify the start point.
3. You can use the pointing device or enter coordinate values on the command line.
4. Complete the first line segment by specifying the endpoint.
5. To undo the previous line segment during the LINE command, enter u or click Undo on the toolbar.
6. Specify the endpoints of any additional line segments.
7. Press ENTER to end or c to close a series of line segments.

To start a new line at the endpoint of the last line drawn, start the LINE command again and press ENTER at the Specify Start Point prompt.

9.4.3   Polyline

A polyline is a connected sequence of line segments created as a single object. You can create straight line segments, arc segments, or a combination of the two. The steps for drawing a line and arc combination Polyline are as follows:

1. On the Draw menu, click Polyline.
2. Specify the start point of the polyline segment.
3. Specify the endpoint of the polyline segment.
4. Switch to Arc mode by entering a (Arc) on the command line.
5. Return to Line mode by entering L (Line).
6. Specify additional polyline segments as needed.
7. Press ENTER to end or c to close the polyline

9.4.4   Arc

Arc is a segment of a circle. You can create arcs in several ways (Figure 9.7), such as:

1. Draw arcs by specifying Three Points.
2. Draw arcs by specifying Start, Centre, End.
3. Draw arcs by specifying Start, Centre, Angle.
4. Draw arcs by specifying Start, Centre, Length.
5. Draw arcs by specifying Start, End, Direction/Radius.

9.4.5   Circle

You can create circles in several ways. The default method is to specify the centre and the radius. Three other ways to draw a circle are shown in Figure 9.8.

1. Centre and radius
2. Two points defining diameter
3. Three defining the circumference
4. Tangent, tangent and radius

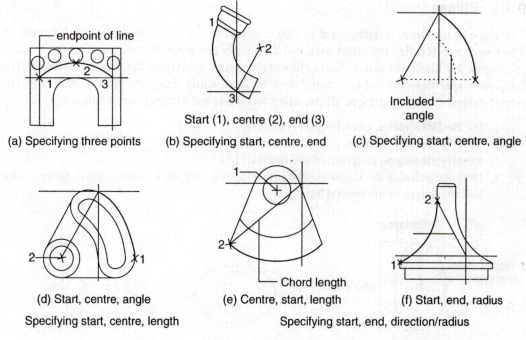

(a) Specifying three points

(b) Specifying start, centre, end
Start (1), centre (2), end (3)

(c) Specifying start, centre, angle
Included angle

(d) Start, centre, angle
Specifying start, centre, length

(e) Centre, start, length
Chord length

(f) Start, end, radius
Specifying start, end, direction/radius

Fig. 9.7 Drawing arcs.

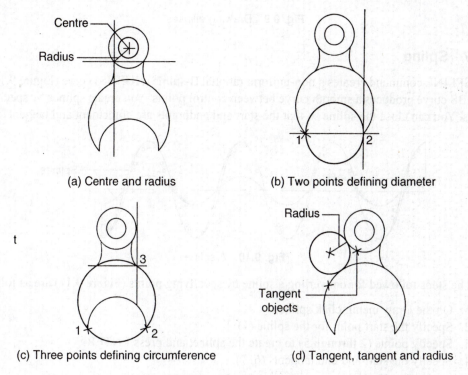

(a) Centre and radius

(b) Two points defining diameter

(c) Three points defining circumference

(d) Tangent, tangent and radius

Fig. 9.8 Drawing circles.

9.4.6 Ellipse

The shape of an ellipse is determined by two axes that define its length and width (Figure 9.9). The longer axis is called the major axis, and the shorter one is the minor axis.

Figure 9.9 illustrates two different ellipses created by specifying the axis and distance. The third point specifies only a distance and does not necessarily designate the axis endpoint. The steps followed for drawing a true ellipse using endpoints and distance are as follows:

1. On the Draw menu, click Ellipse: Axis, End.
2. Specify the first endpoint of the first axis (1).
3. Specify the second endpoint of the first axis (2).
4. Drag the pointing device away from the midpoint, and click to specify a distance (3) for half the length of the second axis

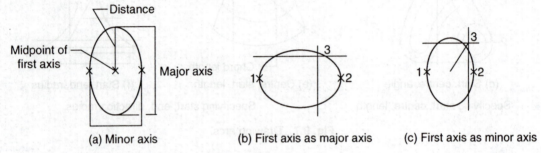

(a) Minor axis　　　　(b) First axis as major axis　　　　(c) First axis as minor axis

Fig. 9.9 Drawing ellipses.

9.4.7 Spline

The SPLINE command creates a non-uniform rational B-spline (NURBS) curve (Figure 9.10). A NURBS curve produces a smooth curve between control points. You create splines by specifying points. You can close the spline so that the start and endpoints are coincident and tangent.

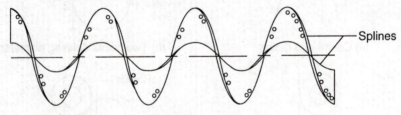

Fig. 9.10 A spline.

The steps followed for converting a spline by specifying points (Figure 9.11) are as follows:

1. On the Draw menu, click spline.
2. Specify the start point for the spline (1).
3. Specify points (2 through 5) to create the spline, and press ENTER.
4. Specify the start and end tangents (6, 7).

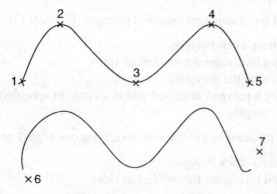

Fig. 9.11 Drawing a spline.

9.4.8 Rectangle

A rectangle can be created by using the specified points as diagonally opposite corners (Figure 9.12). The sides of the rectangle are parallel to the *X*- and *Y*-axis of the current UCS.

Fig. 9.12 Drawing a rectangle.

9.4.9 Polygon

Polygons are closed polylines between 3 and 1,024 equal-length sides. Creating polygons is a simple way to draw squares, equilateral triangles, octagons, and so on. Figure 9.13 illustrates the polygons drawn by using the three methods. In the first two illustrations, point 1 is the centre of the polygon and point 2 defines the radius length, which is being specified with the pointing device. The three methods of drawing polygons are:

1. Specifying the radius when you know the distance between the centre of the polygon and the endpoint of each side (inscribed).
2. Specifying the radius when you know the distance between the centre of the polygon and the midpoint of each side (circumscribed).
3. Specifying the length of an edge and where you want to place it

The steps followed for drawing a circumscribed polygon (Figure 9.13a) are as follows:

1. On the Draw menu, click Polygon.
2. On the command line, enter the number of sides.
3. Specify the centre of the polygon (1).
4. Enter c to specify a polygon circumscribed about a circle.
5. Enter the radius length (2).

The steps followed for drawing an inscribed polygon (Figure 9.13b) are as follows:

1. On the Draw menu, click Polygon.
2. On the command line, enter the number of sides.
3. Specify the centre of the polygon.
4. Enter i to specify a polygon inscribed within a circle of specified points.
5. Enter the radius length.

The steps followed for drawing a polygon by specifying one edge (Figure 9.13c) are as follows:

1. On the Draw menu, click Polygon.
2. On the command line, enter the number of sides.
3. Enter e (Edge).
4. Specify the start point for one polygon segment.
5. Specify the endpoint of the polygon segment.

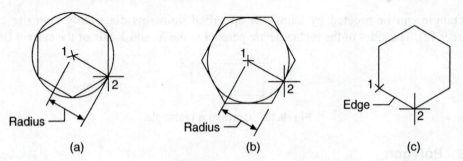

Fig. 9.13 Drawing polygons.

9.4.10 Donut

Donuts are filled rings or solid-filled circles that are actually closed polylines with width (Figure 9.14a). To create a donut, you have to specify its inside and outside diameters and its centre. You can continue creating multiple copies with the same diameter by specifying different centre points. To create solid-filled circles, specify an inside diameter of 0. The steps followed for creating a donut (Figure 9.14b) are as follows:

1. On the Draw menu, click Donut.
2. Specify the inside diameter (1).
3. Specify the outside diameter (2).
4. Specify the centre of the donut (3).
5. Specify the centre point for another donut, or press ENTER to complete the command.

The applications of donut are shown in Figure 9.14c.

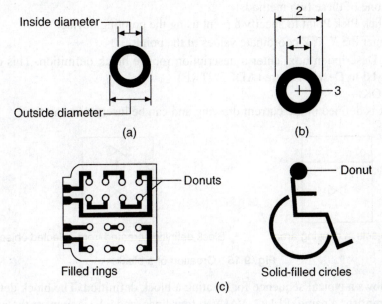

Inside diameter

Outside diameter

(a)

2

1

3

(b)

Donuts

Filled rings

Donut

Solid-filled circles

(c)

Fig. 9.14 Donuts.

9.4.11 Block

A block can be composed of objects drawn on several layers with various colours, linetypes, and lineweight properties. Although a block is always inserted on the current layer, the block reference preserves information about the original layer, colour, and linetype properties of the objects that are contained in the block. You can control whether objects in a block retain their original properties or inherit their properties from the current layer, colour, linetype, or lineweight settings. The following methods can be used to create blocks:

1. Combine objects to create a block definition in your current drawing.
2. Create a drawing file and later insert it as a block in other drawings.
3. Create a drawing file with several related block definitions to serve as a block library.

The steps followed for defining a block for the current drawing are as follows:

1. Create the objects you want to use in the block definition.
2. On the Draw menu, click Block.
3. In the Block Definition dialog box, enter a block name in the Name box.
4. Under Objects, select Convert to Block. If you want the original objects used to create the block definition to remain in your drawing, make sure the Delete option is not selected. If this option is selected, the original objects are erased from the drawing. If necessary, you can use OOPS to restore them.
5. Click Select Objects.
6. Use your pointing device to select the objects to be included in the block definition. Press ENTER to complete object selection.

7. In the Block Definition dialog box under Base Point, specify the block insertion point using one of these two methods:
   (a) Click Pick Point to specify a point using the pointing device.
   (b) Enter the X, Y, Z coordinate values of the point.
8. In the Description box, enter a description for the block definition. This description is displayed in Design Centre (ADCENTRE).
9. Click OK.

The block is defined in the current drawing and can be inserted at any time.

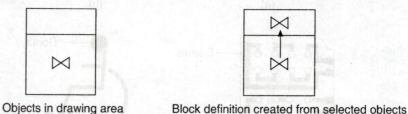

Objects in drawing area   Block definition created from selected objects

Fig. 9.15   Creation of a block.

Figure 9.15 shows a typical sequence for creating a block definition. The block definition in the illustration comprises a name, PLUG_VALVE, four lines, and a base point at the intersection of the two diagonal lines. The applications of block are shown in Figure 9.16.

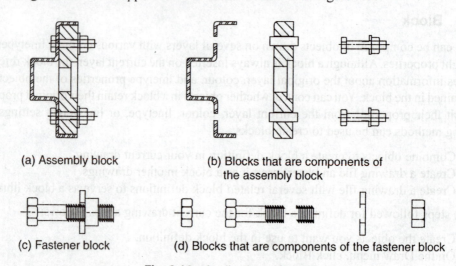

(a) Assembly block   (b) Blocks that are components of
                                    the assembly block

(c) Fastener block   (d) Blocks that are components of the fastener block

Fig. 9.16   Applications of block.

9.4.12 Table

A table is an array of rows and columns. The steps followed for creating a table are as follows:

1. On the Draw menu, click Table.
2. In the Insert Table dialog box, select a table style from the list, or click the [...] button to create a new table style.

3. Select one of the following two insertion methods:
   - Specify an insertion point for the table.
   - Specify a window for the table to fit.
4. Set the number of columns and the column width.
   If you used the window insertion method, you can select the number of columns or the column width, but not both.
5. Set the number of rows and the row height.
   If you used the window insertion method, the number of rows is determined by the size of the window you specified and the row height.
6. Click OK.

9.4.13 Text

All text in an AutoCAD drawing has a text style associated with it. When you enter text, AutoCAD uses the current text style, which sets the font, size, obliquing angle, orientation, and other text characteristics. If you want to create text by using a different text style, you can make another text style current. Table 9.1 shows the settings for the STANDARD text style.

Table 9.1 Text style settings

Setting	Default	Description
Style name	STANDARD	Name with up to 255 characters
Font name	txt.shx	File associated with a font (character style)
Big Font	none	Special shape definition file used for a non-ASCII character set, such as Kanji
Height	0	Character height
Width factor	1	Expansion or compression of the characters
Obliquing angle	0	Slant of the characters
Backwards	No	Backwards text
Upside down	No	Upside-down text
Vertical	No	Vertical or horizontal text

9.5 LAYERS

Layer is a logical grouping of data that are like transparent acetate overlays on a drawing. You can view layers individually or in combination. Layers are the equivalent of the overlays used in paper-based drafting. Layers are the primary organisational tools in AutoCAD. You use them to group information by function and to enforce linetype, colour, and other standards. By creating layers, you can associate similar types of objects by assigning them to the same layer. For example, you can put construction lines, text, dimensions, and title blocks on separate layers (Figure 9.17). You can then control:

1. Whether objects on a layer are visible in any viewports
2. Whether and how objects are plotted

3. What colour is assigned to all objects on a layer
4. What default linetype and lineweight are assigned to all objects on a layer
5. Whether objects on a layer can be modified

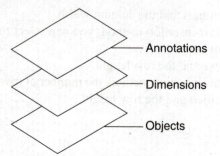

Annotations

Dimensions

Objects

Fig. 9.17   Layers.

Every drawing includes a layer named 0. Layer 0 cannot be deleted or renamed. It has the following two purposes:

1. It ensures that every drawing includes at least one layer.
2. It provides a special layer that relates to controlling colours in blocks.

A typical pop-up window for altering the layers in a given drawing is shown in Figure 9.18.

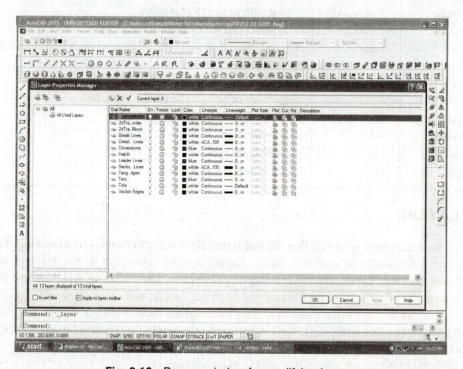

Fig. 9.18   Pop-up window for modifying layers.

The steps followed for creating a new layer are as follows:

1. On the Format menu, click Layer.
2. In the Layer Properties Manager, click the New Layer button.
   A layer name, such as LAYER1, is automatically added to the layer list.
3. Enter a new layer name by typing over the highlighted layer name.
   A layer name can include up to 255 characters: letters, digits, and the special characters dollar sign ($), hyphen (-), and underscore (_). Use a reverse quote (') before other special characters so that the characters are not interpreted as wild-card characters. Layer names cannot include blank spaces.
4. To change the properties, click icons.
   When you click Colour, Linetype, Lineweight, or Plot Style, a dialog box is displayed.
5. (Optional) Click in the Description column and enter text.
6. Click Apply to save your changes, or click OK to save and close.

9.6 DISPLAY CONTROL COMMANDS

The display control commands are:

1. Zoom
2. Pan
3. Window
4. Aerial view
5. Viewport

9.6.1 Zoom

You can change the magnification of a view by zooming in and out, which is similar to zooming in and out with a camera (Figure 9.19). ZOOM does not change the absolute size of objects in the drawing; it changes only the magnification of the view.

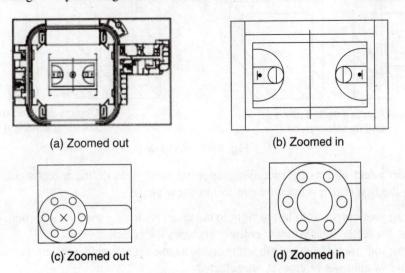

(a) Zoomed out   (b) Zoomed in

(c) Zoomed out   (d) Zoomed in

Fig. 9.19 Zoom.

9.6.2 Pan

It is used to shift the view of a drawing without changing magnification. The cursor changes to a hand cursor. By holding down the pick button on the pointing device, you lock the cursor to its current location relative to the viewport coordinate system. The drawing display is moved in the same direction as the cursor.

The cursor changes to a hand cursor (Figure 9.20a). By holding down the pick button on the pointing device, you lock the cursor to its current location relative to the viewport coordinate system. The drawing display is moved in the same direction as the cursor.

When you reach a logical extent (edge of the drawing space), a bar is displayed on the hand cursor on that edge. Depending on whether the logical extent is at the top, bottom, or side of the drawing, the bar is either horizontal (top or bottom) or vertical (left or right side) as shown in Figure 9.20b.

When you release the pick button, panning stops. You can release the pick button, move the cursor to another location in the drawing, and then press the pick button again to pan the display from that location. To stop panning at any time, press ENTER or ESC.

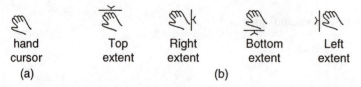

| hand cursor | Top extent | Right extent | Bottom extent | Left extent |
| (a) | | (b) | | |

Fig. 9.20 Pan.

9.6.3 Window

It plots any portion of the drawing you specify (Figure 9.21). Click the Window button to use a pointing device to specify opposite corners of the area to be plotted.

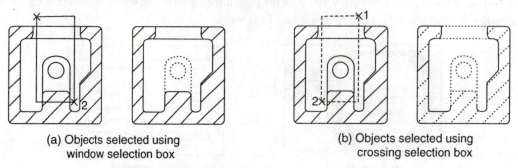

(a) Objects selected using window selection box

(b) Objects selected using crossing selection box

Fig. 9.21 Window.

You can select objects by specifying opposite corners to define a rectangular area. After specifying the first corner point, you can follow these steps:

1. Drag your cursor from left to right to create an enclosing window selection. Only objects that the rectangular window entirely encloses are selected.
2. Drag your cursor from right to left to create a crossing selection. Objects that the rectangular window encloses or crosses are selected.

With a window selection, usually the entire object must be contained in the window selection box. However, if an object with a non-continuous (dashed) linetype is only partially visible in the viewport and all the visible vectors of the linetype can be enclosed within the selection window, the entire object is selected.

9.6.4 Aerial View

You can use the Aerial View window to change the view in your current viewport quickly (Figure 9.22). If you keep the Aerial View window open as you work, you can zoom and pan without interrupting your current command. You can also specify a new view without having to choose a menu option or enter a command.

Within the Aerial View window is a view box, a heavy rectangle that displays the boundary of the view in your current viewport. You can change the view in the drawing by changing the view box in the Aerial View window. To zoom in to the drawing, make the view box smaller. To zoom out of the drawing, make the view box larger. All pan and zoom operations are performed by left-clicking. Right-click to end a pan or zoom operation.

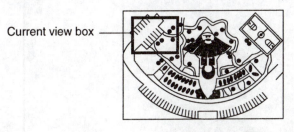
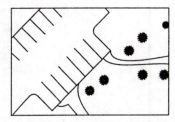

Current view box

Aerial view window

Current view in drawing area

Fig. 9.22 Aerial view.

9.6.5 Viewport

It is a bounded area that displays some portion of the model space of a drawing (Figure 9.23). You can arrange the elements of your drawing by aligning the view in one layout viewport with the view in another viewport. For angled, horizontal, and vertical alignments, you can move each layout viewport relative to distances defined by the model-space geometry displayed.

Dominant viewport

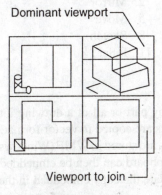

Viewport to join

Fig. 9.23 Viewport.

9.7 EDITING A DRAWING

With AutoCAD, you can easily modify the size, shape, and location of objects. You can either enter a command first and then select the objects to modify, or you can select the objects first and then enter a command to modify them. Double-clicking an object displays the Properties palette or, in some cases, a dialog box that is specific to that type of object. Various options available are shown in Figure 9.24.

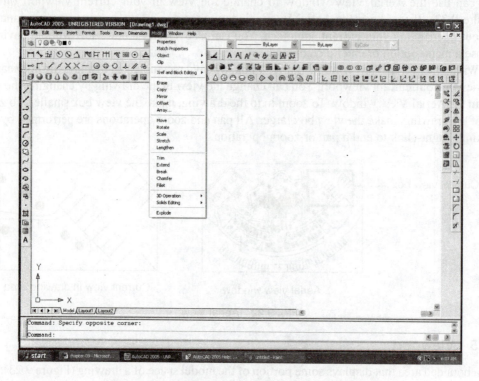

Fig. 9. 24 Editing options available in AutoCAD.

The important drawing editing commands are:

1. Copy
2. Mirror
3. Offset
4. Array
5. Move
6. Rotate
7. Scale
8. Sketch
9. Trim
10. Chamfer
11. Fillet

9.7.1 Copy

You can use the Clipboard to copy part or all of a drawing into a document created by another application. The AutoCAD objects are copied in vector format, which retains the high resolution in other applications. These objects are stored in WMF (Windows metafile) format in the Clipboard. The information stored in the Clipboard can then be embedded in the other document. Updating the original drawing does not update the copy embedded in the other application.

Single copy: If you specify two points, AutoCAD uses the first point as a base point and places a single copy relative to that base point. The two points you specify define a displacement to determine how far the selected objects are moved and in what direction (Figure 9.25a).

If you press ENTER at the Specify Second Point of Displacement prompt, the first point is interpreted as a relative X, Y, Z displacement. For example, if you specify 2, 3 for the base point and press ENTER at the next prompt, the object moves 2 units in the X direction and 3 units in the Y direction from its current position. In this case, the first point is usually entered at the keyboard.

Multiple copies using one COPY command: AutoCAD prompts for an insertion base point for the selection object. If you specify a point, AutoCAD places a copy at that point relative to the base point. The Specify Second Point of Displacement prompt is repeated for placement of multiple copies of the object. If you press ENTER, the command ends (Figure 9.25b).

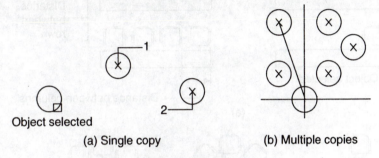

(a) Single copy   (b) Multiple copies

Fig. 9.25 Copy.

9.7.2 Mirror

It places the reflected image into the drawing (Figure 9.26).

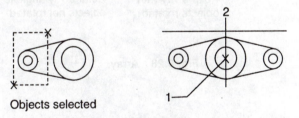

Objects selected

Fig. 9.26 Mirror.

9.7.3 Offset

It creates an object at a specified distance from an existing object (Figure 9.27).

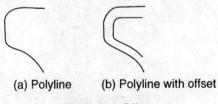

(a) Polyline   (b) Polyline with offset

Fig. 9.27 Offset.

9.7.4 Array

It creates multiple copies of objects in a pattern. Use the Rectangular Array option to create an array of rows and columns of copies of the selected object. Use the Polar Array option to create an array by copying the selected objects around a centre point.

   Rectangular array: It creates an array of rows and columns of copies of the selected objects (Figure 9.28a).

   Polar array: It creates an array defined by specifying a centre point or base point about which AutoCAD replicates the selected objects (Figure 9.28b).

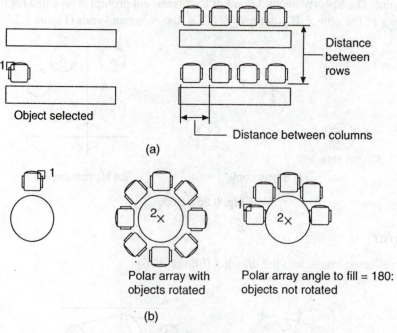

(a)

Polar array with
objects rotated

Polar array angle to fill = 180:
objects not rotated

(b)

Fig. 9.28   Array.

9.7.5 Move

You can move objects without changing their orientation or size (Figure 9.29). By using coordinates and object snaps, you can move objects with precision.

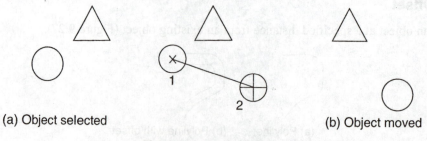

(a) Object selected

(b) Object moved

Fig. 9.29   Move function.

The two points you specify define a displacement vector that indicates how far the selected objects are to be moved and in what direction. If you press ENTER at the Specify Second Point of Displacement prompt, the first point is interpreted as relative X, Y, Z displacement. For example, if you specify 2,3 for the base point and press ENTER at the next prompt, the object moves 2 units in the X direction and 3 units in the Y direction from its current position.

9.7.6 Rotate

You can rotate objects in your drawing around a specified point. To determine the angle of rotation, you enter an angle value or specify a second point.

Entering a positive angle value rotates the objects counter-clockwise or clockwise, depending on the Direction Control setting in the Drawing Units dialog box. The plane of rotation and the direction of the zero angle depend on the orientation of the user coordinate system.

You rotate objects by choosing a base point and a relative or absolute rotation angle. Specify a relative angle to rotate the object from its current orientation around the base point by that angle. Specify an absolute angle to rotate the object from the current angle to a new absolute angle.

You can rotate an object by specifying a relative angle using one of the following two methods:

- Enter a rotation angle value from 0 to 360 degrees. You can also enter values in radians, grads, or surveyor bearings.
- Drag the object around the base point and specify a second point. Turning on Ortho and Polar Tracking, or using object snaps for the second point, is often useful in this method.

For example, you rotate the plan view of a house by selecting the object (1), specifying a base point (2), and specifying an angle of rotation by dragging to another point (3) as shown in (Figure 9.30).

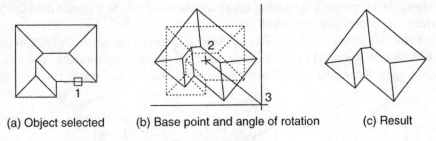

(a) Object selected   (b) Base point and angle of rotation   (c) Result

Fig. 9.30 Rotate.

9.7.7 Scale

This multiplies the dimensions of the selected objects by the specified scale (Figure 9.31). A scale factor greater than 1 enlarges the objects. A scale factor between 0 and 1 shrinks the objects.

(a) Scale factor = .5   (b) Scale factor = 2

Fig. 9.31 Scale.

9.7.8   Sketch

Drawing with the SKETCH command controls a screen-based pen with a pointing device. SKETCH is useful for entering map outlines, signatures, or other freehand drawings. Sketched lines are not added to the drawing until they are recorded. The standard digitiser tablet button menu is not available while SKETCH is in progress. The following information is based on the assumption that the Tablet mode is on.

The record increment value defines the length of the line segments. The pointing device must be moved at a greater distance than the increment value to generate a line (Figure 9.32).

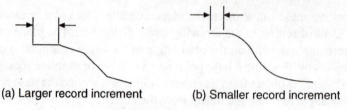

(a) Larger record increment   (b) Smaller record increment

Fig. 9.32   Sketch.

9.7.9   Trim

Objects that can be trimmed include arcs, circles, elliptical arcs, lines, open two- and three-dimensional polylines, rays, splines, hatches, and xlines (Figure 9.33).

Select the objects that define the cutting edges at which you want to trim an object, or press ENTER to select all objects as potential cutting edges. Valid cutting edge objects include two- and three-dimensional polylines, arcs, circles, ellipses, lines, layout viewports, rays, regions, splines, text, and xlines. TRIM projects the cutting edges and the objects to be trimmed onto the XY plane of the current user coordinate system (UCS).

When AutoCAD prompts you to select boundary edges, you can press ENTER and select the object to be trimmed. AutoCAD trims the object against the nearest candidate. You can use only the single, crossing, fence, and implied selection options to select boundaries that include blocks.

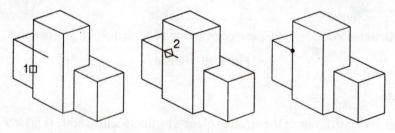

Fig. 9.33   Trim.

9.7.10   Chamfer

If both the objects you want to chamfer are on the same layer, the chamfer is created on that layer (Figure 9.34), otherwise, the chamfer is created on the current layer. This is also true for colour, linetype, and lineweight.

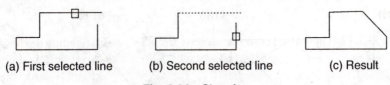

(a) First selected line   (b) Second selected line   (c) Result

Fig. 9.34 Chamfer.

9.7.11 Fillet

FILLET rounds the edges of two arcs, circles, elliptical arcs, lines, polylines, rays, splines, or *x*-lines with the arc of a specified radius (Figure 9.35).

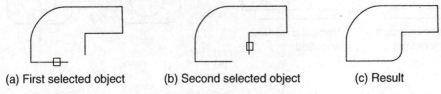

(a) First selected object   (b) Second selected object   (c) Result

Fig. 9.35 Fillet.

9.8 DIMENSIONING

You can create all of the standard types of dimensions, such as:

1. *Create linear dimensions:* You can create linear dimensions with horizontal, vertical, and aligned dimension lines. These linear dimensions can also be stacked, or they can be created end to end (Figure 9.36a).
2. *Create radial dimensions:* Radial dimensions measure the radii and diameters of arcs and circles with optional centrelines or a centre mark (Figure 9.36b).
3. *Create angular dimensions:* Angular dimensions measure the angle between two lines or three points (Figure 9.36c).
4. *Create ordinate dimensions:* Ordinate dimensions measure the perpendicular distance from an origin point called the datum to a dimensioned feature, such as a hole in a part (Figure 9.36d).

9.9 GEOMETRIC TOLERANCES

Geometric tolerances show acceptable deviations of form, profile, orientation, location, and runout of a feature. Geometric tolerances are added in feature control frames. These frames contain all the tolerance information for a single dimension. Geometric tolerances can be created with or without leader lines, depending on whether you create them with TOLERANCE or LEADER (Figure 9.37).

A feature control frame consists of two or more components. The first feature control frame contains a symbol that represents the geometric characteristic to which a tolerance is being applied, such as, location, profile, form, orientation, or runout. Form tolerances control straightness, flatness, circularity and cylindricity; profiles control line and surface. In the illustration, the characteristic is position.

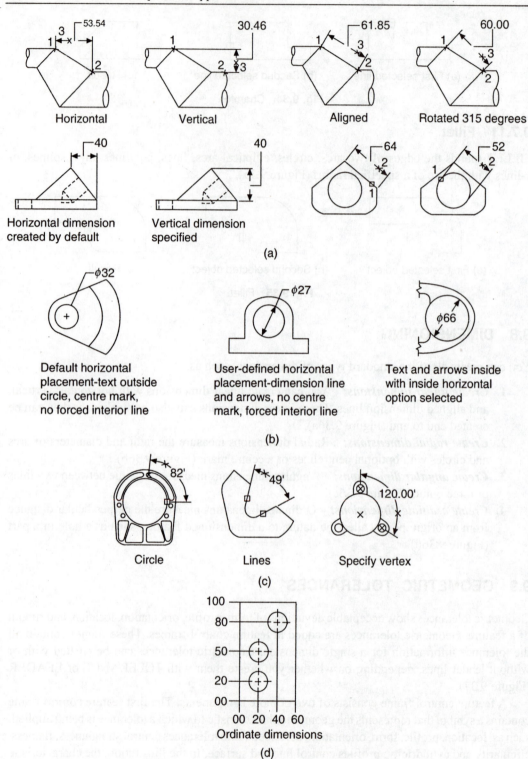

Fig. 9.36 Various methods of dimensioning.

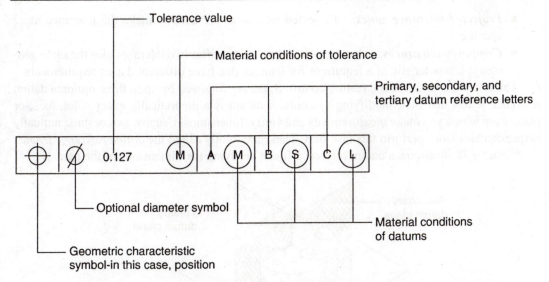

Tolerance value

Material conditions of tolerance

Primary, secondary, and
tertiary datum reference letters

Ø 0.127 M A M B S C L

Optional diameter symbol

Material conditions
of datums

Geometric characteristic
symbol-in this case, position

Fig. 9.37 Tolerance.

Geometric tolerances define the maximum allowable variations of form or profile, orientation, location, and runout from the exact geometry in a drawing. They specify the accuracy required for proper function and fit of the objects you draw in AutoCAD.

AutoCAD adds geometric tolerances to a drawing in feature control frames. These frames are divided into compartments that contain the geometric characteristic symbols followed by one or more tolerance values. Where applicable, the tolerance is preceded by the diameter symbol and followed by datums and symbols for their material conditions.

The second compartment contains the tolerance value. Depending on the control type, the tolerance value is preceded by a diameter symbol and followed by a material condition symbol. Material conditions apply to features that can vary in size:

- At maximum material condition (symbol M, also known as MMC), a feature contains the maximum amount of material stated in the limits.
- At MMC, a hole has minimum diameter, whereas a shaft has maximum diameter.
- At the least material condition (symbol L, also known as LMC), a feature contains the minimum amount of material stated in the limits.
- At LMC, a hole has the maximum diameter, whereas a shaft has the minimum diameter.
- 'Regardless of feature size' (symbol S, also known as RFS) means that a feature can be of any size within the stated limits.

You can add geometric tolerances that show acceptable deviations of form, profile, orientation, location, and runout of a feature. These tolerances are:

- *Material conditions:* Material conditions apply to features that can vary in size.
- *Datum reference frames:* The tolerance values in the feature control frame are followed by up to three optional datum reference letters and their modifying symbols.

- *Projected tolerance zones:*   Projected tolerances are used to make the tolerance more specific.
- *Composite tolerances*:   A composite tolerance specifies two tolerances for the same geometric characteristic of a feature or for features that have different datum requirements.

The tolerance values in the feature control frame are followed by up to three optional datum reference letters and their modifying symbols. A datum is a theoretically exact point, axis, or plane from which you make measurements and verify dimensions. Usually, two or three mutually perpendicular planes perform this task best. These are jointly called the *datum reference frame*.

Figure 9.38 illustrates a datum reference frame verifying the dimensions of the part.

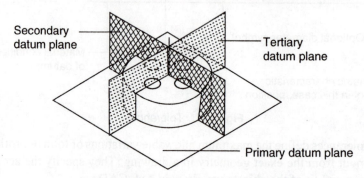

Fig. 9.38   Datum reference frame.

Projected tolerances are specified in addition to positional tolerances to make the tolerance more specific. For example, projected tolerances control the perpendicularity tolerance zone of an embedded part (Figure 9.39).

The symbol for projected tolerance (*p*) is preceded by a height value, which specifies the minimum projected tolerance zone. The projected tolerance zone height and symbol appear in a frame below the feature control frame, as shown in Figure 9.39.

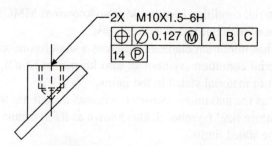

Fig. 9.39   Projected tolerance.

A composite tolerance specifies two tolerances for the same geometric characteristic of a feature or for features that have different datum requirements. One tolerance relates to a pattern of features and the other to each feature within the pattern. The individual feature tolerance is more restrictive than the pattern tolerance.

A composite tolerance can specify both the diameter of the pattern of holes and the diameter of each individual hole, as shown in Figure 9.40.

When you add composite tolerances to a drawing, you specify the first line of a feature control frame and then choose the same geometric characteristic symbol for the second line of the feature control frame. AutoCAD extends the geometric symbol compartment over both lines. You can then create a second line of tolerance symbols.

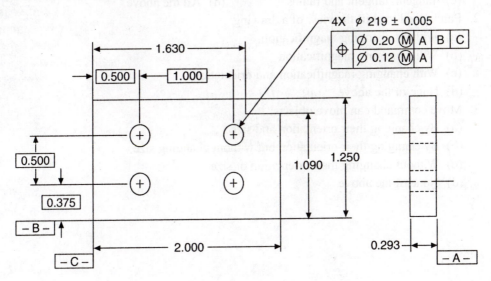

Fig. 9.40 Composite tolerance.

A. Descriptive Questions

1. Describe drafting set-up.
2. What is the importance of grid and snap commands in drafting?
3. Explain the drafting structure with an example.
4. What are the basic commands in drafting? Explain the use of any five commands with examples.
5. Explain the different methods of constructing a circle.
6. Explain the different methods of constructing an ellipse.
7. Explain the different methods of constructing a polygon.
8. What is the importance of layers in drafting? Explain with an example.
9. What are the various types of display control commands? Explain their use with examples.
10. What are the various types of editing commands used in drafting? Explain their use with examples.
11. Explain various methods of dimensioning.
12. Explain various methods of tolerancing.

B. Multiple Choice Questions

1. You can create circles in the following ways:
   (a) Centre and radius   (b) Two points defining diameter
   (c) Tangent, tangent and radius   (d) All the above

2. Pan is used to shift the view of a drawing:
   (a) Without changing magnification
   (b) With changing magnification
   (c) With changing magnification and orientation
   (d) None of the above

3. Move command can move objects:
   (a) By changing their orientation and size
   (b) By changing their orientation but without changing size
   (c) Without changing their orientation or size
   (d) None of the above

Chapter **10**

Finite Element Modelling

OBJECTIVES

After reading this chapter, the reader will be able to understand the following concepts:

- ➲ A generalised procedure of FEM
- ➲ Variational formulation: The total potential energy functional and the minimum potential energy principle
- ➲ Finite element discretisation
- ➲ A two-node bar element
- ➲ Shape functions
- ➲ The element strain–displacement matrix
- ➲ Derivation of finite element equations using the P.E. method: Element stiffness matrix, body force vector, traction load vector and point load vector
- ➲ Degrees of freedom
- ➲ Boundary conditions
- ➲ Assembly of global stiffness matrix and load vector
- ➲ Treatment of boundary conditions: Elimination approach and penalty approach
- ➲ Finite element analysis software
- ➲ Advantages of FEM

10.1 INTRODUCTION

The finite element method (FEM) is a powerful tool for the numerical solution of a wide range of engineering problems. The basic concept in the physical interpretation of the FEM is the sub-division of the mathematical model into disjoint (non-overlapping) components of simple geometry called *finite elements* (Figure 10.1). The response of each element is expressed in terms of a finite number of degrees of freedom characterised as the value of an unknown function, or functions, at a set of nodal points. The response of the mathematical model is then considered to be approximated by that of the discrete model obtained by connecting or assembling the collection of all elements.

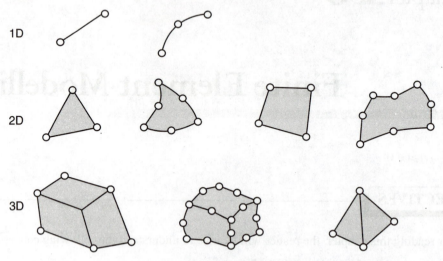

Fig. 10.1   Typical finite elements.

10.2   A GENERALISED PROCEDURE OF FEM

A finite element method typically involves the following steps:

1. Discretise the structure or continuum into finite elements. The finite elements may be triangles, group of triangles, or quadrilaterals for a two-dimensional continuum. For the three-dimensional analysis, the finite elements may be tetrahedron, or hexahedron. Mesh generation programs, called preprocessors, help the user in doing this work.
2. Specify the approximation equation. The order of the approximation, linear or quadratic, must be specified and the equations must be written in terms of the unknown nodal values. An equation is written for each element.
3. Determine the shape functions for each element.
4. Formulate the properties of each element.
5. Determine stiffness matrices and equivalent load vectors for all elements. The stiffness matrix consists of the coefficients of the equilibrium equations derived from the material and geometric properties of an element. It is obtained by use of the principle of minimum potential energy.
6. Assemble elements to obtain the finite element model of the structure or continuum.
7. Apply the known loads: nodal forces and/or moments in stress analysis, nodal heat fluxes in heat transfer.

8. Apply boundary conditions. In stress analysis, specify how the structure is supported. This involves setting several nodal displacements to known values (which are often zero). In heat transfer, impose all known values of nodal temperature.

9. Solve simultaneous linear algebraic equations to determine nodal degrees of freedom (dof) (nodal displacements in stress analysis, nodal temperatures in heat transfer analysis).

10. In stress analysis, calculate element strains form the nodal dof and the element displacement field interpolation, and finally compute stresses from the strains. In heat transfer analysis, calculate element heat fluxes from the nodal temperatures and the element temperature field interpolation.

11. Interpret the results. The interpretation of the numerical results is in terms of their mathematical and physical significance. An important ingredient of this step is the assessment of the modelling and discretisation errors. The last step is crucial in engineering applications, and its importance cannot be over-emphasised.

10.3 VARIATIONAL FORMULATION

10.3.1 The Total Potential Energy Functional

We will derive the finite element equations of the bar from the Minimum Potential Energy principle. In Mechanics of Materials it is shown that the *internal energy density* at a point of a linear-elastic material subjected to a one-dimensional state of stress σ and strain ε is $U = \frac{1}{2}\sigma\varepsilon$, where σ is to be regarded as linked to the displacement u through Hooke's law $\sigma = E\varepsilon$ and the strain displacement relation $\varepsilon = \frac{du}{dx}$. This U is also called the *strain energy density*. Integration over the volume of the bar gives the total internal energy:

$$U = \frac{1}{2}\int_0^v \sigma^T \varepsilon \, dv \;\; = \;\; \frac{1}{2}\int_0^l (E\varepsilon)^T \, \varepsilon A dx \;\; = \;\; \frac{1}{2}\int_0^l (\varepsilon)^T EA\varepsilon dx \tag{10.1}$$

in which all integrand quantities may depend on x.

The *external energy* due to the applied mechanical loads is contributed by the following three sources:

(i)   The traction force, q
(ii) Body force, b
(iii) Any applied point load (s).

The third contribution may be folded into the first or second by conventionally writing any point load P that acts at a cross-section $x = a$ as a contribution $p\delta(a)$ to q, where $\delta(a)$ is the one-dimensional delta function at $x = a$. The total external energy can then be concisely expressed as:

$$W = \int_0^v u^T bA dx + \int_0^l u^T q dx + \sum_i u_i p_i \tag{10.2}$$

The total potential energy of the bar is given by

$$\Pi = U - W \tag{10.3}$$

Mathematically, this is a functional, called the *Total Potential Energy* functional (TPE). It depends only on the axial displacement u.

10.3.2 The Minimum Potential Energy Principle

The Minimum Potential Energy (MPE) Principle states that the actual displacement solution $u(x)$ is that which renders Π stationary:

$$\delta\Pi = \delta U - \delta W = 0 \tag{10.4}$$

10.4 FINITE ELEMENT DISCRETISATION

In order to apply the MPE functional (Equation 10.4) to the derivation of finite element equations, we replace the mathematical model by a discrete one consisting of a union of bar elements. For example, Figure 10.2 illustrates the sub-division of a bar member into four two-node elements.

Functionals are scalars. Consequently, corresponding to a discretisation such as that shown in Figure 10.2, the TPE functional (Equation 10.3) may be decomposed into a sum of contributions of individual elements:

$$\Pi = \Pi_1 + \Pi_2 + ... + \Pi_n \tag{10.5}$$

where n is the number of elements. The same decomposition applies to the internal and external energies, as well as to the condition of minimum potential energy principle (Equation 10.4):

$$\delta\Pi = \delta\Pi_1 + \delta\Pi_2 + ... + \delta\Pi_n \tag{10.6}$$

Using the fundamental lemma of variational calculus, it can be shown that (Equation 10.6) implies that for a generic element (e) we may write:

$$\delta\Pi_e = \delta U_e + \delta W_e = 0 \tag{10.7}$$

This *variational equation* is the basis for the derivation of element stiffness equations once the displacement field has been discretised over the element.

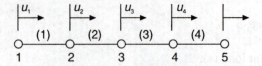

Fig. 10.2 FEM discretisation of bar member.

10.5 A TWO-NODE BAR ELEMENT

Figure 10.3 depicts a generic bar element (e) in the Cartesian coordinate system. The element is referred to the local axis x. In the local number scheme, the first node is numbered 1 and the second node 2. The notation $x_1 = x$-coordinate of node 1, $x_2 = x$-coordinate of node 2 is employed. The two degrees of freedom are u_1 and u_2.

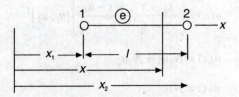

Fig. 10.3   Generic two-node bar element in the Cartesian coordinate system.

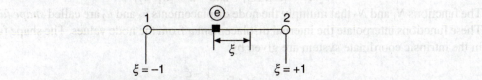

Fig. 10.4   Generic two-node bar element in the intrinsic coordinate system.

We define an intrinsic or natural coordinate system, denoted by ξ, as:

$$\xi = \frac{2}{x_2 - x_1}(x - x_1) - 1 \tag{10.8}$$

From Figure 10.4, we see that $\xi = -1$ at node 1 and $\xi = 1$ at node 2. The length of the element is covered when ξ changes from -1 to 1. We use this system of coordinates in defining shape functions, which are used in interpolating the displacement field.

10.6   SHAPE FUNCTIONS

For a two-node bar element as shown in Figure 3.5, the only possible variation of the displacement u which satisfies the inter-element continuity requirement stated above is linear. The displacement polynomial function is assumed to be:

$$u(x) = c_0 + c_1 x \tag{10.9}$$

where

c_0 and c_1 are the coefficients of the displacement polynomial function.

The displacement vector of the two-node bar element is defined by:

$$u = [u_1 - u_2]^T \tag{10.10}$$

At $x = x_1$,

$$u_e = u_1 = c_0 + c_1 x_1 \tag{10.11}$$

At $x = x_2$,

$$u = u_2 = c_0 + c_1 x_2 \tag{10.12}$$

Upon solving Equations 3.12 and 3.13 for the polynomial coefficients, we obtain:

$$c_0 = \frac{u_2 - u_1}{x_2 - x_1} \quad \text{and} \quad c_0 = \frac{u_1 x_2 - u_2 x_1}{x_2 - x_1} \tag{10.13}$$

The linear displacement polynomial function within the element can be written in terms of the nodal displacements u_1 and u_2 as:

$$u(x) = \left[\frac{x_2 - x}{x_2 - x_1}, -\frac{x - x_1}{x_2 - x_1} \right] [u_1, u_2]^T \tag{10.14}$$

$$u(x) = N_1 u_1 + N_2 u_2 \tag{10.15}$$

$$u(x) = Nu \tag{10.16}$$

where

$$N = [N_1, N_2] \quad \text{and} \quad u = [u_1, u_2]^T \tag{10.17}$$

The functions N_1 and N_2 that multiply the node displacements u_1 and u_2 are called *shape functions*. These functions interpolate the internal displacement u from the node values. The shape functions in the intrinsic coordinate system are given by:

$$N_1(\xi) = \frac{1 - \xi}{2} \tag{10.18}$$

$$N_2(\xi) = \frac{1 + \xi}{2} \tag{10.19}$$

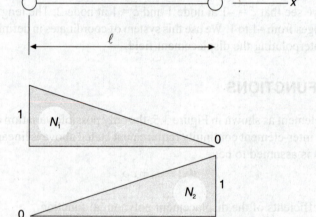

Fig. 10.5   Generic two-node bar element and its two shape functions.

The graphical representation of shape functions is shown in Figure 10.5. The matrix N describes how u is to be interpolated from nodal values u_1 and u_2 over the elements, that is, over the range. $0 \leq x \leq l$. Here the shape function matrix happens to be a row matrix. Note that the shape function N_1 has the value 1 at node 1 and 0 at node 2. Conversely, the shape function N_2 has the value 0 at node 1 and 1 at node 2. We shall see later that this is a general property of the shape functions, required by interpolation considerations. The sum of the shape functions, also called interpolation functions, over the element is always equal to unity. It may be noted that the transformation from x to ξ in Equation 3.9 can be written in terms of N_1 and N_2 as:

$$x = N_1 x_1 + N_2 x_2 \qquad (10.20)$$

Comparing Equations 10.15 and 10.20, we observe that both the displacement u and the coordinate x are interpolated within the element using the same functions N_1 and N_2. This is referred to as the Isoparametric formulation. In general, the shape functions need to satisfy the following conditions:

(i)   First the derivatives must be finite within an element.
(ii) Displacement must be continuous across the elementary boundary.

10.7   THE ELEMENT STRAIN–DISPLACEMENT MATRIX

The axial strain over the element is:

$$\varepsilon = \frac{du}{dx} = \left[\frac{dN_1}{dx}, \frac{dN_2}{dx} \right] \begin{Bmatrix} u_1 \\ u_2 \end{Bmatrix} = \frac{1}{l}[-1 \ 1] \begin{Bmatrix} u_1 \\ u_2 \end{Bmatrix} = Bu \qquad (10.21)$$

where

$$B = \frac{dN}{dx} = \frac{1}{l}[-1 \ 1] \qquad (10.22)$$

is called the strain–displacement matrix.

The stress, from Hooke's law is:

$$\sigma = E\varepsilon = EBu \qquad (10.23)$$

The stress given by Equation 10.23 is constant within the element. The stress may be considered to be the value at the centroid of the element for interpolation.

10.8   DERIVATION OF FINITE ELEMENT EQUATIONS USING THE P.E. METHOD

The total potential energy for the general elastic body is given by:

$$\pi = \frac{1}{2} \int_v \sigma^T \varepsilon \, dv - \int_v u^T b \, dv - \int_l u^T q \, dx - \sum_i u_i^T p_i \qquad (10.24)$$

Since the continuum has been discretised into finite elements, the expression for π becomes:

$$\pi = \sum_e \frac{1}{2} \int_e \sigma^T \varepsilon A \, dx - \sum_e \int_e u^T b A \, dx - \sum_e \int_e u^T q \, dx - \sum_i u_i p_i \qquad (10.25)$$

10.8.1   Element Stiffness Matrix

For the two-node bar element, the internal energy U is:

$$U = \frac{1}{2} \int_0^l \varepsilon E A \varepsilon \, dx \qquad (10.26)$$

where the strain is related to the nodal displacements through (Equation 3.23). Inserting $\varepsilon = Bu$ into the second ε and $\varepsilon^T = u^T B^T$ into first ε yields:

$$U = \frac{1}{2} \int_0^l u^T B^T EABu dx \qquad (10.27)$$

The nodal displacements can be moved out of the integral, giving:

$$U = \frac{1}{2} u^T \left[\int_0^l B^T EAB dx \right] u = \frac{1}{2} u^T k_e u \qquad (10.28)$$

where

$$k_e = \int_0^l B^T EAB dx \qquad (10.29)$$

is the element stiffness matrix.

$$k_e = \int_0^l \frac{EA}{l^2} \begin{Bmatrix} -1 \\ 1 \end{Bmatrix} [-1 \; 1] dx = \int_0^l \frac{EA}{l^2} \begin{bmatrix} 1 & -1 \\ -1 & 1 \end{bmatrix} dx$$

If the axial rigidity is constant over the length of the element,

$$k_e = \frac{EA}{l} \begin{bmatrix} 1 & -1 \\ -1 & 1 \end{bmatrix} \qquad (10.30)$$

It is observed that k_e is linearly proportional to the axial rigidity and inversely proportional to the length of the element.

10.8.2 Body Force Vector

The body force is a distributed force acting on every elemental volume of the body, and has the units of force per unit volume. The self-weight due to gravity is an example of a body force. The body force vector F_e comes from the element contribution to the external work potential W:

$$W_b = \int_0^v u^T b dv = \int_0^l (Nu)^T - bA dx = u^T bA \int_0^l N^T dx = u^T bA \int_0^l \begin{bmatrix} N_1 \\ N_2 \end{bmatrix} dx \qquad (10.31)$$

Further, transformation from x to ξ in (Equation 10.8) yields:

$$dx = \frac{x_2 - x_1}{2} d\xi = \frac{1}{2} d\xi \qquad (10.32)$$

where $-1 \le \xi \le 1$, and l is the length of the element, $l = |x_2 - x_1|$.

$$W_b = u^T bA \left\{ \begin{array}{c} \int\limits_0^l N_1 dx \\ \int\limits_0^l N_2 dx \end{array} \right\} \tag{10.33}$$

The integrals of the shape functions above can be evaluated by making the substitution $dx = \dfrac{l}{2} d\xi$. Thus:

$$\left. \begin{array}{l} \int\limits_0^l N_1 dx = \dfrac{l}{2} \int\limits_{-1}^{+1} \dfrac{1-\xi}{2} d\xi = \dfrac{l}{2} \\[4mm] \int\limits_0^l N_2 dx = \dfrac{l}{2} \int\limits_{-1}^{+1} \dfrac{1+\xi}{2} d\xi = \dfrac{l}{2} \end{array} \right\} \tag{10.34}$$

$$W_b = u^T \frac{bAL}{2} \left\{ \begin{array}{c} 1 \\ 1 \end{array} \right\} = u^T f_e \tag{10.35}$$

where

$$f_e = \frac{bAl}{2} \left\{ \begin{array}{c} 1 \\ 1 \end{array} \right\} \tag{10.36}$$

is the body force vector. If the force b is constant over the element, one obtains the same results as those obtained with the load lumping method.

10.8.3 Traction Load Vector

The traction force is a distributed load acting on the surface of the body. The traction force is defined as the force per unit area. For the one-dimensional bar members, the traction force is defined as the force per unit length. This is done by taking the traction force to be the product of the force per unit area with the perimeter of the cross-section. Frictional resistance, viscous drag, and surface shear are examples of the traction forces.

The potential energy due to the traction force is given by:

$$W_t = \int\limits_e u^T q dx = \int\limits_e (uN)^T q dx = u^T \int\limits_e N^T q dx = u^T \Gamma_e \tag{10.37}$$

where

$$\Gamma_e = \int\limits_e N^T q dx \tag{10.38}$$

Since the traction force is constant and $\int\limits_e N_1 dx = \int\limits_e N_2 dx = \dfrac{l}{2}$, we have:

$$\Gamma_e = \frac{ql}{2}\begin{Bmatrix} 1 \\ 1 \end{Bmatrix} \qquad (10.39)$$

10.8.4 Point Load Vector

The potential energy due to point loads $\sum_i u_i p_i$ (10.40)

where p_i represents a point force acting at point i and u_i is the displacement at that point.

The point load vector, $p_e = [p_1, p_2, \ldots, P_n]^T$. (10.41)

10.9 DEGREES OF FREEDOM

The degrees of freedom (dof) specify the state of the element. They also function as 'handles' through which adjacent elements are connected. Degrees of freedom are defined as the values (and possibly derivatives) of a primary field variable at nodal points. For mechanical elements, the primary variable is the displacement field and the dof for many (but not all) elements are the displacement components at the nodes.

10.10 BOUNDARY CONDITIONS

A key strength of the FEM is the ease and elegance with which it handles arbitrary boundary and interface conditions. One of the biggest hurdles that an FEM newcomer faces is the need for understanding and proper handling of boundary conditions. In the present section, we summarise some basic rules for treating boundary conditions.

In mechanical problems, essential boundary conditions are those that involve displacements (but not strain-type displacement derivatives). The support conditions for the truss problem furnish a particularly simple example. But there are more general boundary conditions that occur in practice. A structural engineer must be familiar with displacement B.C. of the following types:

10.11 ASSEMBLY OF GLOBAL STIFFNESS MATRIX AND LOAD VECTOR

In the finite element analysis, the continuum is discretised into finite elements. The potential energy of the continuum is given by:

$$\Pi = \sum_e \frac{1}{2} u^T k_e u - \sum_e u^T f_e - \sum_e u^T \Gamma_e - \sum_i p_i u_i \qquad (10.42)$$

This can be written in the form:

$$\Pi = \frac{1}{2} d^T K d - d^T F \qquad (10.43)$$

This step involves the assembling of K and F from element stiffness and force matrices.

Consider an axially loaded bar structure as shown in Figure 10.6. The bar structure is discretised into two elements. The stiffness matrices associated with elements 1 and 2 are given by:

$$k_1 = \frac{A_1 E_1}{l_1} \begin{bmatrix} 1 & -1 \\ -1 & 1 \end{bmatrix} \quad \text{and} \quad k_2 = \frac{A_2 E_2}{l_2} \begin{bmatrix} 1 & -1 \\ -1 & 1 \end{bmatrix}$$

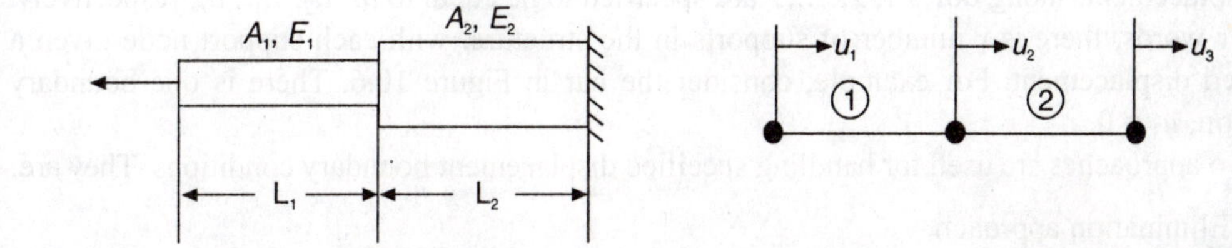

(a) An axially loaded bar   (b) Finite elements used to model the bar

Fig. 10.6

The dof are axial displacements u_1, u_2 and u_3 where 1, 2 and 3 are arbitrary labels assigned to identify the structural nodes. Now imagine two hypothetical states: in the first only element ❶ is present; in the second, only element ❷ is present. Therefore, the respective stiffness matrices would be:

$$k_1 = \begin{bmatrix} \dfrac{A_1 E_1}{l_1} & -\dfrac{A_1 E_1}{l_1} & 0 \\ -\dfrac{A_1 E_1}{l_1} & \dfrac{A_1 E_1}{l_1} & 0 \\ 0 & 0 & 0 \end{bmatrix} \begin{matrix} 1 \\ 2 \\ 3 \end{matrix} \quad \text{and} \quad k_2 = \begin{bmatrix} 0 & 0 & 0 \\ 0 & \dfrac{A_2 E_2}{l_2} & \dfrac{A_2 E_2}{l_2} \\ 0 & \dfrac{A_2 E_2}{l_2} & \dfrac{A_2 E_2}{l_2} \end{bmatrix} \begin{matrix} 1 \\ 2 \\ 3 \end{matrix}$$

whose column headings indicate the global dof associated with the matrix coefficients. As elements are connected to form a finite element model, elemental matrices are added to form a global stiffness matrix. By addition of the elemental matrices, the global stiffness matrix is given by:

$$K = \begin{bmatrix} \dfrac{A_1 E_1}{l_1} & -\dfrac{A_1 E_1}{l_1} & 0 \\ -\dfrac{A_1 E_1}{l_1} & \dfrac{A_1 E_1}{l_1} + \dfrac{A_2 E_2}{l_2} & -\dfrac{A_2 E_2}{l_2} \\ 0 & -\dfrac{A_2 E_2}{l_2} & \dfrac{A_2 E_2}{l_2} \end{bmatrix} \begin{matrix} 1 \\ 2 \\ 3 \end{matrix}$$

$$K = \sum_e k_e \tag{10.44}$$

Similarly the global load vector F is assembled from elemental force vectors and point loads as:

$$F = \sum_e f_e + \sum_e \Gamma_e + P_e \tag{10.45}$$

10.12 TREATMENT OF BOUNDARY CONDITIONS

Boundary conditions avoid the possibility of the structure moving as a rigid body. Boundary conditions are usually of the type:

$$u_1 = a_1, u_2 = a_2, ..., u_r = a_r \qquad (10.46)$$

The displacements along dof's 1, 2,...., r are specified to be equal to $a_1, a_2, ..., a_r$, respectively. In other words, there is r number of supports in the structure, with each support node given a specified displacement. For example, consider the bar in Figure 10.6. There is one boundary condition, $u_3 = 0$.

Two approaches are used for handling specified displacement boundary conditions. They are:

- Elimination approach
- Penalty approach

10.12.1 Elimination Approach

Consider the boundary conditions: $u_1 = a_1, u_2 = a_2, ..., u_r = a_r$

1. Store the 1st, 2nd, ..., and r^{th} rows of the global stiffness matrix K and force vector F. These rows will be used subsequently.
2. Delete the 1st row and column, 2nd row and column, ... and the rth row and column from the K matrix. The resulting stiffness matrix K is of dimension $(n - r, n - r)$. Similarly, the corresponding load vector F is of dimension $(n - r, 1)$. Modify each load component as:

$$F_i = F_i - (K_{i,1} a_1 + K_{i,2} a_2 +, ..., K_{i,r} a_r) \qquad (10.47)$$

   for each dof i that is not a support.
3. Solve $Kd = F$ for the global displacement vector d.
4. For each element, extract the element displacement vector u from the d vector, using element connectivity, and determine the element stresses.
5. Using the information stored in Step 1, evaluate the reaction forces at each support dof from

$$R_1 = K_{11}u_1 + K_{12}u_2 + ... + K_{1n}u_n - F_1$$

$$R_2 = K_{21}u_1 + K_{22}u_2 + ... K_{2n}u_n - F_2$$

....

....

$$R_r = K_{r1}u_1 + K_{r2}u_2 + ... K_{rn}u_n - F_r \qquad (10.48)$$

10.12.2 Penalty Approach

This approach is simple and easy to implement in a computer program. Consider the boundary conditions:

$$u_1 = a_1, u_2 = a_2, ..., u_r = a_r$$

1. Modify the structural stiffness matrix K by adding a large number C to each of the 1st, 2nd, ..., r^{th} diagonal elements of K. Also, modify the global load vector F by adding Ca_1, Ca_2, ..., Ca_r to $F_1, F_2, ..., F_r$ respectively.

2. Solve $Kd = F$ for the displacement vector d.
3. For each element, extract the element displacement vector u from the d vector, using element connectivity, and determine the element stresses.
4. Evaluate the reaction force at each support from:

$$R_i = -C(u_i - a_i) \qquad I = 1, 2,..., r \tag{10.49}$$

The magnitude of $C = \max |K_{ij}| \times 10^5$

$$I \le i \le n \qquad \text{and} \qquad 1 \le j \le n \tag{10.50}$$

Example 10.1   The structure consists of two bars. An axial load $P = 200$ kN is loaded as shown in Figure 10.7(a). Determine the following:

   (i)   Element stiffness matrices
  (ii)   Global stiffness matrix
 (iii)   Global load vector
  (iv)   Nodal displacements
   (v)   Stress in each bar
  (vi)   Reaction forces

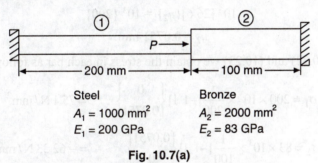

Fig. 10.7(a)

Solution
The finite element model is shown in Figure 10.7(b).

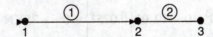

Fig. 10.7(b)   Representation of finite element model of Example 3.2.

The displacement vector is:

$$d = [u_1 \ u_2 \ u_3]^T$$

The element stiffness matrices are given below:
The global stiffness matrix which is assembled from k_1 and k_2 is given by:

$$k_1 = \frac{200 \times 10^3 \times 1000}{200} \begin{bmatrix} 1 & -1 \\ -1 & 1 \end{bmatrix} \begin{matrix} 1 \\ 2 \end{matrix}$$

$$k_2 = \frac{83 \times 10^3 \times 2000}{100} \begin{bmatrix} 1 & -1 \\ -1 & 1 \end{bmatrix} \begin{matrix} 2 \\ 3 \end{matrix}$$

$$K = k_1 + k_2 = 10^5 \begin{bmatrix} 10 & -10 & 0 \\ -10 & 26.6 & -16.6 \\ 0 & -16.6 & 16.6 \end{bmatrix} \begin{matrix} 1 \\ 2 \\ 3 \end{matrix}$$

The structure is loaded by point force only. The global point load vector is given by:

$$F = [0 \quad 2000 \quad 0]^T$$

The finite element equations are given by $Kd = F$

$$10^5 = \begin{bmatrix} 10 & -10 & 0 \\ -10 & 26.6 & -16.6 \\ 0 & -16.6 & 16.6 \end{bmatrix} \begin{Bmatrix} u_1 \\ u_2 \\ u_3 \end{Bmatrix} = 10^3 \begin{Bmatrix} 0 \\ 200 \\ 0 \end{Bmatrix}$$

The known boundary conditions are:

$$u_1 = u_3 = 0$$

When the known boundary conditions are applied and the elimination approach is used, the finite element equations take the following form:

$$10^5 [26.6]\{u_2\} = 10^3 \{200\}$$

Thus

$$u_2 = 0.0751 \text{ mm.}$$

Using Equations (10.22) and (10.23) we obtain the stress in each bar as follows:

$$\sigma_1 = 200 \times 10^3 \times \frac{1}{200}[-1 \quad 1] \begin{Bmatrix} 0 \\ 0.0751 \end{Bmatrix} \qquad = 75.1 \text{ N/mm}^2$$

$$\sigma_2 = 83 \times 10^3 \times \frac{1}{100}[-1 \quad 1] \begin{Bmatrix} 0.0751 \\ 0 \end{Bmatrix} \qquad = -62.33 \text{ N/mm}^2$$

The reaction forces R_1 at node 1 and R_3 at node 3 are obtained from Equation (10.49). Thus:

$$R_1 = 10^5 [10 \quad -10 \quad 0] \begin{Bmatrix} 0 \\ 0.0751 \\ 0 \end{Bmatrix} - 0 = -75 \text{ KN}$$

$$R_3 = 10^5 [0 \quad -16.6 \quad 16.6] \begin{Bmatrix} 0 \\ 0.0751 \\ 0 \end{Bmatrix} - 0 = -125 \text{ KN}$$

10.13   FINITE ELEMENT ANALYSIS SOFTWARE

ANSYS is one of the finite element analysis computer programming software. It has various modules. ANSYS-Mechanical product is designed for linear and non-linear, structural and thermal, static, buckling, sub-structure, acoustics and dynamic/transient analyses. It enables users to solve a wide variety of analyses in mechanical engineering applications.

ANSYS-Structural product supports the following types of structural analyses: structural elastic, modal, harmonic response, transient dynamic, spectrum, buckling, non-linear structural, and *p*-method structural static analysis. The product also enables the user to solve fracture mechanics problems and model composites, and to perform fatigue evaluations.

Example 10.2 Structural analysis of the steel support is shown in Figure 10.8. This is a typical bracket used to support towel rods. The bracket is fixed at the screw holes. The bracket is loaded at one point in the centre of the large hole. The load is 2000 N. The thickness of the bracket is 3.125 mm. Determine the deformed shape.

The modulus of elasticity, $E = 200$ GPa

Poisson's ratio = 0.3

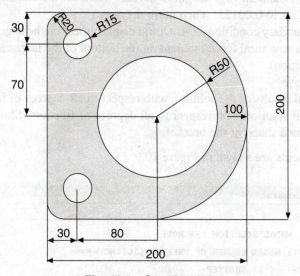

Fig. 10.8 Steel bracket.

Solution

The bracket is meshed with a solid eight-node plane stress element. By a plane stress element we are assuming that there are no stresses in the thickness direction of the bracket. The ANSYS software is used to solve this problem.

The procedure is as follows:

1. Turn on the keypoint numbering function in the ANSYS Utility Menu.
2. Create the keypoints to form the area that will become the bracket.
3. Then connect the keypoints with lines and define an area to form the bracket master area.
4. Fillet the lines to form the curve on the right side. Use a fillet radius of 0.1.
5. Create two areas defined by the fillet curve and the respective corner of the bracket master area.
6. Create the circular areas in the centre and left side of the bracket.
7. Subtract the areas defined by the fillet, the centre circle, and the two smaller circles to form the shape of the bracket intended to be analysed.

8. Add the two lines forming the bottom of the circle together to form one arc that encompasses the lower semi-circle of the centre circle.

9. Define the Material Properties of the Steel (Elastic Modulus and Poisson's Ratio are the important qualities).

10. Define the Element Properties as a Quad 8 node Structural Solid.

11. In the Element Type Window, set the option of setting the plane stresses to the thickness. (Hint: in the window it is the value for K3).

12. Set the Real Constant Set No. to 1 and the Real Constant for the plane stress with thickness upto 3.125 mm.

13. Mesh the bracket. (Do so by picking the lines around the outer boundary of the bracket and setting the element edge length to 0.0125. Next set the element edge length around the small circles to 0.00125. Then mesh the area.)

14. Apply the boundary conditions. (Structural displacement on the edges of the 'screw' equal to zero, and a structural force/moment on the bottom of the large circle equal to – 900 N in the Y direction).

15. Solve the above.

16. List the nodal results of the solution with respect to all degrees of freedom.

17. Plot the nodal solution with respect to all degrees of freedom. Show both the deformed and undeformed shape of the bracket.

The nodal displacements are shown in Figure 10.9.

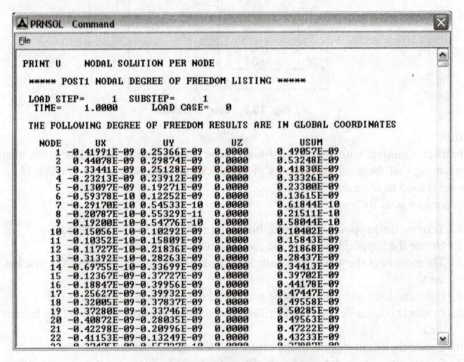

```
PRNSOL  Command                                                    X

File

PRINT U    NODAL SOLUTION PER NODE

***** POST1 NODAL DEGREE OF FREEDOM LISTING *****

LOAD STEP=    1   SUBSTEP=    1
  TIME=    1.0000      LOAD CASE=   0

THE FOLLOWING DEGREE OF FREEDOM RESULTS ARE IN GLOBAL COORDINATES

  NODE      UX          UY          UZ          USUM
    1  -0.41991E-09  0.25366E-09  0.0000   0.49057E-09
    2   0.44078E-09  0.29874E-09  0.0000   0.53248E-09
    3  -0.33441E-09  0.25128E-09  0.0000   0.41830E-09
    4  -0.23213E-09  0.23912E-09  0.0000   0.33326E-09
    5  -0.13097E-09  0.19271E-09  0.0000   0.23300E-09
    6  -0.59378E-10  0.12252E-09  0.0000   0.13615E-09
    7  -0.29170E-10  0.54533E-10  0.0000   0.61844E-10
    8  -0.20787E-10  0.55329E-11  0.0000   0.21511E-10
    9  -0.19200E-10 -0.54776E-10  0.0000   0.58044E-10
   10  -0.15056E-10 -0.10292E-09  0.0000   0.10402E-09
   11  -0.10352E-10 -0.15809E-09  0.0000   0.15843E-09
   12  -0.11727E-10 -0.21836E-09  0.0000   0.21868E-09
   13  -0.31392E-10 -0.28263E-09  0.0000   0.28437E-09
   14  -0.69755E-10 -0.33699E-09  0.0000   0.34413E-09
   15  -0.12367E-09 -0.37727E-09  0.0000   0.39702E-09
   16  -0.18847E-09 -0.39956E-09  0.0000   0.44178E-09
   17  -0.25627E-09 -0.39932E-09  0.0000   0.47447E-09
   18  -0.32005E-09 -0.37837E-09  0.0000   0.49558E-09
   19  -0.37288E-09 -0.33746E-09  0.0000   0.50285E-09
   20  -0.40872E-09 -0.28035E-09  0.0000   0.49563E-09
   21  -0.42298E-09 -0.20996E-09  0.0000   0.47222E-09
   22  -0.41153E-09 -0.13249E-09  0.0000   0.43233E-09
```

Fig. 10.9 Nodal displacements.

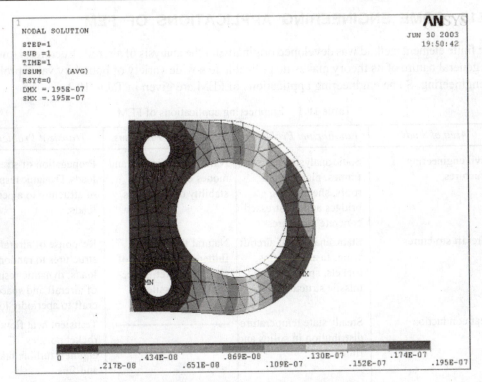

Fig. 10.10 Deformed and undeformed shape.

10.14 ADVANTAGES OF FEM

As previously indicated, FEM has been applied to numerous problems, both structural and non-structural. This method has a number of advantages that have made it very popular. They include the ability to:

1. Model complex shaped bodies quite easily.
2. Handle several load conditions without difficulty.
3. Handle different kinds of boundary conditions.
4. Model bodies composed of several different materials.
5. Discretise the bodies with a combination of different elements because the element equations can be evaluated individually.
6. Vary the size of the elements to make it possible to use small elements where necessary.
7. Include dynamic effects.
8. Handle non-linear behaviour of different plastic deformation processes and non-linear materials.
9. Handle steady and unsteady, compressible and incompressible, laminar and turbulent flow problems.
10. Handle time-dependent and time-independent heat transfer problems.

10.15 SOME ENGINEERING APPLICATIONS OF FEM

The finite element method was developed originally for the analysis of aircraft structures. However, the general nature of its theory makes it applicable to a wide variety of boundary value problems in engineering. Some engineering applications of FEM are given in Table 10.1.

Table 10.1 Engineering applications of FEM

Area of Study	Equilibrium Problems	Eigen Value Problems	Transient Problems
Civil engineering structures	Static analysis of trusses, frames, plates, shell roofs, shear walls, bridges and prestressed concrete structures	Natural frequencies and modes of structures stability of structures	Propagation of stress loads. Dynamic response of structure to a periodic loads.
Aircraft structures	Static analysis of aircraft wing, fuselages, fins, rockets, spacecraft and missile structures	Natural frequencies, flutter, and stability of aircraft, rocket, space-craft and missile structures	Response of aircraft structures to random loads, dynamic response of aircraft and space-craft to aperiodic loads
Heat conduction	Steady state temperature distribution in solids and fluids	---------------------------	Transient heat flow in rocket nozzles, IC engines, turbine blades, and fins.
Soil mechanics, foundation engineering, and rock mechanics	Analysis of excavations, retaining walls, under-ground openings, rock joints. Stress analysis in soils, dams, layered piles and machine foundation	Natural frequencies and modes dam-reservoir systems and soil structure interaction problems	Time-dependent soil structure interaction problems, transient seepage in soil and rocks, stress wave propagation in soils and rocks.
Hydrodynamics, hydraulic engineering and water resources	Analysis of potential flows, free surface flows, boundary layer flows, viscous flows, transonic aerodynamic problems, analysis of dams	Natural periods and modes of shallow basins, lakes and harbours, sloshing of liquids in rigid and flexible containers	Analyses of unsteady fluid flow and wave propagation problems. Transient seepage in aquifers and porous media.
Mechanical design	Stress concentration problems, stress analysis of pressure vessels, composite materials, linkages and gears	Natural frequencies and stability of linkages, gears and machine tools	Crack and fracture problems under dynamic loads
Nuclear engineering	Analysis of nuclear pressure vessels and	Natural frequencies and stability containment	Response of reactor containment structures

(Cont...)

Table 10.1   Engineering applications of FEM. (*Cont...*)

Area of Study	Equilibrium Problems	Eigen Value Problems	Transient Problems
	containment structures, steady state temperature distribution in reactor components	structures, neutrons flux distribution	to dynamic loads, unsteady temperature distribution in reactor components, thermal and visco-elastic analysis of reactor structures
Biomedical engineering	Stress analysis of eyeballs, bones and teeth, load-bearing capacity in plant and prosthetic systems, mechanics of heart values	---------------------------	Impact analysis of skull, dynamics of anatomical structures
Electrical machines and electromagnetics	Steady state analysis of synchronous and induction machines, eddy current and core losses in electric machines, magnetostics	---------------------------	Transient behaviour of electro-mechanical devices such as motors and actuators, magnetodynamics.

QUESTION BANK

A. Descriptive Questions

1. Explain the generalised procedure of FEM.
2. Explain the variational formulation of FEM.
3. Explain finite element discretisation with an example.
4. Define two-bar element.
5. Derive the shape functions of a two-node bar element.
6. Derive the strain-displacement matrix of a two-node bar element.
7. Derive the finite element equation of a two-node bar element using the potential energy method.
8. Derive the stiffness matrix of a two-node bar element.
9. Derive the body force vector of a two-node bar element.
10. Derive the traction load vector of a two-node bar element.
11. What is meant by degrees of freedom in FEM? Explain.
12. What are the boundary conditions in FEM? Explain with examples.
13. Derive the assembly of global stiffness matrix and load vector.
14. What are the different methods of treating boundary conditions? Explain them.
15. Explain the use of typical finite element software with an example.
16. What are the advantages of FEM?

17. What are the applications of FEM?

18. A stepped bar as shown in Figure 10.11 is axially loaded. $P = 250$ KN. Using the penalty approach for handling boundary conditions, determine the following:
    (a) The nodal displacements
    (b) Stress in each material
    (c) The reaction forces.

19. A two-stepped bar is subjected to loading condition as shown in Figure 10.12 is fixed at one end and the free end is at a distance of 3.0 mm. Using the elimination approach for handling boundary conditions, determine the following:
    (a) The nodal displacements
    (b) Stress in each material
    (c) The reaction forces.

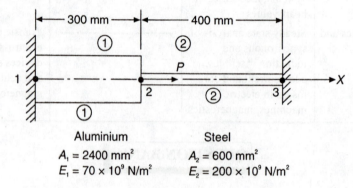

Aluminium
$A_1 = 2400$ mm^2
$E_1 = 70 \times 10^9$ N/m^2

Steel
$A_2 = 600$ mm^2
$E_2 = 200 \times 10^9$ N/m^2

Fig. 10.11

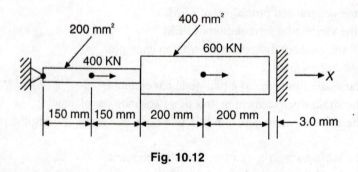

Fig. 10.12

B. Multiple Choice Questions

1. The finite element method _____ .
   (a) Is based on numerical methods
   (b) Gives approximate solution
   (c) Is the subdivision of the mathematical model into disjoint components of simple geometry called finite elements
   (d) All the above

2. The degrees of freedom of a two-node bar element are:
   (a) 1   (b) 2   (c) 3   (d) 4

3. The shape functions of a two-node bar element are:
   (a) Linear   (b) Quadratic   (c) Constant   (d) None of the above

4. The sum of the shape functions over the element is always equal to:
   (a) Zero   (b) Infinity   (c) Unity   (d) None of the above

5. Stiffness is _____ to the length of the element.
   (a) Inversely proportional   (b) Directly proportional
   (c) Exponential   (d) Independent

Chapter 11

Numerical Control

After reading this chapter, the reader will be able to understand the following concepts:

- ➲ Numerical control
- ➲ Numerical control elements: Program of instructions, machine control unit, NC machine tools, and NC cutting tools
- ➲ NC coordinate system
- ➲ NC tool positioning methods
- ➲ Numerical control modes: Point-to-point NC mode and straight-cut NC mode
- ➲ Contouring NC mode
- ➲ Numerical control applications
- ➲ Advantages of numerical control
- ➲ Limitations of NC

11.1 INTRODUCTION

Conventional machine tools have developed over a period of more than 160 years and enable a tool to cut metal by power-assisted movements. The metal-cutting machine tools are developed with two kinematic systems. These are:

1. Based on the displacement of the workpiece.
2. Based on the displacement of the cutting tool.

The linear displacements are associated with slideways. The rotary displacements take place about spindle axes. The geometric shapes are machined by controlling the relative movements between the workpiece and the tool.

With the advent of new materials and requirements for tolerances of precision, skilled human operators have reached the limit of their ability. There is also a huge demand for a variety of products in view of the varying tastes of the consumer and global competition. Hence, the need for flexible and just-in-time manufacturing is felt. These requirements have led to a form of automatic machine control known by the generic name *numerical control* (NC).

By 1957, the first successful NC machines were used in production. Initially, the part programs were prepared manually and input into the machine controller through the tape reader. In order to resolve the difficulty in generating part programs manually, a computer-based part programming language called APT (automatically programmed tools) was introduced.

The development of NC technology has taken place on the following two platforms:

1. Hardware development to improve control systems and machine tools.
2. Software development to generate computer-aided part programming.

11.2 NUMERICAL CONTROL

Numerical control may be defined as a method of programmable automation in which various functions of machine tools are controlled by numbers, letters and symbols. In NC, the numbers form a program of instructions. The instructions may be:

1. To start or stop the machine tool spindle
2. To control the spindle speed
3. To change the tool
4. To change the feed rate
5. To switch the coolant on/off
6. To position the tool at a desired position.

The principle of operation of an NC machine is shown in Figure 11.1. The program of instructions in terms of part geometry, cutting process parameters and type of cutting tool serves as the input to the machine control unit (MCU), which, in turn, commands the machine tool to make the product. The machine axes are connected to servomotors, which work under the control of the MCU. The servomotors control the movement of the cutting tool with respect to the workpiece.

The control of an axis in an NC machine is shown in Figure 11.2. It is a closed loop positioning system. The MCU generates a pulse signal until the signal returned from the feedback transducer agrees with the original number of pulses required to execute the movement. The comparator compares the count of feedback pulses with the original number, and the error signal is the output until the table reaches the desired position. The feedback transducers are linear/rotary encoders used to obtain the appropriate position or velocity feedback.

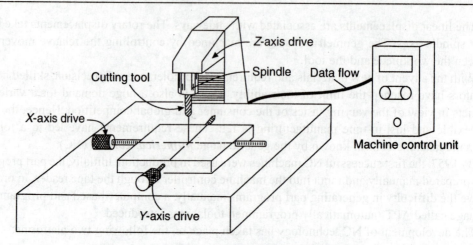

Fig. 11.1   Principle of operation of an NC machine.

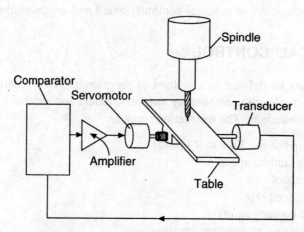

Fig. 11.2   Control of an axis in an NC machine tool.

11.3   NUMERICAL CONTROL ELEMENTS

The basic elements of an NC machine system are:

1. Program of instructions
2. Machine control unit (MCU)
3. NC machine tool
4. NC cutting tools

11.3.1   Program of Instructions

The program of instructions is the detailed step-by-step set of operations, which are to be implemented by the machine control unit. The program is coded in alphanumerical form on an input medium to the MCU. The input medium, in general, is a punched tape or a magnetic tape. Two methods are used to program for NC. They are:

- Manual part programming
- Computer-aided part programming

11.3.2 Machine Control Unit

The machine control unit (MCU) consists of the electronics and hardware that read and interpret the part program of instructions and convert them into mechanical actions of the machine tool. The MCU consists of two main units: data processing unit (DPU) and control loops unit (CLU). The function of the DPU is to read and decode the instructions available on the tape, and to provide the decoded data to the CLU. The function of the CLU is to control the drives attached to the axes and to receive the feedback signals from the machine tool. CLU also prompts a signal that the previous data segment is completed and that the DPU can read the next block of the part program.

The DPU consists of the following elements:

- Input device, e.g., tape reader
- Reading circuit
- Parity checking logic
- Decoding circuits
- Interpolator

The CLU consists of the following:

- Positional control unit with a feedback device such as a linear encoder
- Velocity control unit with a feedback device such as a rotary encoder
- Acceleration, retardation and backlash correction circuits
- Auxiliary function control unit for coolant on and off, etc.

11.3.3 NC Machine Tools

The quality of the product demands the use of expensive tooling when conventional machine tools are employed, and there is a considerable impact on the cost of each component in proportion to the tooling cost. The machining of small and medium quantities is a high-cost area of production. The prime objective of NC machines is to reduce the cost of production, to improve the quality of the product, and to decrease the manufacturing lead times by saving the tool set-up time and the material handling time.

The general characteristics for the implementation of NC machine tools in the manufacturing industry are:

1. The part geometry is so complex that cannot be manufactured by the conventional machine tools.
2. Parts are produced in small lots, but frequently.
3. Products demand high accuracy and precision.
4. Many operations must be performed on the part.
5. A lot of metal needs to be removed.
6. Hard materials need to be machined.
7. Parts are subjected to frequent engineering design changes.
8. Parts require 100 per cent inspection.

The machine tool performs the machining operation on the work. The machine tool consists of a work table, spindle, cutting tools, jigs and fixtures, motors with the necessary controls to drive them and other auxiliary equipment needed in the machining operation. The NC machine tool may be used for turning, drilling, milling, boring, grinding, welding, etc. Some practical NC machines are illustrated in Figures 11.3 to 11.6.

Fig. 11.3 NC milling machine (Courtesy: Bridgeport Machines, Textron Inc.).

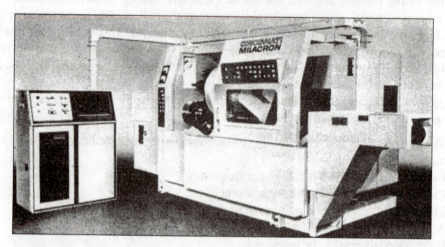

Fig. 11.4 Four-axis NC turning machine (Courtesy: Cincinnati Milacron).

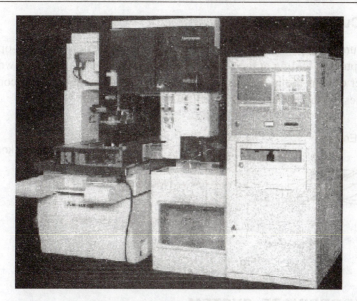

Fig. 11.5 Wire EDM (Courtesy: Mitsubishi Electric Corp., Tokyo).

Fig. 11.6 Coordinate measuring machine (Courtesy: UPMC-CARAT, Tokyo Seimitsu).

11.3.4   NC Cutting Tools

The ISO procedure is adopted for the designation of NC cutting tools. A power-operated draw bar may be used to pull the tooling at the retention knob. A typical end mill is shown in Figure 11.7. The programmer obtains the history of the tools such as tool number, cutter compensation, etc. from the tool files, which are updated periodically.

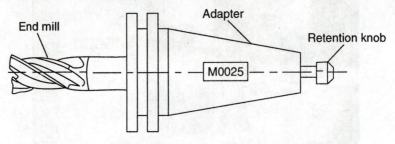

Fig. 11.7   NC end mill cutter.

11.4   NC COORDINATE SYSTEM

A Cartesian coordinate system consists of three axes positioned at 90 degrees from each other. The nomenclature of the tree main axes (x, y and z) is based on the 'right hand rule'. The x-, y- and z-axes are represented by the thumb, index and middle fingers of the right hand, respectively (Figure 11.8). The right-hand rule is used to define the positive direction of the coordinate axes as shown in Figure 11.9. The three rotational axes defined in NC are the a-, b- and c-axes.

For turning operations, two axes are normally required to control the movement of the tool relative to the rotating workpiece. The z-axis is the axis of rotation of the workpiece, and the x-axis is the radial location of the cutting tool. The arrangement is shown in Figure 11.10. For drilling operations, the NC machining tool axis system is shown in Figure 11.11. Two axes, x- and y-, are defined in the plane of the table and the z-axis is perpendicular to this plane and movement in the z direction is controlled by the vertical motion of the spindle.

An NC milling machine use an axis system similar to that of a drilling machine. In addition to three linear axes, the milling machine may use one or more rotational axes i.e. the a-, b- or c-axes.

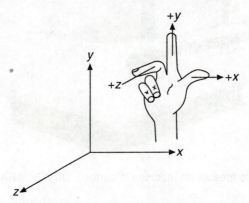

Fig. 11.8   Cartesian coordinate system.

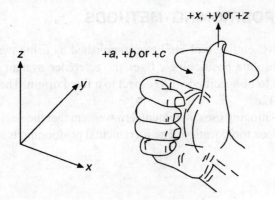

Fig. 11.9 Right hand rule.

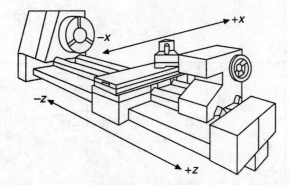

Fig. 11.10 NC machine tool axis system for turning operation.

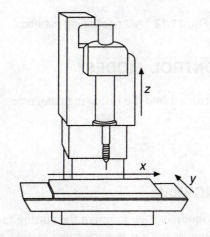

Fig. 11.11 NC machine tool axis system for drilling operation.

11.5   NC TOOL POSITIONING METHODS

The positioning of the NC cutting tool can be accomplished by using two distinct methods. The first method, called 'absolute positioning', fixes the reference system and enables the actual x-, y-, and z-coordinates to be specified with respect to a fixed origin. The absolute positioning is illustrated in Figure 11.12a.

The incremental positioning uses incremental movement that the next tool location is defined with respect to the previous tool location. The incremental positioning is shown in Figure 11.12b.

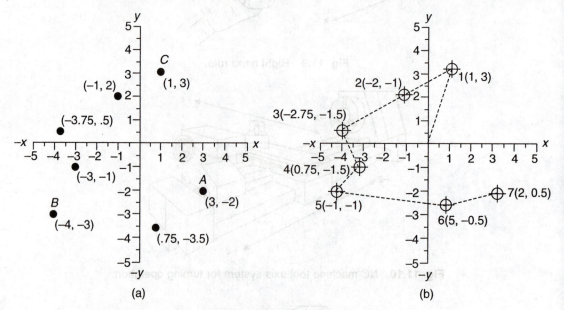

(a)   (b)

Fig. 11.12   NC positioning methods.

11.6   NUMERICAL CONTROL MODES

The NC modes are broadly classified into the following categories:

1. Point-to-point cut mode
2. Straight cut mode
3. Contouring cut mode

11.6.1   Point-to-Point NC Mode

The point-to-point (PTP) NC mode is used to move the cutting tool to a pre-defined position (Figure 11.13a). The machining operation is performed at that position. The speed or tool path is not important in the PTP NC mode. An NC drilling machine is the best example of a PTP NC.

11.6.2   Straight Cut NC Mode

In a straight cut NC mode, the cutting tool is moved parallel to one of the major axes (*x* or *y* or *z*) at a controlled rate as shown in Figure 11.13b. Pocket milling is an example of the straight-cut NC mode.

11.6.3   Contouring NC Mode

In this mode, the tool motion in more than one axis is controlled continuously and simultaneously (Figure 11.13c). This mode facilitates two-dimensional or three-dimensional profiles to be contour-machined, and is used in milling turning and grinding machines.

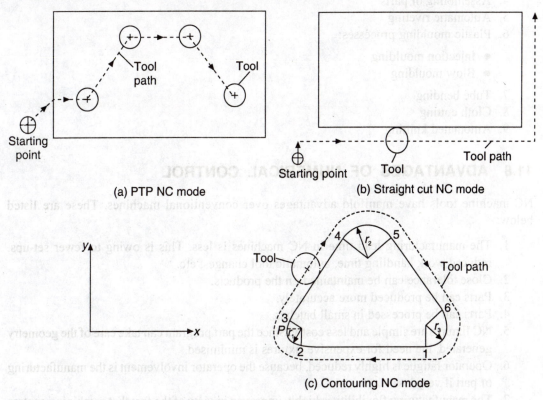

Fig. 11.13   Numerical control modes.

11.7   NUMERICAL CONTROL APPLICATIONS

Numerical control machines are widely used for:

1. Material removal processes:
   - Turning
   - Drilling

- Boring
- Milling
- Grinding

2. Welding and cutting processes:
   - Spot welding
   - Arc welding
   - Laser beam welding
   - Plasma arc cutting

3. Automatic drafting
4. Assembling of parts
5. Automatic riveting
6. Plastic moulding processes:
   - Injection moulding
   - Blow moulding

7. Tube bending
8. Cloth cutting
9. Automated knitting

11.8 ADVANTAGES OF NUMERICAL CONTROL

NC machine tools have manifold advantages over conventional machines. These are listed below:

1. The manufacturing lead time in NC machines is less. This is owing to fewer set-ups, reduced work handling time, automatic tool changes, etc.
2. Close tolerance can be maintained on the products.
3. Parts can be produced more accurately.
4. Parts can be processed in small batches.
5. NC fixtures are simple and less costly. Since the part program can take care of the geometry generated, the need for expensive fixtures is minimised.
6. Operator fatigue is highly reduced, because the operator involvement is the manufacturing of part if very less.
7. The manufacturing flexibility is highly improved in view of the fact that machining centres can perform a variety of machining operations and alterations of the production schedule, etc.
8. Floor space requirements are reduced because one NC machine centre can accomplish the production of several conventional machines.
9. The quality of the products is improved because of automation and the absence of inter-related human factors.
10. Cutting tools can be used at optimum speeds and feeds.
11. The inventory is reduced due to shorter lead times and fewer set-ups.

11.9 LIMITATIONS OF NC

Along with the advantages, NC machines also have certain limitations, which must be considered for their implementation. The limitations are as follows:

1. The initial cost is high.
2. The maintenance cost is high on account of its complex and sophisticated technology.
3. NC machines require part programmers. There is a problem of finding, hiring and training the programmers.

QUESTION BANK

A. Descriptive Questions

1. What is numerical control?
2. What are the basic elements of NC? Explain them.
3. What are general characteristics to be considered for the implementation of NC machine tools in the manufacturing industry?
4. Explain the importance of a machine control unit in NC.
5. Explain the functions of DPU.
6. Discuss NC positioning systems.
7. Discuss NC coordinate systems.
8. What are the different types of NC modes? Explain them schematically.
9. What are the applications where NC is the most suitable?
10. Give the advantages and limitations of NC.
11. Explain the designation of axes in an NC system.

B. Multiple Choice Questions

1. Control loop unit of MCU is a:
   - (a) Software unit
   - (b) Hardware unit
   - (c) Software and hardware unit
   - (d) Control unit
2. The first NC machine was developed in the year:
   - (a) 1950
   - (b) 1952
   - (c) 1954
   - (d) 1956
3. The repeatability of NC machine depends on:
   - (a) Mechanical errors
   - (b) Electrical errors
   - (c) Software errors
   - (d) Control loop errors
4. The axes of turning machine are:
   - (a) z and x-axes
   - (b) x and y-axes
   - (c) z and y-axes
   - (d) x, y and z-axes
5. Rotation about the Z-axis is called:
   - (a) a-axis
   - (b) b-axis
   - (c) c-axis
   - (d) None of the above

Chapter **12**

Computer Numerical Control

OBJECTIVES

After reading this chapter, the reader will be able to understand the following concepts:

➲ Development in MCU technology

➲ Computer numerical control

➲ Features of computer numerical control

➲ Mechanical design criterion of CNC machine tools: Structure of CNC machine tools, sources of lost motion, and friction of CNC machine slides

➲ Types of computer numerical control: Hybrid CNC configuration and straight CNC configuration

➲ Features of CNC machining centres

➲ Features of CNC turning centres

➲ Advantages of CNC

12.1 INTRODUCTION

The physical size and cost of a digital computer has been significantly reduced at the same time that its computational capabilities have been substantially increased. The result of these advances is that machine control units based on the digital computer have replaced the large hard-wired machine control units of conventional numerical control.

Computer numerical control (CNC) is an NC system using a dedicated microcomputer as the machine control unit (MCU).

12.2 DEVELOPMENT IN MCU TECHNOLOGY

The hardware technology in NC controls has changed dramatically over the years. At least seven generations of technology of controller hardware can be identified. These are:

GENERATION—0: Mechanical computers (1642–1945)
GENERATION—1: Vacuum tubes (1945–1952)
GENERATION—2: Electromechanical relays (1952–1955)
GENERATION—3: Discrete semiconductors (1955–1960)
GENERATION—4: Integrated circuits (1960–1965)
GENERATION—5: Digital computers (1965–1968)
GENERATION—6: Direct numerical control (1968-1970)
GENERATION—7: Computer numerical control (1970–1975)
GENERATION—8: Microprocessors and microcomputers (1975–1980)
GENERATION—9: Personal computers and VLSI (1980–2001)

GENERATION—0

The first person to build a working calculating machine was the French scientist Blaise Pascal (1623–1662), in whose honour the programming language Pascal is named. This device, built in 1642, when Pascal was only 19, was designed to help his father, a tax collector for the French government. It was entirely mechanical, using gears, and powered by a hand-operated crank. Pascal's machine could only do addition and subtraction.

But thirty years later the great German mathematician Baron Gottfried Wilhelm von Leibniz (1646–1716) built another mechanical machine that could multiply and divide as well. Nothing much happened for 150 years until a professor of mathematics at the University of Cambridge, Charles Babbage (1792–1871), inventor of the speedometer, designed and built his *difference engine*. This mechanical device, which like Pascal's could only add and subtract, was designed to compute tables of numbers useful for naval navigation.

GENERATION—1

The initial NC prototype machine built in the MIT Servomechanism Laboratories used vacuum tubes for the controller hardware. These components were so large that the control unit consumed more space than the machine tool. But that was the state of the technology in controls at that time.

GENERATION—2

By the time the first NC machines were sold in the commercial market several years later, electromechanical relays were substituted for the vacuum tubes. The problem with these relay-based controls was their large size and poor reliability. Even the relatively simple point-point logic required large cabinets filled with relays. The relays were susceptible to wear and tear, and controls requiring a large number of these components were inherently unreliable.

GENERATION—3

The use of transistors helped reduce the number of electromechanical relays required. Accordingly, this increased the reliability because the use of transistors avoided the wear problem. It also contributed to a downsizing of the controller cabinet and allowed systems designers to build more complex circuitry into the NC controller. Features such as circular interpolation became practical with these controls. But the electronics were sensitive to heat, and fans or air conditioners were required in the cabinets to operate under factory conditions.

GENERATION—4

Electronic hardware using integrated circuits brought about significant improvements in size and reliability. The number of separate components could be reduced by 90 per cent. There were corresponding savings in cost to the user. The trend towards LSI circuits has allowed more control features to be packaged into smaller control cabinets. Among these features are circular and hyperbolic interpolation routines, inch-to-metric conversions, and vector federate computations.

GENERATION—5

The next development in NC control marked the introduction of digital computers. All the previous controls were made of hard-wired components. The functions that were performed by these control systems could not be easily changed due to the fixed nature of the hard-wired design. Digital computers, on the other hand, are based on a different approach. In this new approach, the control functions were programmed into the computer memory and could be changed by altering the program.

GENERATION—6

DNC was the first of the computer control systems. In the evolution of computer technology, the computers of that era were quite large and expensive, and the only feasible approach seemed to be to use one large computer to control a number of machine tools on a time-shared basis. The advantage of DNC was that it established a direct control link between the computer and the machine tool, thereby eliminating the necessary for using punched tape input.

GENERATION—7

The CNC systems were introduced when the recognised trend toward small and less expensive computers became practical. They soft-wired the controller approach to good advantage. One standard computer control unit could be adapted to various types of machine tools by programming the control functions into the computer memory for that particular machine.

GENERATION—8

Advances in computer technology have continued to provide smaller and smaller digital control devices, which offer greater speed and capacity at lower cost. This has allowed machine tool builders to design the CNC control panel as an integral part of the machine tool rather than as a separate stand-alone cabinet. This reduces floor space requirements for the machine.

GENERATION—9

VLSI had made it possible to put first tens of thousands, then hundreds of thousands, and finally millions of transistors on a single chip. This development has led to the advent of smaller and faster computers. Fewer components in the controller means that it is easier and less expensive for the machine tool builder to fabricate. Fewer circuit boards, which are readily replaced, reduce the burden on the user for maintenance and repair.

12.3   COMPUTER NUMERICAL CONTROL

The basic elements of CNC machine are:

1. Microcomputer
2. Tape reader

3. NC program storage
4. Computer hardware interface and servosystem
5. Machine tool

As illustrated in Figure 12.1, the controller has a tape reader for the initial entry of a part program. In this regard, the outward appearance of a CNC system is similar to that of a conventional NC machine. However, the manner in which the program is used in CNC is different. With a conventional NC system, the punched tape is cycled through the tape reader for each work part in the batch.

The MCU reads in a block of instructions on the tape, executing that block before proceeding to the next block. In CNC, the entire program is entered once and stored in computer memory. The machining cycle for each part is controlled by the program contained in memory rather than from the tape itself. Controller algorithms contained in the computer convert the part program instructions into actions of the machine tool.

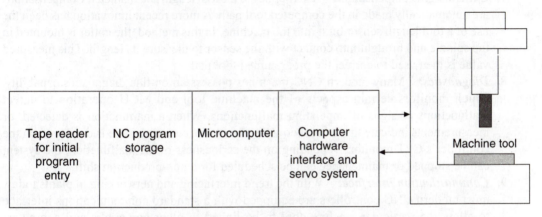

Fig. 12.1   Basic configuration of a CNC machine.

12.4 FEATURES OF COMPUTER NUMERICAL CONTROL

The salient features of CNC system are as follows:

1. *Storage of more than one program:* With improvements in computer technology, many of the newer CNC controllers have a large capacity to store more than a single program.

2. *Use of diskettes:* There is a growing use of floppy disks for part programs in manufacturing. The capacity of an 8-inch diskette is the approximate equivalent of 8000 feet of punched tape.

3. *Program editing at the machine tool site:* In order to deal with the mistakes in part programming, CNC systems permit the program to be edited while it is computer memory. Hence, the process of testing and correcting the program can be done entirely at the machine site rather returning to the programming office in the shop to make the corrections. In addition to the part program corrections, editing can also be done to optimise the cutting conditions of the machining cycle.

4. *Fixed cycles and programming sub-routines:* The increased memory capacity and ability to program the control computer in CNC provides the opportunity to store frequently used machining cycles in memory that can be called by the part program. Instead of writing the instructions for the particular cycle into every program, a code is written into the program to indicate that the cycle should be executed.

5. *Interpolation:* Linear and circular interpolation are often hard-wired into the control unit. Helical, parabolic, and cubic interpolations are usually executed in a stored program algorithm.

6. *Programming features for set-up:* Setting up the machine tool for a certain job involves installing and aligning the fixture on the machine tool table. This must be accomplished so that the machine axes are aligned with the work part. The alignment can be facilitated by using certain features that are made possible by software options in a CNC system. Position set is one of these features.

7. *Cutter length compensation:* This applies to the tool length and diameter. Compensations are automatically made in the computed tool path. A more recent innovation has been the use of a tool length sensor built into the machine. In this method, the cutter is mounted in the spindle and brought into contact with the sensor to measure its length. This measured value is then used to correct the programmed tool path.

8. *Diagnostics:* Many modern CNC machines possess an on-line diagnostics capability, which monitors certain aspects of the machine tool and MCU operation to detect malfunctions or signs of impending malfunctions. When a malfunction is detected, or measurements indicate that a breakdown is about to occur, a message is displayed on the controller's CRT monitor. Depending on the seriousness of the malfunction, the system can be stopped or maintenance can be scheduled for a non-production shift.

9. *Communication interface:* With the trend interfacing and networking in plants today, most modern CNC controllers are equipped with a standard communications interface to allow the particular machine tool to be linked to other computers and computer-driven devices.

12.5 MECHANICAL DESIGN CRITERION OF CNC MACHINE TOOLS

The benefits of a CNC machine are directly related to its accuracy, speed and degree of automation. These demands impose design problems. The design considerations should handle elastic deformations, vibrations, backlash, etc. The CNC machine should be stronger and stiffer and should perform more accurately than a conventional NC machine.

12.5.1 Structure of CNC Machine Tools

A general criterion for the design of structures for CNC machine tools is to provide adequate static stiffness with the best stiffness-to-weight ratio for a wide range of loading conditions. The large static stiffness allows a small deflection of CNC machine tools. The dynamic response of the CNC machine is directly related to the stiffness-to-weight ratio.

Vibrations resulting from the tool chatter can influence the surface finish of the products. The structures of CNC machine tools are cast iron-based for damming vibrations. The structures are provided with ribs to achieve the best stiffness-to-weight ratio.

The design parameters that are to be considered along with operating conditions are given in Table 12.1.

Table 12.1 CNC machine tool design criteria

Machine response	Component characteristics	Operating and cost characteristics
Type of command signal	Undamped natural frequency	Reliability
Input configuration	Power requirement	Maintainability
Maximum feed rate	Friction characteristics	Cost of operation
Static accuracy	Inertia	Capital investment
Dynamic accuracy	Stiffness	Installation requirements
Magnitude of load	Amount of backlash	
Range of travel	Speed range	
Weight of moving members	Bandwidth	
Power source		

12.5.2   Sources of Lost Motion

The lost motion in CNC machine tool is on account of backlash in gearing, wind-up of drive shafts and deflection of machine tool members. The backlash is associated with gearing, looseness in bearings, play between leadscrew and nut, and the effect of cocking of the machine slide. Rigid mounting of bearings and screws can considerably eliminate the backlash.

Wind-up is the angular deflection or twisting of drive shafts or screws due to applied torque. The wind-up is a function of stiffness of the member and the load. The deflection of lead screw and spindle is owing to the longitudinal compression load. Increasing the diameter of the leadscrew and very little overhang of the spindle beyond the end bearings can minimise the deflection (Figure 12.2).

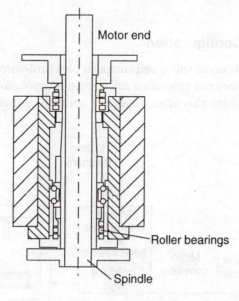

Fig. 12.2   Spindle.

12.5.3   Friction of CNC Machine Slides

The initial large coefficient of friction between the table and slides requires a considerable frictional force to initiate movement. Since the dynamic friction coefficient is smaller than the static friction coefficient, the drive force required to sustain movement decreases thereby causing the table to advance beyond the desired position. Anti-friction bearings are used to reduce the coefficient of friction. Hydrostatic and roller bearings can be used. The lead screw can be replaced by the ball screw (Figure 12.3).

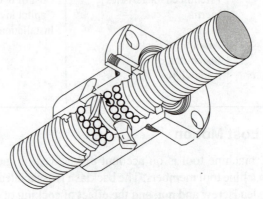

Fig. 12.3   Ball screw.

12.6   TYPES OF COMPUTER NUMERICAL CONTROL

CNC machines are classified into two types on the basis of the controller design: Hybrid CNC and Straight CNC.

12.6.1   Hybrid CNC Configuration

In this, the controller consists of the soft-wired computer plus hard-wired logic circuits. The hard-wired components perform feed rate generation and circular interpolation. The computer performs the remaining control functions plus other duties not normally associated with a conventional hard-wired controller.

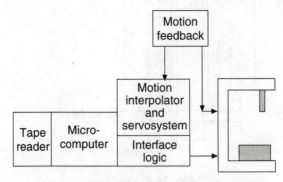

Fig. 12.4   Hybrid CNC configuration.

12.6.2 Straight CNC Configuration

This uses a computer to perform all the NC functions. The only hard-wired elements are those required to interface the computer with the machine tool and the operator's console. Interpolation, tool position, and all other functions are performed by the computer software. Accordingly, the computer required in a straight CNC system must be more powerful than that needed for a hybrid system.

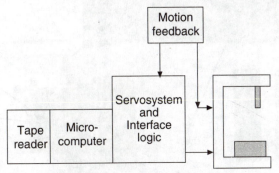

Fig. 12.5   Straight CNC configuration.

12.7 FEATURES OF CNC MACHINING CENTRES

The machining centre, developed in the late 1950s, is a machine tool capable of performing several different machining operations on a work part in one set-up under program control. The machining centre is capable of milling, drilling, reaming, tapping, boring, facing, and similar operations.

Machining centres are classified as vertical or horizontal, on the basis of the orientation of the machine tool spindle.

Horizontal machining centre: It has its spindle on a horizontal axis. It is used for cube-shaped parts where tool access can best be achieved on the sides of the cube (Figure 12.6).

Vertical machining centre: It has its spindle on a vertical axis relative to the table. It is used for flat work that requires tool access from the top (Figure 12.7).

The main features of a machining centre are:

1. *Automatic tool-changing capability:*   A variety of machining operations means that a variety of tools is required. The tools are contained in a tool magazine or drum. When a tool needs to be changed, the tool drum rotates to the proper position, and an automatic tool changing mechanism, operating under program control, exchanges the tool in the spindle and tool in the drum.

2. *Automatic work part positioning:*   Most machining centres have the capability to rotate the job relative to the spindle, thereby permitting the cutting tool to access four surfaces of the part.

3. *Pallet shuttle:*   The machining centre has two or more separate pallets that can be presented to the cutting tool. While machining is being performed with one pallet in position in front of the tool, the other pallet is in a safe location away from the spindle. In

this way, the operator can be unloading the finished part from the prior cycle and fixturing the raw work part for the next cycle while machining is being performed on the current workpiece.

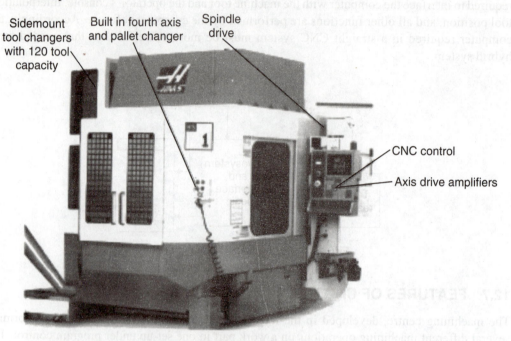

Fig. 12.6 Horizontal machining centre (Courtesy: Haas Automation, Inc., California).

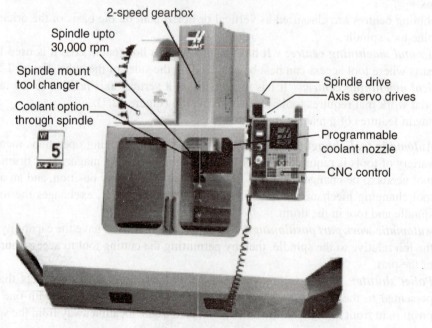

Fig. 12.7 Horizontal machining centre (Courtesy: Haas Automation, Inc., California).

12.8 FEATURES OF CNC TURNING CENTRES

CNC lathes are used to produce the cylindrical shape products. A majority of the components machined in industry are of cylindrical shape. Hence, CNC lathes are called turning centres (Figure 12.8). The main features of CNC turning centres are:

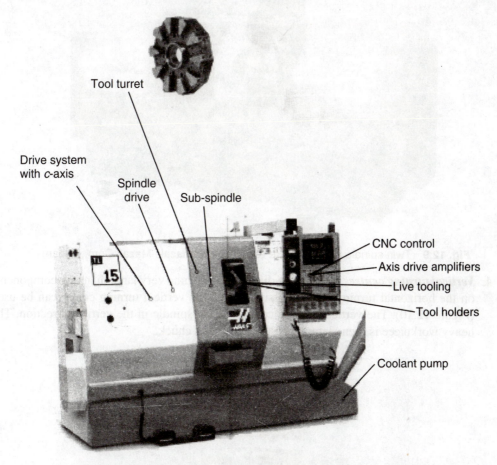

Fig. 12.8 CNC turning centre. (Courtesy: Hass Automotion, Inc, California)

1. *Tool turret:* Most of the turning centres are provided with a tool turret, which may have a capacity of 8 to 12 tools of various types.
2. *Multiple axis turning centres:* A larger number of axes is provided in addition to the x- and z-axes of turning. The turning centre area available with z-, x- and c-axes of operation. The main spindle holding the workpiece can be indexed to get the variety of profiles. This is called the c-axis.
3. *Multiple spindle turning centres:* For a large volume production of small and medium-sized components, it may be necessary to incorporate multiple spindles. A twin spindle turning centre is shown in Figure 12.9. The two spindles and turrets are separately

controlled. Two set-ups are possible for a component. If the machining is completed on the left spindle, the component can be transferred to the right spindle.

Fig. 12.9 Twin spindle turning centre (Courtesy: Yamazaki Mazak Corp., Japan).

4. *Vertical turning centres:* It is very difficult to machine very large diameter components on the horizontal turning centre. In such cases, the vertical turning centre can be used (Figure 12.10). The vertical turning centre has the spindle in the vertical direction. The heavy workpiece is then clamped on the horizontal chuck.

Fig. 12.10 CNC vertical turning centre.

12.9 ADVANTAGES OF CNC

CNC possesses a number of advantages over the conventional NC. These are as follows:

1. The part program tape and tape reader are used only once to enter the program into memory
2. CNC can edit tool path, spindle speeds, feeds, etc., at the site of the machine tool.
3. CNC is more compatible with the use of computer-integrated CAD and CAM facilities to make the total manufacturing system.
4. It is possible for the user to generate specialised part programs. These programs generally take the form of sub-routines or functions stored in CNC memory, which can be called by the part program to execute frequently used cutting sequences.
5. New options like new interpolation can be added to the system easily and at a relatively low cost.
6. CNC can convert programs prepared in the inch units into the metric units.

QUESTION BANK

A. Descriptive Questions

1. What are the developments of MCU technology?
2. What are the basic elements of CNC? Explain.
3. What are the salient features of the CNC system? Explain.
4. What design criteria should be used while designing CNC machine tools?
5. What are the requirements of structure in the case of CNC machine tools?
6. What are the sources of lost motion?
7. What is the influence of friction of CNC machine slides?
8. What are the different types of CNC systems? Explain them schematically.
9. What are the salient features of CNC machining centres?
10. What are the salient features of CNC turning centres?
11. What are the advantages of CNC systems?

B. Multiple Choice Questions

1. Computer will perform the data processing functions in _____.
   (a) NC (b) CNC (c) DNC (d) ACS
2. The first commercial CNC machine was developed in the year:
   (a) 1970 (b) 1972 (c) 1976 (d) 1980
3. CNC drilling machine is considered to be a:
   (a) Point-to-point controlled machine (b) Straight line controlled machine
   (c) Continuous path controlled machine (d) Servo-controlled machine
4. The lost motion in CNC machine tool is on account of:
   (a) Backlash in gearing (b) Wind-up of drive shafts
   (c) Deflection of machine tool members (d) All the above

Chapter **13**

Manual Part Programming

OBJECTIVES

After reading this chapter, the reader will be able to understand the following concepts:

- ⊃ Part programming fundamentals: Process planning, machine tool selection, drive axes selection, cutting tool setup planning, part programming, testing the part-program and documentation of part-program.

- ⊃ Methods of manual part programming: Fixed sequential tape format, block address tape format, tab sequential tape format and word address tape format

- ⊃ ISO standards for coding

- ⊃ Basic CNC input data: Sequence numbers, coordinate function, feed function, speed function, tool function and preparatory functions

13.1 INTRODUCTION

Part programming consists of a sequence of instructions to be performed on the NC/CNC machine. There are two methods of part programming. These are:

1. Manual part programming
2. Computer-aided part programming

In this chapter, manual part programming is described. In the subsequent chapters, turning centre programming and computer-aided part programming are described.

13.2 PART PROGRAMMING FUNDAMENTALS

In order to prepare part programming, the programmer decides the order of the machining operations required to produce a component. The choice of the machine tools and cutting tools depends upon the operations. Each line of the program is numbered in sequence, details of the operations are stated, and the x, y and z coordinates are given. The total steps involved in the development of a part program (Figure 13.1) are as follows:

1. Prepare the process plan.
2. Identify the machine tool.
3. Select the drive axes.
4. Choose tools.
5. Determine machining parameters such as feed rate, depth of cut, spindle speed, etc.
6. Make job and tool set-up plans.
7. Decide the tool path.
8. Write the part program.
9. Test the program.
10. Document the program.

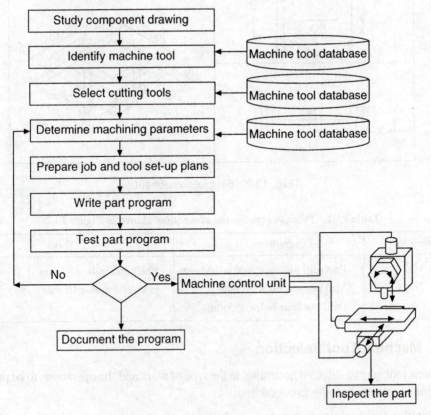

Fig. 13.1 Steps involved in the preparation of a part program.

13.2.1 Process Planning

The use of NC/CNC machine tools necessitates a detailed process planning of steps involved in the machining of a component. The programmer makes a detailed study of the part drawing and prepares the process plan. The process plan consists of:

1. Sequence of operations
2. Machine tools used
3. Jigs and fixtures required
4. Tool type and size
5. Feed rates and spindle speeds
6. Coolant requirement

The process plan of the component shown in Figure 13.2 is given in Table 13.1.

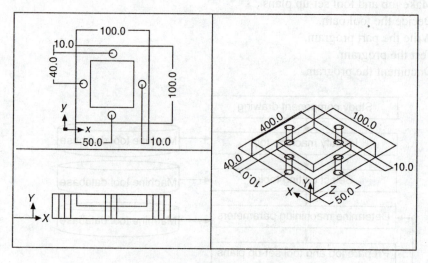

Fig. 13.2   Simple component.

Table 13.1   Process plan for the component shown in Figure 13.2

Operation No.	Description	Tools
10	End mill top face, 100×100 mm	Shell end mill, $\phi 50$ mm
20	Mill pocket, 60×60 mm	HSS end mill, $\phi 10$ mm
30	Drill the four holes, $\phi\,5$ mm	

13.2.2 Machine Tool Selection

The machine tool may be selected according to the type of work and the operations to be performed. The machine tools are broadly grouped into:

1. **Positional** (i.e., point-to-point), e.g., drilling machine, boring machines, punching press, spot welder, and pipe bending machine.

2. **Paraxial** (i.e., straight line), e.g., lathes, milling machines and machining centres.
3. **Continuous path,** e.g., lathes, milling machines, routers, grinding machines, machining centres, draughting machine, flame cutting equipment, and inspection machine.

The positional machine tool is one in which the slides are controlled in order to reach a particular fixed coordinate position where machining is to take place. No machining occurs until the slide movement ceases. The movement path is not critical, but care must be taken during programming to ensure that the tool does not collide with the workpiece or a projection such as clamp when it is moving from one position to the next.

Slide displacements from one position to the next position can be stated by reference to either:

- A fixed datum (Figure 13.3a), or
- The present position of the slide (Figure 13.3b).

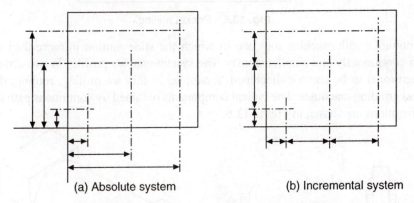

(a) Absolute system   (b) Incremental system

Fig. 13.3 Specification of slide displacements.

Systems in which all positional dimensions are stated with reference to a common datum point are termed as 'absolute systems'. Systems in which each position dimension as stated with reference to previous position are termed as 'incremental systems'.

In paraxial machine tools, the cutting process occurs while the machine slides are moving and the movement path must follow a controlled route. The machine control unit must ensure that transient behaviour in slide displacements does not change in a slide hunting or oscillating about its desired position. If surfaces are to be machined at an angle to the axes, the machine control unit (MCU) must be capable of displacing the slides simultaneously and at suitable rates of feed in order to produce a cutter path at the desired angle as shown in Figure 13.4.

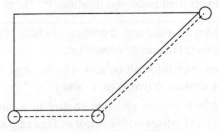

Fig. 13.4 Machining at an angle using paraxial machine tool.

The milling of a recess or pocket is a common example of straight line cutting. In straight line NC milling machines the operation can be programmed by defining the path step-by-step from *A* to *B*, etc. (Figure 13.5).

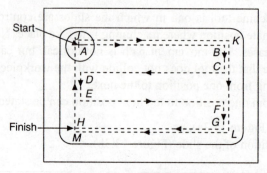

Fig. 13.5   Pocket milling.

A continuous path machine tool one in which the slide motion in more than one axis is controlled continuously and simultaneously. The system enables profiles in two-dimensional or three-dimensional to be contour-machined. Examples of this are milling, routing, die-sinking, turning and grinding machines. The typical components obtained by continuous path turning and milling operations are shown in Figure 13.6.

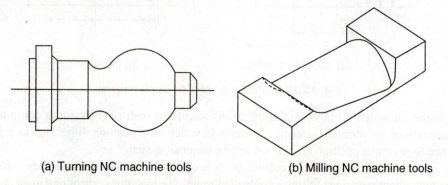

(a) Turning NC machine tools   (b) Milling NC machine tools

Fig. 13.6   Examples of components produced by continuous path.

13.2.3   Drive Axes Selection

All the CNC machine tools rely on the axes system for defining the axes motion. The number of axes in the machine tool are specified under the heading 'P', 'C' or 'L'.

2P	Positional control in two axes; e.g., a drilling machine controlled in *x*- and *y*-axes but with the spindle axis (*z*) manually controlled.
2L	Line control of two axes for position and velocity; e.g., a milling machine equipped with line milling facilities in two axes, *x*- and *y*-.
2P, L	Positional control in two axes and line control in a third axis; a drilling machine controlled in the *x*- and *y*-axes with control of feed rate and depth in the *z*-axis.

(Cont...)

3L	Line control of three axes for position and velocity, e.g., a milling machine equipped with linear feed rate facilities in three axes, x-, y- and z.
2C	Continuous path control in two axes, e.g., a lathe or a milling machine.
2C, L	Continuous path control in two axes and line control for velocity and position in the third axis, e.g., a milling machine.
3C	Continuous path control in three axes x-, y- and z.
4C, L	Continuous path control in four axes and line control along one axis, e.g., a milling machine having continuous path control in x- and y-axes and in two rotary displacements of the table and linear control of the spindle in the z-axis.
5C	Continuous path control in five axes, e.g., x- and y- and z-axes and rotations of the table about x- and z-axes.
6C	Continuous path control in six axes, e.g., x- and y- and z-axes, rotations of the table about x- and z-axes and rotary displacement of the spindle about some axis other than the z-axis.

The axes' system of all the CNC machine tools would generally have a fixed datum called '*machine zero datum point*'. When the workpiece is clamped on the machine table, the workpiece datum and the machine datum will not normally coincide. In order to relate the slide displacements called for in the part program with the position of the workpiece on the machine table, a *floating zero* facility is provided. By this means, an operator can arbitrarily designate as zero any point on each axis within the range of the slide displacement.

13.2.4 Cutting Tool Selection

The selection of cutting tool is a very vital function because many cuttings are feasible for a given operation. It is more appropriate to choose the right tool for the job based on the economy of manufacturing. The MCU must be able to compensate for the variations in cutter size, if accurate components are to be produced.

Compensation for the variation of the cutter diameter is manually registered on the machine console dials by the operator. Provision is made at the programming stage for the MCU to modify the cutter path by the amount registered on the console. This is called *tool diameter compensation*.

At times, it is required to provide tool length compensation. In this case, the compensation is easier to apply because the machined surface is situated at the end of the cutter. Consequently, when a cutter is either too long or too short, the cutter path can be modified by dialling the error and its direction (+ or −) on the console.

13.2.5 Machining Parameters Planning

For a given cutting tool and the operation selected, the appropriate process parameters have to be selected to ensure that each cutting tool achieves the maximum metal removal rate in roughing operations, and the maximum machined surface coverage in finishing operations. This can be done by increasing:

1. Cutting speed
2. Feed rate
3. Depth of cut

It is also necessary to minimise the floor-to-floor time by limiting the time needed for the non-cutting activities by reducing:

1. Machine down time during the initial set-up period
2. Machine idle time during the setting of each individual component
3. Machine idle time during the period required for changing from one cutting g tool to the next.

The machine tool must be designed with sufficient power for driving the spindle and feed mechanisms, and the spindle speeds are suitable for the use of cutting tools employing cemented carbide, or other hard tool materials.

13.2.6 Tool Path Planning

In order to machine profiles with a sufficient degree of accuracy, a very large number of coordinates need to be determined and fed into the MCU. In milling a straight line parallel to an axis, it is only necessary to specify the coordinates of the beginning and end points of the line and the feed rate. The cutter will take up a position at the first point, the slide will be displaced along its slideway and the cutter will machine a straight line parallel to the slide axis until the endpoint of the line is reached.

In a continuous tool path, the coordinates of a series of consecutive points on the contour are supplied MCU. The slides move from point-to-point in such a way that the cutter generates a smooth curve. The tool path between the points may be in the form of a series of straight lines, curves from a circular arc, or curves from a parabolic arc. The capacity to perform these movements in straight lines or curves, carefully computed to fit the overall pattern of the curve is known as *interpolation*.

During machining of the profile, the cutter must follow a path, which takes into account the diameter of the cutter, and the movement of the slides must be coordinated in order to produce the correct profile between change points. A typical contoured tool path is shown in Figure 13.7.

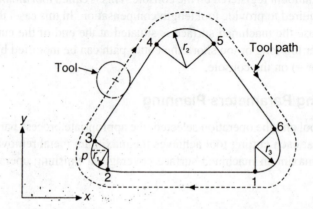

Fig. 13.7 Tool path for two-dimensional contour machining.

13.2.7 Job and Tool Set-up Planning

The planning of job and tool setting is very important. If the component and its locating fixture are small in relation to the size of the machine table, two or more components can be set up side-by-side on the surface of the table as shown in Figure 13.8. If the machine table can accommodate only one component, the machine tools are designed with twin tables. One table is used for the component being machined, while the other table is clear of the spindle and the machining area, and on this table the operator sets the unmachined component (Figure 13.9).

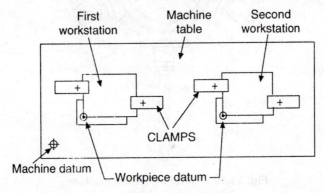

Fig. 13.8 Two-station machining on a CNC machine: Loading can take place at one station while machining takes place at the second station.

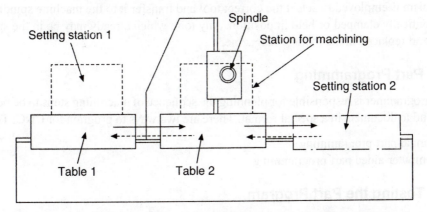

Fig. 13.9 Arrangement of twin-table machine. The workpiece is machined at one station while second workpiece is being set at the setting station.

The number of tools needed for completing the operations depends upon the complexity of the job. The use of tools with indexing tool tips or throw-away tips also speeds up tool setting. For simple drilling operations, six or eight tools may be adequate. The indexing turret used on drilling machines is shown in Figure 13.10. The indexing movement is powered by a hydraulic motor and employs a Geneva mechanism.

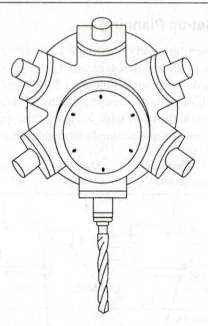

Fig. 13.10 Turret for drilling machine.

Automatic tool changers with magazines of the drum, chain and egg-box type work on the principle that the magazine provides storage for a wide selection of tools (24 to 120). Some form of mechanism is employed to select the correct tool and transfer it to the machine spindle, where it is automatically clamped or held in position. Any tool, which already may be in the spindle, is removed and replaced in the storage magazine.

13.2.8 Part Programming

The part programmer is responsible for planning the sequence of machining steps to be performed by CNC and to document in a special format. There are two ways to program for CNC: These are:

- Manual part programming
- Computer-aided part programming

13.2.9 Testing the Part Program

Once the part program is prepared, it should be tested before it is loaded on the MCU for the production of component. A trial run can be carried out with or without the tool or workpiece to enable visualisation of movements taking place and of any collision possible between the tool, the workpiece and the clamping device. During the trial runs, the program is run block by block. This is vital for eliminating the possibility of collisions during machining.

With the workpiece and tool in position, dry runs are made during these trial runs, and if any mistakes are noticed the part program is corrected. The *acid test* of the program involves trying it on the machine tool to make the part. A foam or plastic may be used for this try-out. After this, one component is made and checked. Based on this run, speeds and feeds are modified on the basis of the quality of the component.

Graphical simulation is also possible on the computer. The simulation shows the workpiece and the tool, the motion of the cutting tool and progressive material removal. The simulation can be carried out at a fast speed without much loss of time.

13.2.10 Documentation of Part Program

Documentation is an essential aspect of CNC manufacturing. The documentation involves the following:

1. Part drawing
2. Process planning sheet
3. Tools cards
4. Setting card
5. Programming sheet

13.3 METHODS OF MANUAL PART PROGRAMMING

Numerical control information is passed to the MCU in the block format. Each block of NC data may be arranged differently, depending on the control system requirements of the system configuration.

The four basic tape formats used for NC input are:

1. Fixed sequential format
2. Tab sequential format
3. Block address format
4. Word address format

Regardless of the format, each NC block must be capable of specifying dimension and non-dimension data. By convention, data within an NC block is specified in the following order:

$n\ g\ xyzabc\ f\ s\ t\ m\ eob$

where

n = sequence number
g = preparatory function
$xyzabc$ = dimension data
f = feed function
s = speed function
t = tool function
m = miscellaneous function
eob = eond-of-block

13.3.1 Fixed Sequential Tape Format

It is necessary for each NC block to be of the same length and to contain the same number of characters. This restriction enables the block to be divided into sub-strings corresponding to each of the data types specified above. Since the block length is invariant, all values must appear. For example, even if feed and speed are the same for ten blocks of NC data, f and s must be coded in each block.

13.3.2 Block Address Tape Format

This eliminates the need for specifying redundant information in subsequent NC blocks through the specification of a *change code*. The change code follows the blocks and the block, sequence number, and indicates which values are to be changed relative to the preceding blocks.

13.3.3 Tab Sequential Tape Format

This uses a special symbol called the *tab* to separate data values within a block. Two or more tabs immediately following one another indicate that the data, which would normally occupy the null locations, is redundant and has been omitted.

001	tab	1.0	tab	4.0	tab	5.00	tab	5.92	tab	13	eob
002	tab		tab	1.0	eob						
003	tab	2.5	tab	3.0	tab		tab		tab	06	eob

13.3.4 Word Address Tape Format

It uses alphanumeric data specification. Each data value is preceded by a letter, which indicates the type of data that follows. Hence, redundant information is merely omitted along with the appropriate letter.

| N001 | G90 | G00 | X50.0 | Y45.0 | Z40.0 |
| N002 | Go1 | X90.0 | Y90.0 | Z70.0 | F350 |

13.4 ISO STANDARDS FOR CODING

All the 26 letters of the English alphabet are standardised (Table 13.2).

Table 13.2 Standardisation of all letters of the English alphabet

Letter	Address
A	Angular dimension about X-axis
B	Angular dimension about Y-axis
C	Angular dimension about Z-axis
D	Angular dimension about special axis
E	Angular dimension about special axis
F	Feed function
G	Preparatory function
H	Unassigned
I	Distance to arc centre or thread lead parallel to X
J	Distance to arc centre or thread lead parallel to Y
K	Distance to arc centre or thread lead parallel to Z
L	Do not use
M	Miscellaneous function

(Cont...)

Table 13.2   Standardisation of all letters of English alphabet (*Cont...*)

Letter	Address
N	Sequence number
O	Reference rewind stop
P	Third rapid traverse dimension
Q	Second rapid traverse dimension
R	First rapid traverse dimension
S	Spindle speed function
T	Tool function
U	Secondary motion dimension parallel to X
V	Secondary motion dimension parallel to Y
W	Secondary motion dimension parallel to Z
X	Primary X motion dimension
Y	Primary Y motion dimension
Z	Primary Z motion dimension

The part program for a given component consists of a beginning code of per cent which represents the start of the tape. Each block always starts with a block number used as identification and is programmed with an N word address. As per ISO 2539, it has a minimum of three digits, e.g., N005. a typical ISO format for block is given as follows:

N001   G01   X±25   Y±50   Z±10   U..V..W..J..K..F10   S600   T4   M2   *

This shows a typical sequence in which the word addresses should occur in the block. However, it is not mandatory to present all addresses and in the same sequence. Since each function is indicated in its address character, the order of writing words in a block is not important except that the letter N should come in the beginning and the end-of-block (*) should be placed where the information for that block is completed.

13.5   BASIC CNC INPUT DATA

13.5.1   Sequence Numbers (N code)

It is used to identify each block within the CNC program and provides a means by which CNC commands may be rapidly located. Some control units require that sequence numbers be input in ascending order, whereas other systems allow any three-digit numbers to appear after the N symbol.

N025 Y25 Z0 *

13.5.2   Coordinate Function

The coordinates of the tool tip are programmed for generating a given component geometry. The coordinates are specified by using the word addresses X, Y, Z, U, V, W, I, J, K, etc. For example

X = 100.125 Y-25.005 Z-5.565

13.5.3 Feed Function

The feed rate for slide displacement or spindle feed rate is expressed in mm/min and is a three-digit number prefixed by the letter 'F'. For example, F125 indicates that the feed rate is 125 mm/min.

     Once the feed rate is programmed in a block, it remains in force in all the subsequent blocks till it is replaced by another 'F' value.

13.5.4 Speed Function

The spindle speed is expressed in rev/min, and is a three-digit number prefixed by the letter 'S'. For example, S1000 indicates that the spindle speed is 1000 rpm.

13.5.5 Tool Function

The tool function is used in conjunction with the miscellaneous function for tool changes (M06), and as a means of addressing the new tool. For example, T05 M06. The execution of the above statement ensures that the new tool numbered 05 is set-up.

13.5.6 Preparatory Functions

The preparatory functions are represented by a two-digit number prefixed by the letter 'G'. The purpose of the preparatory function is to command the machine toll to perform the function represented by the selected code number. For example, G90 specifies absolute input dimensions. ISO has standardised a number of these preparatory functions as shown in Table 13.3.

Motion group

G00   rapid positioning
G01   linear interpolation
G02   circular interpolation CW
G03   circular interpolation CCW

Dwell

G04   dwell

Table 13.3   G codes

Code	Function
G00	Point-to-point positioning, rapid traverse
G01	Linear interpolation
G02	Circular interpolation, clockwise
G03	Circular interpolation, counter-clockwise
G04	Dwell
G05	Hold/delay
G06	Parabolic interpolation

(Cont...)

Table 13.3   G codes (*Cont...*)

Code	Function
G07	Unassigned
G08	Acceleration of feed rate
G09	Deceleration of feed rate
G10	Linear interpolation for long dimensions (10 inches–100 inches)
G11	Linear interpolation for short dimensions (up to 10 inches)
G12	Unassigned
G13-G16	Axis designation
G17	XY plane designation
G18	ZX plane designation
G19	YZ plane designation
G20	Circular interpolation CW for long dimensions
G21	Circular interpolation CW for short dimensions
G22-G29	Unassigned
G30	Circular interpolation CCW for long dimensions
G31	Circular interpolation CCW for short dimensions
G32	Unassigned
G33	Thread cutting, constant lead
G34	Thread cutting, linearly increasing lead
G35	Thread cutting, linearly decreasing lead
G36-G39	Unassigned
G40	Cutter compensation, cancels to zero
G41	Cutter radius compensation, offset left
G42	Cutter radius compensation, offset right
G43	Cutter radius compensation, positive
G44	Cutter radius compensation, negative
G45-G52	Unassigned
G53	Deletion of zero offset
G54-G59	Datum point/zero shift
G60	Target value, positioning tolerance 1
G61	Target value, positioning tolerance 2 or loop cycle
G62	Rapid traverse positioning
G63	Tapping cycle
G64	Change feed rate or speed
G65-G69	Unassigned
G70	Dimensioning in inch units
G71	Dimensioning in metric units
G72-G79	Unassigned

(Cont...)

Table 13.3   G codes (*Cont...*)

Code	Function
G80	Canned cycle cancelled
G81-G89	Canned drilling and boring cycle
G90	Specifies absolute input dimensions
G91	Specifies incremental input dimensions
G92	Programmed reference point shift
G93	Unassigned
G94	Feed rate/min
G95	Feed rate/rev
G96	Spindle feed rate for constant surface feed
G97	Spindle speed in revolution per minute
G98-G99	Unassigned

Active Plane Selection Group

G17   XY plane
G18   XZ plane
G19   YZ plane

Cutter Compensation Group

G40   cutter compensation, cancel
G41   cutter radius compensation, left
G42   cutter radius compensation, right

Units Group

G70   inch units
G71   metric units

Hole Making Canned Cycle Group

G80   canned cycle cancel
G81-G89   canned cycles definition and ON

Coordinate System Group

G90   absolute coordinate system
G91   incremental coordinate system

Pre-set

G92   absolute pre-set

13.5.7   Miscellaneous Functions

Miscellaneous functions involve actions that are necessary for machining (i.e., spindle on/off, coolant on/off). These are used to designate a particular mode of operation for a CNC machine tool. The number codes for miscellaneous functions are listed in Table 13.4.

Table 13.4 M codes

Code	Function
M00	Program stop
M01	Optional stop
M02	End of program
M03	Spindle CW
M04	Spindle CCW
M05	Spindle off
M06	Tool change
M07	Coolant No.2 ON
M08	Coolant No.1 ON
M09	Coolant OFF
M10	Clamp
M11	Unclamp
M12	Unassigned
M13	Spindle CW and coolant ON
M14	Spindle CCW and coolant ON
M15	Motion +
M16	Motion –
M17–M29	Unassigned
M30	End of tape + tape rewind
M31	Interlock bypass
M32–M35	Constant cutting speed
M36–M39	Unassigned
M40–M45	Gear changes if used; otherwise unassigned
M46–M49	Reserved for control use only
M50–M99	Unassigned

13.5.8 Program Number

The symbol used for the program number is 'O' or ':', followed by its number, for example, O123 or :123. The program number does not interfere with the execution of the CNC program.

13.6 INTERPOLATION

The two most common types of interpolation found in practice are linear and circular. Parabolic and cubic interpolations are also available for use in the more advanced systems.

Linear interpolation may be defined as a method that develops intermediate coordinate points on a straight line between the given start and finish points. The input contains discrete information in the form of absolute coordinates or incremental movements. The G code for linear interpolation is G01. When the motion is desired along a straight line at a given feed rate, this function is used. If a cut has to be made from A to B at a feed rate of 200 mm/min as shown in Figure 13.11, then the block is written as

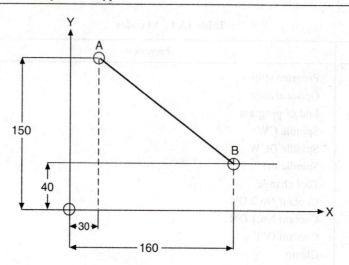

Fig. 13.11 Linear interpolation.

Absolute programming A to B

    N010 G90 G01 X160.0 Y40.0 F200

Incremental programming A to B

    N020 G91 G01 X130.0 Y-110.0 F200

The circular interpolation is used to traverse along an arc. The G code for circular interpolation is G02 (for clockwise movement) or G03 (counter-clockwise movement).

When the motion is from *A* to *B* in an *XY* plane as shown in Figure 13.12, the program block is written by

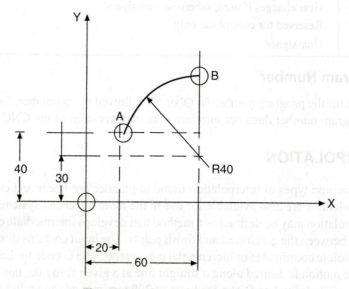

Fig. 13.12 Circular interpolation.

N030 G02 X60.0 Y70.0 I40.0 J-10.0 F200

If the motion is from B to A, then the program block is written by

N040 G03 X20.0 Y40.0 J-40.0 F200

For the circular interpolation, (X, Y) are the coordinates of the destination and (I, J) the coordinates of the centre of the arc from the starting point of the arc.

Example 13.1   The part drawing of a component is shown in Figure 13.13. Five holes of 12.5 mm diameter are to be drilled at five places. The speed and feed rate are 592 rpm and 100 mm/min, respectively. The machine has a floating zero feature and absolute positioning. The thickness of plate is 10 mm. Write the manual part program.

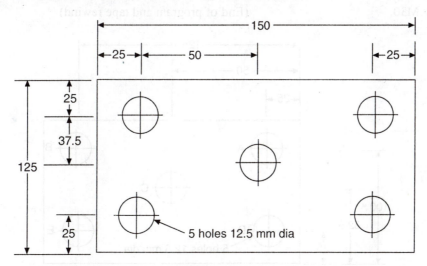

Fig. 13.13

Solution
The coordinate system is defined for a part as shown in Figure 13.14.
   Assume that the spindle is initially at (–25, –25, 0).

%
:001

N001 G92 X0 Y0 Z2.0	(Absolute presetting)
N002 G90	(Absolute programming)
N003 G00 X25.0 Y25.0 T01 S592 M03	(Tool brought rapidly at D above XY plane)
N004 G01 Z-14.0 F100	(Tool goes down to full depth at D)
N005 G00 Z2.0	(Tool comes rapidly above XY plane)
N006 G00 X25.0 Y100.0	(Tool brought rapidly at A above XY plane)
N007 G01 Z-14.0 F100	(Tool goes down to full depth at A)
N008 G00 Z2.0	(Tool comes rapidly above XY plane)

N009 G00 X50.0 Y 62.5   (Tool brought rapidly at C above XY plane)

N010 G01 Z-14.0 F100   (Tool goes down to full depth at C)

N011 G00 Z2.0   (Tool comes rapidly above XY plane)

N012 G00 X125.0 Y100.0   (Tool brought rapidly at B above XY plane)

N013 G01 Z-14.0 F100   (Tool goes down to full depth at B)

N014 G00 Z2.0   (Tool comes rapidly above XY plane)

N015 G00 X125.0 Y25.0   (Tool brought rapidly at E above XY plane)

N016 G01 Z-14.0 F100   (Tool goes down to full depth at E)

N017 G00 Z2.0 M05   (Tool comes rapidly above XY plane and spindle OFF)

N018 X-25.0 Y-25.0   (Tool goes rapidly to clearance point)

N019 M30   (End of program and tape rewind)

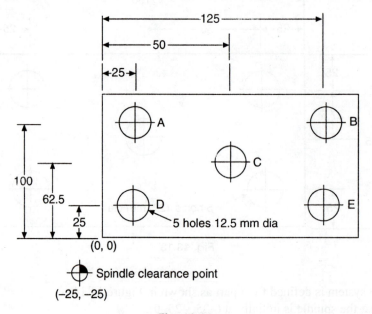

Fig. 13.14

13.7 CANNED CYCLES

A canned cycle consists of a series of motions repeated a number of times like drilling, boring and tapping, etc. For example, a drilling cycle (Figure 13.15) consists of the following motions of the drill bit:

1. Rapid approach to workpiece
2. Drill at feed rate
3. Rapid return to initial position

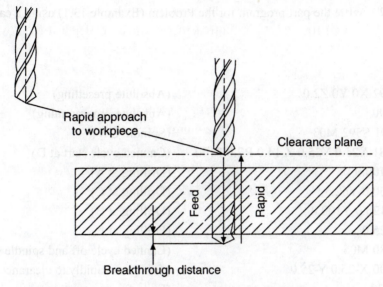

Fig. 13.15 Canned cycle of drilling operation.

The format of canned cycle is given by

N   G81   X   Y   Z   R

where

N	=	sequence number
G81	=	canned cycle
X, Y	=	coordinates of the point where the drilling is to be performed
Z	=	depth of hole to be drilled
R	=	position of the clearance plane

Code	Application
G81	Drilling
G82	Counter sinking, counter boring
G83	Deep hole drilling
G84	Tapping
G85	Reaming
G86	Boring
G87	Multiple
G88	Boring
G89	Boring

Example 13.2 Write the part program for the Problem (Example 13.1) using a canned cycle.

Solution

```
%
:001
```

N001	G92 X0 Y0 Z2.0	(Absolute presetting)
N002	G90	(Absolute programming)
N003	T01 S592 M03	(Spindle CW)
N004	G81 X25.0 Y25.0 Z-14.0 R2.0 F100	(Canned cycle start at D)
N005	Y100.0	(Drilling at A)
N006	X50.0 Y62.5	(Drilling at C)
N007	X125.0 Y100.0	(Drilling at B)
N008	Y25.0	(Drilling at E)
N009	G80 M05	(Canned cycle off and spindle OFF)
N010	G00 X-25.0 Y-25.0	(Tool goes rapidly to clearance point)
N011	M30	(End of program and tape rewind)

13.8 TOOL LENGTH COMPENSATION

The CNC program is written for the movement of the slides whereas it is the path of the tool tip. In cases where there is more than one tool, the programmer has to take care of the individual tool lengths for the purpose of programming the Z-depth in each case.

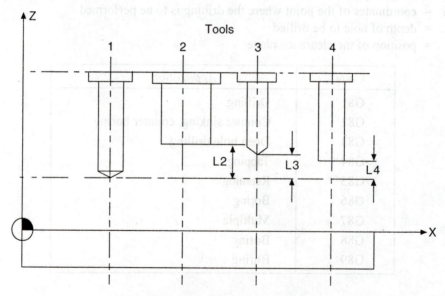

Fig. 13.16 Tool length compensation.

In CNC practice, all tools are measured in the assembled state by using a tool pre-setter, which can be mechanical, optical or electronic. Whenever a tool is changed, it is necessary to measure the new tool length offset and input it into the memory of the CNC machine. Tool length compensation functions in a machine centre are:

G45 = extension of axis travel by the amount stored in the offset data memory

G46 = reduction by the amount stored in the offset data memory
For example

   G00 G45 z-75.0 H04

H04 is the offset stored in number '04' of the offset data memory.

13.9 CUTTER RADIUS COMPENSATION

In profile turning or pocketing, the cutter radius affects accuracy of the workpiece. Therefore, it becomes necessary to compute the tool path by offsetting the contour by an amount equal to the cutter radius. Figure 13.17 shows the part contour and the tool path for a typical component. The preparatory functions G40, G41 and G42 are used for cutter radius compensation.

G40 = Compensation OFF.
G41 = It is used when the cutter is on the left of the tool path when looking in the direction of the tool movement.
G42 = It is used when the cutter is on the right of the tool path when looking in the direction of the tool movement.

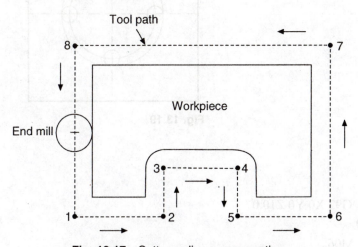

Fig. 13.17 Cutter radius compensation.

Example 13.3 It is required to mill the cavity of the component shown in Figure 13.18. The cutter diameter is 20 mm. Write a manual program considering the cutter size into account. The spindle speed is 600 rpm. The feed rate is 100 mm/min.

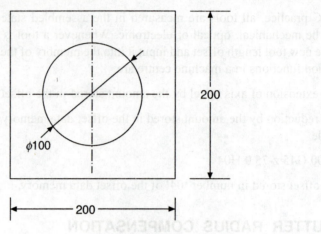

Fig. 13.18

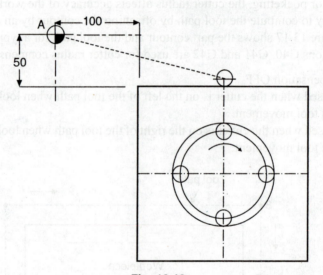

Fig. 13.19

Solution

```
%
:003
N010  G71 G92 X0 Y0 Z10.0
N020  G90
N030  T01 M06
N040  X2000.0 Y-50.0 Z2.0 S600 M03
N050  Y-120.0
N060  G01 Z-10.0 F100
N070  G42 Y-100.0
```

N080 G02 I0 J-50.0
N090 G00 Z10.0
N100 G40 X0 Y0 M05
N110 T0 M06
N120 M02

13.10 TYPES OF MEDIA

There are five types of NC media. These are:

1. Punched cards
2. Punched tape
3. Magnetic tape
4. Magnetic disks
5. Computer-transmitted NC data

13.10.1 Punched Cards

The punched cards are almost obsolete as an input media for NC. The standard 80-column 'IBM card' is 3.250 in wide, 7.375 in long and 0.007 in thick (Figure 13.20). Hole size and spacing are precisely specified. Each card contains 12 rows of hole locations with 80 horizontal positions across the card.

The most common code used for punched cards is BCD (Binary Coded Decimal). The code for each character is represented by defining two sections on the card. The upper three rows are called zone rows, while the bottom nine rows represent the digits 1, 2, 3, 4, 5, 6, 7, 8, 9. The letter symbols comprise one zone and digit entry. The hole pattern for each character is unique.

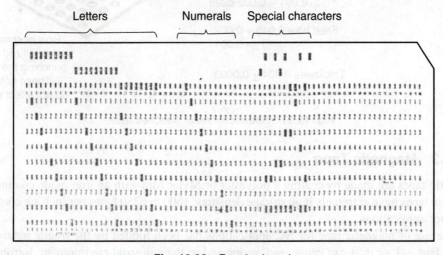

Fig. 13.20 Punched card.

13.10.2   Punched Tape

The specifications for punched tape are standardised by the EIA (Electronics Industries Association), and are illustrated in Figure 13.21. Tapes are made of paper, paper–plastic sandwiches, aluminium–plastic laminates, or other materials.

The flexowriter reads and prints tapes at high speed. Data is entered by using a standard typewriter keyboard and is converted into printed output and perforated tape.

Punched tape can also be generated directly from the output of computer-based NC part programming systems. The tape is prepared directly by the computer by using a device called a 'tape punch'.

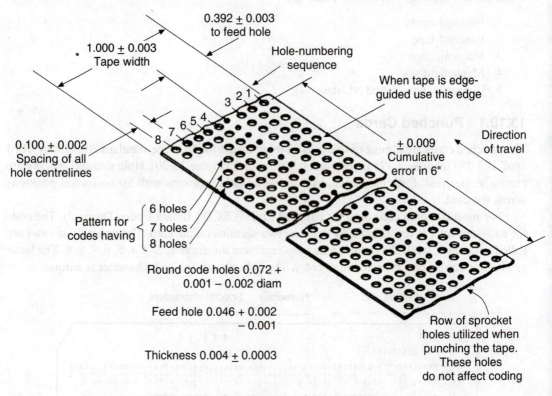

Fig. 13.21   Specifications of punched tape.

13.10.3   Magnetic Tape

Magnetic tapes are made by coating a polyester or Mylar film with an iron oxide coating. Such magnetic tapes have extremely high storage densities: 1600 to 6250 bytes per inch are common in computer applications.

The use of magnetic tape for NC applications has been limited by the fragile nature of the media. Dirt, oil, or dust can cause read errors, and in the industrial environment, ferrous metal fillings and/or magnetised tools cause damage to the data on the tape. The sealed tape cassettes have been used with various NC systems.

13.10.4   Magnetic Disks

A more reliable magnetic storage device, the floppy, has thus been introduced. Nowadays, two sizes are commonly used, 5.25 inch and 3.5 inch. Each of these has a low-density and a high-density version. The 3.5 inch diskettes come in a rigid jacket for protection, so they are not really 'floppy'. Since the 3.5 inch disks store more data and are better protected, they will eventually replace the 5.25 inch ones.

In recent years, optical disks have become available. They have much higher recording densities than conventional magnetic disks. These disks are based on the same technology used in Compact Disc audio players and are called **CD ROMs (Compact Disc Read Only Memory).** This technology has some important consequences. Since the CD ROMs are stamped rather than recorded like conventional floppy disks, fully automated machinery can mass produce them at a very low price.

13.10.5   Computer-transmitted NC Data

In a CNC system, the machine control unit is replaced by a programmable minicomputer. A number of NC programs can be stored in the memory of the computer. After the NC instructions are stored, the computer performs all the basic NC functions.

QUESTION BANK

A. Descriptive Questions

1. What are the steps involved in the development of a part program? Explain.
2. What are the different methods of manual part programming? Explain.
3. What is a preparatory function?
4. What is a miscellaneous function?
5. What are the various methods of interpolation in part programming?
6. What is a canned cycle? Give examples.
7. What is tool length compensation?
8. What is cutter radius compensation?
9. What are the various methods of NC media?
10. Write a manual part programming to cut the profile as shown in Figure 13.22 with the cutter is 6.5 mm dia, cutting speed of 900 rpm and feed rate of 7.5 mm/min.
11. Write a manual part program to cut the profile as shown in Figure 13.23 with a cutting speed of 2000 rpm and 200 m/min feed rate using a cutter of 10 mm dia.
12. Write a manual part program to cut the profile as shown in Figure 13.24 with a cutting speed of 1500 rpm and 100 m/min feed rate using a cuttre of 5 mm dia.

13.10.4   Magnetic Disks

A more reliable magnetic storage device, the floppy disk, was introduced. Nowadays, two sizes are commonly used, 5.2-inch and 3.5-inch, each of which has a low-density and a high-density version. The 3.5-inch diskettes come in a rigid jacket for protection, so they are not really "floppy". Since the 3.5-inch disks store more data and are better protected, they will eventually replace the 5.25-inch ones.

In recent years, optical disks have become available. They have much higher recording densities than conventional magnetic disks. These disks are based on the same technology used in Compact Disc audio players, and are called **CD ROMs** (Compact Disc Read Only Memory). This technology has some shortcomings, however. Since most CD ROMs are stamped rather than recorded like conventional computer disks, only equipped manufacturers can mass produce them at a very low price.

13.10.5   Computer-transmitted NC Data

In a CNC system, the main frame computer is replaced by a separate, small-scale minicomputer. A number of NC programs can be stored in the memory of the computer. Also the NC instructions are stored, the computer performs all of the NC functions.

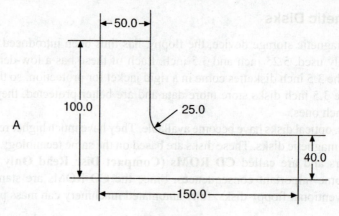

Fig. 13.22

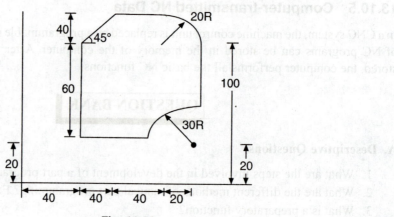

Fig. 13.23

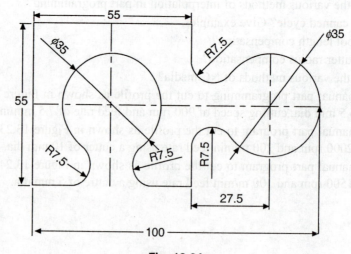

Fig. 13.24

B. Multiple Choice Questions

1. Linear interpolation is carried out by:
   (a) G00 (b) G01 (c) G02 (d) G03
2. M03 code is used for:
   (a) Spindle in anti-clockwise direction (b) Spindle speed on clockwise direction
   (c) Stopping of the spindle (d) None of the above
3. In word address format "I" stands for:
   (a) Tool changing function
   (b) Simultaneous motion of x and y-axes
   (c) Arc centre coordinate parallel to x-axis
   (d) Arc centre coordinate parallel to x-axis
4. The canned cycle G85 stands for:
   (a) Boring operation (b) Drilling operation
   (c) Tapping operation (d) Thread cutting operation

Chapter **14**

Turning Centre Programming

OBJECTIVES

After reading this chapter, the reader will be able to understand the following concepts:

- ⮑ Coordinate system for CNC lathe
- ⮑ Zero points and reference points: Machine zero points (M), Reference point (R), Workpiece zero point (W),
- ⮑ Programming functions: Preparatory functions (G codes)
- ⮑ Miscellaneous functions (M codes): Speed function, feed rate function, tool function, sequence number, program number, and billet size
- ⮑ Canned cycles: Parallel turning, taper turning and thread cutting

14.1   INTRODUCTION

This chapter presents the part programming for turning centre operations. The programs include these used for step turning, taper turning and thread turning operations. Only the manual part programming is discussed in this chapter.

14.2   COORDINATE SYSTEM FOR CNC LATHE

Machining of a workpiece by an NC program requires a coordinate system to be applied to the machine tool. There are three planes in which movement can take place. These are:

1. Longitudinal
2. Vertical
3. Transverse

Each plane is assigned a letter and is referred to as an axis: X-axis, Y-axis and Z-axis. The Z-axis is always parallel to the main spindle of the machine. The X-axis is always parallel to the work-holding surface and always at right angles to the Z-axis. The Y-axis is at right angles to both the Z- and X-axes. The coordinate system for turning operations is shown in Figure 14.1.

In programming, it is assumed that the workpiece is stationary and that the tools move in the coordinate system. The workpiece is positioned within the coordinate system so that the Z-axis coincides with the turning centre (axis of rotation) and the X and Y coordinates always have the same values. Therefore, the Y coordinate is not used in turning.

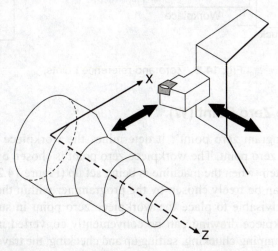

Fig. 14.1   Coordinate system for turning operations.

14.3   ZERO POINTS AND REFERENCE POINTS

On CNC lathes, tool traverses are controlled by coordinate systems. Their accurate position within the machine is established by zero points.

14.3.1   Machine Zero Point (M)

This is specified by the manufacturer of the machine. This is the zero point for the coordinate systems and reference points in the machine (Figure 14.2). On turning lathes, the machine zero point is generally at the centre of the spindle nose face. The main spindle axis represents the Z-axis while the face determines the X-axis. The direction of the positive X- and Z-axes points toward the working area. When the tool traverses in the positive direction, it moves away from the workpiece.

14.3.2   Reference Point (R)

This point is used for calibrating for controlling the measuring system of the slides and tool traverses. The position of the reference point is accurately predetermined in every traverse axis by the trip dogs and limit switches. Therefore, the reference point coordinates always have the same, precisely known numerical value in relation to the machine zero point (Figure 14.2).

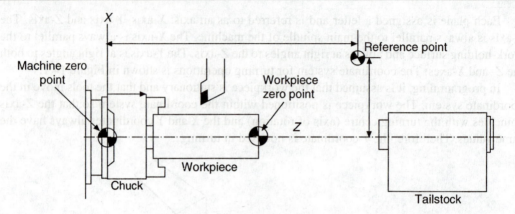

Fig. 14.2   Zero and reference points.

14.3.3   Workpiece Zero Point (W)

This is also called 'program zero point'. It determines the workpiece coordinate system in relation to the machine zero point. The workpiece zero point is chosen by the programmer and input into the CNC system when the machine is being set up (Figure 14.2). The position of the workpiece zero point can be freely chosen by the programmer within the workpiece envelope of the machine. It is advisable to place the workpiece zero point in such a manner that the dimensions in the workpiece drawing can be conveniently converted into coordinate values and orientation when clamping/chucking, setting up and checking, the traverse measuring system can be effected easily.

For turned parts, the workpiece zero point should be placed along the spindle axis in line with the right-hand or left-hand end face of the finished contour.

14.4   PROGRAMMING FUNCTIONS

14.4.1   Preparatory Functions (G Codes)

A two-digit number following address G determines the meaning of the command of the block concerned. The G codes are divided into the following two types:

1. *One-shot G codes:*   The G code is effective only at the block in which it is specified. G00 is not modal.
2. *Modal G codes:*   The G code is effective until another G code in the same group is commanded.

A number of G codes can be specified in a block even if they do not belong to the same group. When a number of G codes of the same group are specified, the G code specified last is effective.

Table 14.1 G codes

Code	Function
G00	Positioning, rapid traverse
G01	Linear interpolation
G02	Circular interpolation, clockwise
G03	Circular interpolation, counter-clockwise
G04	Dwell
G20	Inch inputs
G21	Metric inputs
G28	Reference point return
G32	Thread cutting
G40	Tool nose radius compensation, cancels to zero
G41	Tool nose radius compensation, offset left
G42	Tool nose radius compensation, offset right
G50	Work coordinates change/maximum spindle speed setting
G70	Finishing cycle
G71	Stock removal in turning
G72	Stock removal in facing
G73	Pattern repeating
G74	Peck drilling in Z-axis
G75	Grooving in X-axis
G76	Thread cutting cycle
G90	Cutting cycle A
G92	Thread cutting cycle
G94	Cutting cycle B
G96	Feed rate/rev
G96	Constant surface speed control
G97	Constant surface speed control cancel
G98	Feed per minute

Motion Commands

Rapid traverse (**G00**):   The rapid traverse instruction is defined by the program word G00. A rapid traverse instruction traverses the tool to the target point at the maximum traverse rate (Figure 14.3). As a supplementary function, it will be necessary to input the coordinates of the target point. The tool takes the shortest path from the starting point to the destination point. The rapid traverse is used for movements where no tool is in engagement.

For example,

N040 G00 X40.0 Z –5.0

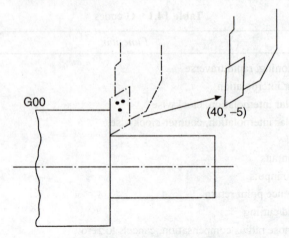

Fig. 14.3 Rapid traverse.

Linear interpolation **(G01):** G01 refers to linear interpolation at a given feed rate. G01 traverses the tool along a linear path to the given target point with the feed rate input (Figure 14.4), the feed rate determines the speed with which the workpiece is machined. The choice of the feed rate depends on the tool, the material being machined, the required surface finish and the rigidity of the machine tool. When giving the instructions G01, the coordinates of the destination point can be expressed by using either absolute or incremental dimensions. For example,

N020 G00 X10.0 Z0
N030 G01 X10.0 Z25.0

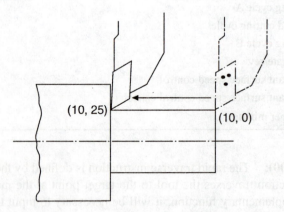

Fig. 14.4 Linear interpolation.

Circular interpolation **(G02/G03):** The circular interpolation is specified by G02 and G03. The clockwise interpolation is specified by G02 and the counter-clockwise interpolation by G03. The circular interpolation is achieved in two ways. These are:

1. Specification of the radius
2. Specification centre coordinates

The radius can be directly specified by using the R word address.

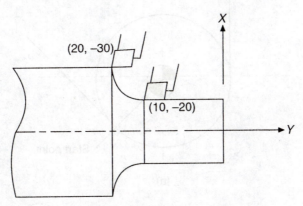

Fig. 14.5 Circular interpolation.

For example,

    N060 G01 X10.0 Z-20.0 F120
    N070 G02 X20.0 Z-30.0 R10.0 F100

***Dwell* (G04):** The Instruction G04 causes the program to wait for a specified amount of time. The time can be specified in seconds with the 'X' or 'U' prefixes or in milliseconds with the 'P' prefix. During the cutter motion, a deceleration at the end of the motion specified by one statement and an acceleration at the start of the motion specified by the next statement, are usually applied by the NC controller. G04 code can be inserted between the two statements to make a sharp corner. For example:

    G04 X2.5
    G04 U2.5
    G04 P2500

Tool Nose Radius Compensation
In turning operations on the lathe, the positions and tool path for contouring motion cannot be defined directly on the basis of the dimensions specified on a part drawing. The coordinates of the end position in each contouring motion statement of the NC program must be computed. This computation is time-consuming and error-prone. On modern CNC machines, tool radius compensation codes are provided to allow the user to employ part-profile coordinates obtained from the part drawing to program the contouring motion. These are G41 and G42 codes for tool radius compensation. G40 code is used to cancel the tool radius compensation. If tool nose radius compensation is used, accurate cutting will be performed (Figure 14.6).

14.4.2 Miscellaneous Functions (M Codes)

Miscellaneous functions (M codes) are used to instruct the actions to the machine. The miscellaneous functions are given in Table 14.2.

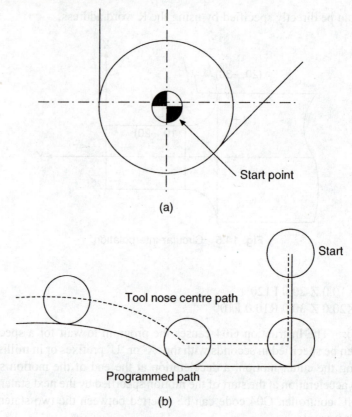

(a)

Fig. 14.6   Programming using the tool nose centre.

Table 14.2   M codes 7

Code	Function
M00	Program stop
M01	Optional stop
M02	End of program
M03	Spindle CW
M04	Spindle CCW
M05	Spindle off
M06	Tool change
M08	Coolant ON
M09	Coolant OFF
M10	Chuck open
M11	Chuck close
M13	Spindle CW and coolant ON
M14	Spindle CCW and coolant ON
M30	End of tape + tape rewind

14.4.3 Speed Function

The spindle speed can be specified in two ways: rpm or m/min.

G96 S300 Spindle speed is set at 300 m/min.
G97 S2000 Spindle speed is set at 2000 rpm.

G50 sets the maximum spindle speed for constant surface control.

G50 S4000 Maximum spindle speed is 4000 rpm.

14.4.4 Feed Rate Function

The feed rate can be specified in two ways: mm/min or mm/rev.

G98 F200	Feed in mm/min
G99 F1.0	Feed in mm/rev

14.4.5 Tool Function

Tools are selected by using the T word. The T word has the format Tmmnn. The first two digits (mm) specify the turret station while the last two digits (nn) specify the location of the tool offsets.

N100 M06 T0214

Block N100 calls for turret station 3 and tool geometry register number is 14.

14.4.6 Sequence Number

The sequence number is used to identify the blocks. The sequence number consists of N and four digits (0000–9999). For example:

N0020

14.4.7 Program Number

The program number is specified with O word address. The number can be a maximum of four digits. For example:

O1234

14.4.8 Billet Size

It defines the workpiece dimensions. The billet size is used only for simulation purpose.

[BILLET X25 Z50

The workpiece size is 50 mm long and 25 mm in diameter.

Example 14.1 Write a manual part programming for turning operation for the component shown in Figure 14.7. Take the billet size is 55 mm long and 20 mm in diameter. The spindle speed is 1000 rpm and the feed rate is 40 mm/min.

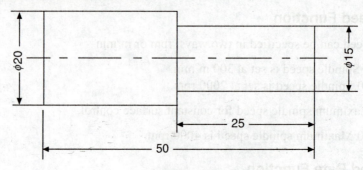

Fig. 14.7

Solution

```
%
O0001
[BILLET X20 Z55
G21   G98                    Initial settings
G28   U0 W0                  Going to home position
M06   T0102                  Selecting tool no.1 with offset no.2
M03   S1000                  Setting spindle speed at 1000 rpm
G00   X20.0 Z1.0             Tool moving to tool entry point
G01   X19.0
G01   Z-25.0 F40
G00   X20.0
G00   Z1.0
G01   X18.0
G01   Z-25.0 F40
G00   X20.0
G00   Z1.0
G01   X17.0
G01   Z-25.0 F40
G00   X20.0
G00   Z1.0
G01   X16.0
G01   Z-25.0 F40
G00   X20.0
G00   Z1.0
G10   X15.0
G01   Z-25.0 F40
G00   X20.0
G00   Z1.0
G28   U0 W0                  Going to home position
M05                          Stop spindle
M30                          Program stop and rewind
```

14.5 CANNED CYCLES

As noticed in Example 14.1, the length of the part program increases when a number of cuts are involved. A majority of the motions are repetitive in nature and therefore, the motions can be embedded in a canned cycle.

14.5.1 Turning Canned Cycle

This cycle is used to produce either a parallel or tapered tool path. This cycle performs the following four distinct moves:

1. Rapid to X position
2. Feed to Z position
3. Feed to start X position
4. Rapid to start Z position

Parallel Turning

A typical parallel turning canned cycle is shown in Figure 14.8. The command used is

G90 $X(U) Z(W) F$

where

X = diameter to which the movement is being made.
U = the incremental distance from the current tool position to the required final diameter.
Z = the Z-axis coordinate to which the movement is being made.
W = the incremental distance from the current tool position to the required Z-axis position.
F = feed

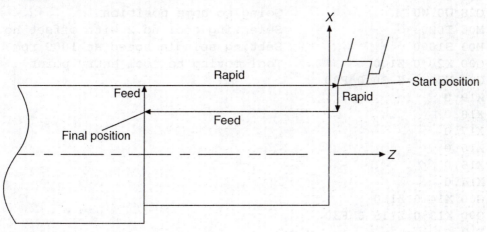

Fig. 14.8 Parallel turning.

With the above command, the cycle will execute the removing material to the required diameter and length. In order to repeat this cycle to reduce the diameter but maintain the same length, only the value to be changed needs to be programmed.

Example 14.2 Write a manual part program for step turning operation using canned cycle for the component shown in Figure 14.9. The spindle speed is 1000 rpm. The feed rate is 30 mm/min. while the tool nose radius is 0.4 mm.

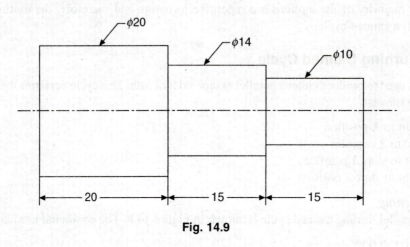

Fig. 14.9

Solution

```
    %
    O0002
    [BILLET X20 Z55

    G21 G98                     Initial settings
    G28 U0 W0                   Going to home position
    M06 T0203                   Selecting tool no.2 with offset no. 3
    M03 S1000                   Setting spindle speed at 1000 rpm
    G00 X20.0 Z1.0              Tool moving to tool entry point
    G90 X20.0 Z-30.0 F30
    X19.0
    X18.0
    X17.0
    X16.0
    X15.0
    X14.0
    G00 X14.0 Z1.0
    G90 X13.0 Z-15.0 F30
    X12.0
    X11.0
    X10.0
    G00 Z1.0
    G28 U0 W0                   Going to home position
    M05                         Stop spindle
    M30                         Program stop and rewind
```

Taper Turning

A typical taper turning canned cycle is shown in Figure 14.10. The command used is:

G90 X(U) Z(W) R F

where

X = diameter to which the movement is being made.

U = the incremental distance from the current tool position to the required final diameter.

Z = the Z-axis coordinate to which the movement is being made.

W = the incremental distance from the current tool position to the required Z-axis position.

R = the difference in incremental of the cut start radius value and the cut finish radius value.

F = feed.

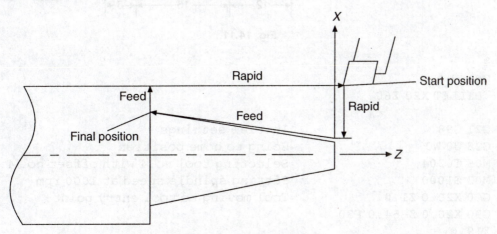

Fig. 14.10 Taper turning.

If the 'R' value is specified in the command format of G90 cycle, tapering will be performed. The sign of 'R' will depend on the direction of the taper. The initial rapid move will be the X position plus the 'R' value.

Example 14.3 Write a manual part programming for taper turning operation for the component shown in Figure 14.11. The spindle speed is 1000, the feed rate is 30 mm/min. and the tool nose radius is 0.4 mm.

Solution

For the right taper,

$$R = \frac{D_1 - D_f}{2} = \frac{10 - 18}{2} = -4.0$$

For the left taper,

$$R = \frac{D_1 - D_f}{2} = \frac{18 - 10}{2} = 4.0$$

where

D_1 = Initial diameter

D_f = Final diameter

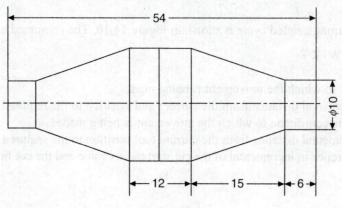

Fig. 14.11

```
%
O0003
[BILLET X20 Z60

G21 G98                      Initial settings
G28 U0 W0                    Going to home position
M06 T0304                    Selecting tool no.4 with offset no. 4
M03 S1000                    Setting spindle speed at 1000 rpm
G00 X20.0 Z1.0               Tool moving to tool entry point
G90 X20.0 Z-54.0 F30
X19.0
X18.0
X17.0 Z-6.0
X16.0
X15.0
X14.0
X13.0
X12.0
X11.0
X10.0
G00   X18.0 Z-6.0
G90   X18.0 Z-21.0 R0 F30
X18.0 R-0.5
X18.0 R-1.0
X18.0 R-1.5
X18.0 R-2.0
X18.0 R-2.5
X18.0 R-3.0
X18.0 R-3.5
X18.0 R-4.0
```

```
G01 X18.0 Z-48 R0 F30
X17.0 R0.5
X16.0 R1.0
X15.0 R1.5
X14.0 R2.0
X13.0 R2.5
X12.0 R3.0
X11.0 R3.5
X10.0 R4.0
G00 X18.0 Z-48
G90 X18 Z-54 F30
X17.0
X16.0
X15.0
X14.0
X13.0
X12.0
X11.0
X10.0
G28 U0 W0                  Going to home position
M05                        Stop spindle
M30                        Program stop and rewind
```

14.5.2 Thread Cutting

Thread cutting is similar to parallel turning. The only difference between the two is that the cutting operation, G32 will be initiated in place of G01 for synchronising the spindle drive and the feed drive. The thread cutting cycle is illustrated in Figure 14.12. The command used is:

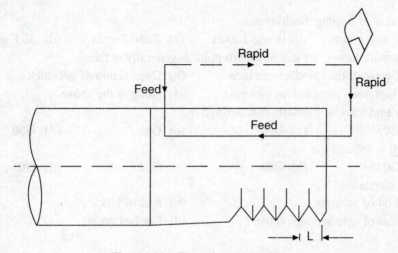

Fig. 14.12 Thread cycle cutting.

G92 X(U) Z(W) F(f)

where

    X = depth of cut (absolute)
    U = depth of cut (incremental)
    Z = length of thread (absolute)
    W = length of thread (incremental)
    f = lead or pitch of thread

For example,

```
G00 X32 Z5
G92 X20.977 Z-20 F2.5
X19.955
X18.932
```

QUESTION BANK

A. Descriptive Questions

1. Explain coordinate system for CNC lathe.
2. What are zero and reference points for turning part programming?
3. What are the preparatory functions for turning part programming?
4. Explain linear and circular interpolations with examples for turning part programming.
5. What is 'dwell'? Explain its importance in turning part programming with an example.
6. Explain tool nose radius compensation for turning part programming.
7. What are the miscellaneous functions for turning part programming?
8. What are canned cycles for turning part programming?

B. Multiple Choice Questions

1. The axes of turning machine are:
    (a) Z and X-axes   (b) X and Y-axes   (c) Z and Y-axes   (d) X, Y and Z-axes
2. On turning lathes, the machine zero point is generally at the:
    (a) Centre of the spindle nose face   (b) Dead centre of tail stock
    (c) Tool point mounted on tool post   (d) None of the above
3. The rapid traverse instruction is defined by:
    (a) G03   (b) G02   (c) G01   (d) G00
4. Dwell is defined by:
    (a) G04   (b) G03   (c) G02   (d) G01
5. M30 stands for:
    (a) End of program   (b) End of block
    (c) End of tape and tape rewind   (d) Coolant on/off

Chapter 15

Computer-aided Part Programming

OBJECTIVES

After reading this chapter, the reader will be able to understand the following concepts:

- ⊃ Part programming languages
- ⊃ APT language structure
- ⊃ Geometry statements: Point, line, plane, and circle
- ⊃ Motion statements: Set-up commands, point-to-point motion commands, and contouring motion commands
- ⊃ Post processor commands
- ⊃ Auxiliary commands
- ⊃ Repetitive programming

15.1 INTRODUCTION

For complex jobs, manual part programming becomes an extremely tedious task and is subject to errors. This chapter presents computer-aided part programming. Many part programming languages have been developed to generate part programs automatically. The computer-aided part programming consists of two parts:

1. Definition of work part geometry
2. Specification of operation sequence and tool path

15.2 PART PROGRAMMING LANGUAGES

Today, several part programming languages are used. Following are some of the important part programming languages:

APT (Automatically Programmed Tools)

This was originated at the Servomechanism Laboratory of the Massachusetts Institute of Technology (MIT). Its development began in June 1956. Versions of APT for particular processes include APTURN (for lathe operations), APTMIL (for milling and drilling operations), and APTPOINT (for point-to-point operations).

ADAPT (Adaptation of APT)

This was developed by IBM. ADAPT was intended to provide many of the features of APT while utilising a smaller computer. It is not as powerful as APT, but can be used to program for both positioning and contouring jobs.

EXAPT (Extended sub-set of APT)

This was developed in Germany on the basis of the APT language. It has three versions: EXAPT I—designed for positioning, EXAPT II—designed for turning and EXAPT III—designed for contouring.

UNIAPT

This was developed by the United Computing Corp. of Carson, California. It is a limited version of APT to be implemented on microcomputers.

PROMPT

This was developed by Weber NC System, Inc., of Milwaukee, Wisconsin. It is designed for use with a variety of machine tools such as lathes, machining centres, flame cutters and punch pressers.

15.3 APT LANGUAGE STRUCTURE

APT is not only an NC language but also a computer program that performs the calculations to generate cutter positions based on APT statements. There are four types of statements in the APT language:

1. Geometry statements
2. Motion statements
3. Post-processor statements
4. Auxiliary statements

The APT language consists of different types of statements composed by the following letters, numerals and punctuation marks:

Letters: ABCDEFGHIJKLMNOPQRSTUVWXYZ

Numerals: 0123456789

Punctuation marks:

/   A slash divides a statement into two sections. For example, GO/PAST

,   A comma is used as a separator between the elements in a statement. For example,

L1 = LINE/P1, P2

= An equal sign is used for assigning an entity to a symbolic name. For example,
P1 = 25.0, –30.0, 0.0

() The parentheses are used for enclosing the nested statements.

$ A single dollar sign when placed at the end of a line in the part program indicates that the statement continues in the following line.

Words: Words are constructed with six letters or numerals with the first one being a letter. No special character is allowed in the words.

Keywords: There are certain reserved names called key words in the language, which have a fixed meaning. These words cannot be used for any other purpose. For example, CIRCLE, LINE, POINT, TANTO, LEFT.

Arithmetic operations: APT provides the facility for arithmetic computations such as:

- Addition   +
- Subtraction   –
- Multiplication   *
- Division   /
- Exponentiation   **

For example:

$A = 3 (5 + 7)$ should be written as $A = 3*(5 + 7)$

$B = \dfrac{2 + 5 + 9}{4}$ should be written as $A = (2 + 5 + 9)/4$

$C = 4^3$ should be written as $C = 4**3$

The priority of arithmetic operations is as follows:

1. ( )
2. **
3. *, /
4. +, –

Library functions: The most commonly used library functions are:

ABS   Absolute value
SQRT   Square root
SIN   Sine of the angle in degrees
COS   Cosine if the angle in degrees
TAN   Tangent of the angle in degrees
ASIN   Angle of Sine in degrees
ACOS   Angle of Cosine in degrees
ATAN   Angle of Tangent in degrees
EXP   Exponential
LOG   Natural logarithm

Symbols: A symbol can be any combination of six or fewer alphabetic and numeric characters. The first character is always an alphabetic character. The symbol cannot be a key word. For example,

L1
P2
C5

15.4 GEOMETRY STATEMENTS

Geometric statements are used to define the geometric elements that comprise work part. The syntax of an APT geometry statement is:

$$\text{Symbol} = \text{geometry type/descriptive data.}$$

The statement is made up of three sections. The first is the symbol used to identify the geometric element. The second section is the key word that identifies the type of geometry element. The third section comprises the descriptive data that define the element precisely, completely, and uniquely.

To specify a point,
    P1 = POINT/2.0, –4.0, 1.0
To specify a line,
    L2 = LINE/P1, P2
To specify a plane,
    PL3 = PLANE/P2, P3, P5
To specify a circle,
    C4 = CIRCLE/CENTRE, P6, RADIUS, 4.0

15.4.1 Point

The point has three coordinates, the x, y and z-axes. The point is specified by the following ways:

  (*a*) *By the rectangular coordinates* (Figure 15.1)
      P1 = POINT/3.0, 1.5, 0.0

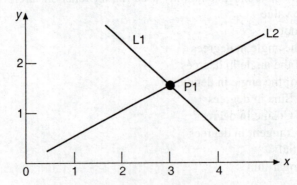

Fig. 15.1 A point by intersection of two lines.

(b) **By the intersection of two lines** (Figure 15.1)

P1 = POINT/L1, L2

(c) **By the intersection of a line and a circle** (Figure 15.2)

P2 = POINT/YLARGE, INTOF, L3, C1

P3 = POINT/XLARGE, INTOF, L3, C1

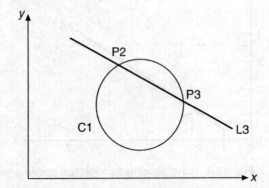

Fig. 15.2 Points by intersection of line and circle.

Any of the descriptive words–XLARGE, XSMALL, YLARGE, YSMALL, can be used to indicate the relative position of the point. For point P2, XSMALL, or YLARGE can be used.

(d) **By intersecting two circles** (Figure 15.3)

P4 = POINT/YLARGE, INTOF, C1, C2

P5 = POINT/YSMALL, INTOF, C1, C2

(e) **By the centre of a circle** (Figure 15.3)

P6 = POINT/ CENTRE, C1

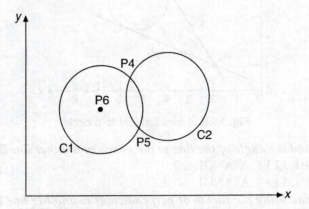

Fig. 15.3 Points by intersections of two circles.

15.4.2 Line

Lines are considered to be of infinite length and do not have a direction. The following are the methods of definition:

(*a*) **By the coordinates of two points** (Figure 15.4)

L1 = LINE/2, 1, 0, 5, 3, 0

(*b*) **By two points** (Figure 15.4)

L1 = LINE/P1, P2

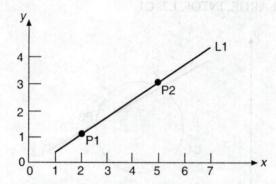

Fig. 15.4 Line passing through two points.

(*c*) **By a point and tangent to a circle** (Figure 15.5)

L1 = LINE/P1, LEFT, TANTO, C1

L2 = LINE/P1, RIGHT, TANTO, C!

The words LEFT and RIGHT are used by looking from the point toward the circle.

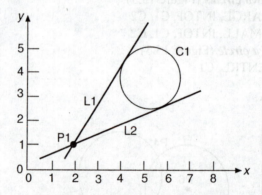

Fig. 15.5 Lines tangent to a circle.

(*d*) **By a point and the angle of the line to the x-axis or another line** (Figure 15.6)

L3 = LINE/P1, LEFT, ATANGL, 20

L4 = LINE/P1, LEFT, ATANGL, 30, L3

(*e*) **By a point and being parallel to or perpendicular to another line** (Figure 15.7)

L5 = LINE/P2, PARLEL, L3

L6 = LINE/P2, PERPTOL, L3

(*f*) **By being a tangent to two circles** (Figure 15.8)

L7 = LINE/LEFT, TANTO, C3, LEFT, TANTO, C4

L8 = LINE/LEFT, TANTO, C3, RIGHT, TANTO, C4

L9 = LINE/RIGHT, TANTO, C3, LEFT, TANTO, C4

L10 = LINE/ RIGHT, TANTO, C3, RIGHT, TANTO, C4

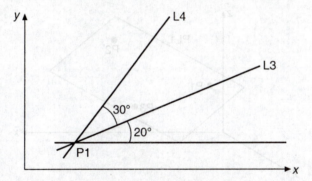

Fig. 15.6 Lines by orientation.

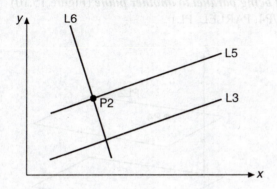

Fig. 15.7 Line normal to another line.

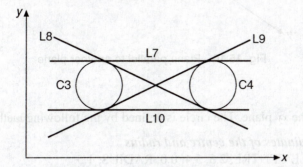

Fig. 15.8 Lines tangent to two circles.

15.4.3 Plane

Planes are surfaces with infinite areas. Planes are defined by following methods:

(*a*) *By three points that do not lie on the same straight line* (Figure 15.9)

PL1 = PLANE/P1, P2, P3

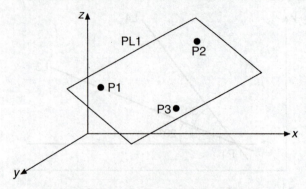

Fig. 15.9   Plane represented by three points.

(*b*) ***By a point and being parallel to another plane*** (Figure 15.10)
PL2 = PLANE/P4, PARLEL, PL1

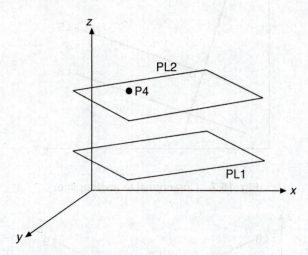

Fig. 15.10   Plane parallel to another plane

15.4.4   Circle

Circle is defined in the *xy* plane. The circle is defined by the following methods:

(*a*) ***By the coordinates of the centre and radius***
C1 = CIRCLE/CENTRE, 2.5, 5.4, 0.0, RADIUS, 1.5

(*b*) ***By the centre point and radius***
C1 = CIRCLE/CENTRE, P1, RADIUS, 1.5

(*c*) ***By the centre point and tangent to a line*** (Figure 15.11)
C1 = CIRCLE/CENTRE, P1, TANTO, L1

(*d*) ***By three points on the circumference***
C1 = CIRCLE/ P1, P2, P3

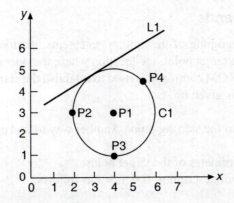

Fig. 15.11 Circle by centre point and tangent.

(*e*) *By intersecting lines and the radius* (Figure 15.12)

C2 = CIRCLE/XSMALL, L2, YSMALL, L3, RADIUS, 1.25
C3 = CIRCLE/YLARGE, L2, YLARGE, L3, RADIUS, 1.25
C4 = CIRCLE/XLARGE, L2, YLARGE, L3, RADIUS, 1.25
C5 = CIRCLE/YSMALL, L2, YSMALL, L3, RADIUS, 1.25

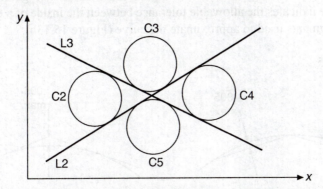

Fig. 15.12 Circle by intersecting lines and radius.

15.5 MOTION STATEMENTS

These are used to describe the path taken by the cutting tool. The syntax of the motion statement is given by

Motion command/descriptive data

For example,

GOTO/P4
GODLTA/1.0, 3.0, 0.0

The motion commands can be broadly divided into the following three groups:

1. Set-up commands
2. Point-to-point motion commands
3. Contouring motion commands

15.5.1 Set-up Commands

Start point: At the beginning of the motion statements, the tool must be given a starting point. This point may be the target point, the location where the operator has positioned the tool at the start of the job. The FROM command is used to establish the starting point of the tool at the start of the job. The syntax is given by

FROM/TARG

TARG is the symbol given to the starting point. Another way to make this statement is

FROM/x, y, z

where x, y and z are the coordinates of the target point.

Cutter: The cutting tool description is defined as follows:

CUTTER/dia

For example,

CUTTER/ 25.0

defines a 25.0 mm diameter milling cutter. The cutter path is offset from the part outline by one-half the diameter.

Tolerances: The tolerances are specified as outside tolerance (OUTTOL) and inside tolerance (INTOL). Outside tolerance indicates the allowable tolerance between the outside of a curved surface and any straight line segments used to approximate the curve (Figure 15.13a).

Inside tolerance indicates the allowable tolerance between the inside of a curved surface and any straight line segments used to approximate the curve (Figure 15.13b).

INTOL/0.005

OUTTOL/0.005

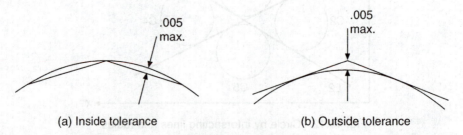

(a) Inside tolerance   (b) Outside tolerance

Fig. 15.13   Tolerances.

15.5.2 Point-to-Point Motion Commands

There are only two basic commands: GOTO and GODLTA. The GOTO command is used to move the tool from the current position to the point specified in the statement. The syntax is given by

GOTO/point

For example,

GOTO/P7

GOTO/2.0, 5.0, 0.0

In the second statement, the tool has been instructed to go to the location whose coordinates are $x = 2.0$, $y = 5.0$ and $z = 0.0$.

The GODLTA command specifies the relative movement along the axes specified. The syntax is given by

GODLTA/dx, dy, dz

For example,

GODLTA/ 1.0, 2.0, 0.0

instructs the tool to move from the present position 1 unit in x-direction and 2.0 units in y-direction. The *z*-coordinate remains unchanged.

15.5.3 Contouring Motion Commands

These are used to specify the continuous path motion involving milling and turning operations to generate a variety of surfaces. Contouring commands are used to continuously control the tool throughout the move. The tool is directed along two intersecting surfaces as shown in Figure 15.14.

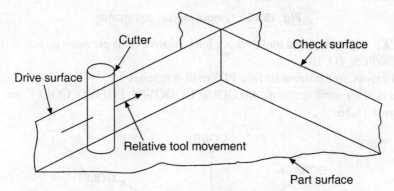

Fig. 15.14 Intersecting surfaces to control the tool movement.

The intersecting surfaces are:

1. *Drive surface*: This is the surface which guides the side of the tool.
2. *Part surface*: This is the surface on which the bottom of the tool rides.
3. *Check surface*: This is the surface that stops the movement of the tool in its current direction. Four modifier words are used to stop the movement of the tool. TO moves the tool into initial contact with check surface. ON moves the tool until the tool centre is on the check surface. PAST moves the tool just beyond the check surface. TANTO moves the tool to point of tangency between two surfaces, at least one of which is circular.

GO: This is used to bring the tool from the starting point against the drive surface (ds), part surface (ps), and check surface (cs). The general format is:

$$
GO/ \begin{Bmatrix} TO \\ ON \\ PAST \end{Bmatrix}, ds, \begin{Bmatrix} TO \\ ON \\ PAST \end{Bmatrix}, ps \begin{Bmatrix} To \\ ON \\ PAST \\ TANTO \end{Bmatrix}, cs
$$

For example,
   Go/TO, L1, TO, PL1, TO, L2
The initial drive surface is the line L1, the part surface is PL1, and the initial check surface is L2.

   The effects of the motion modifier words TO, ON, PAST and TANTO are shown in Figure 15.15.

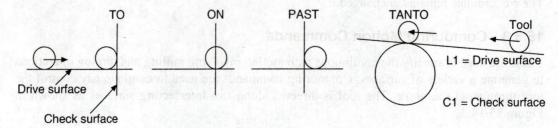

Fig. 15.15   Control motion commands.

GOBACK: It instructs the tool to move back relative to its previous direction of movement.
GOBACK/PL5, TO, L1
The tool moves on the drive surface PL5 until it reaches L1.

   The effects of the motion commands GOUP, GODOWN, FOFWD, GOLFT, and GORGT are shown in Figure 15.16.

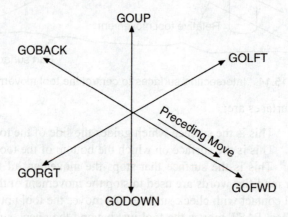

Fig. 15.16   Six motion command words.

15.6   POST-PROCESSOR COMMANDS

These functions are used to specify the machine tool functions. The post-processor commands are as follows:
   COOLNT: Coolant turns on, off.
   COOLNT/ON
   COOLNT/OFF
   COOLNT/FLOOD

COOLNT/MIST

FEDRAT: It is used to specify the feed rate in mm per minute

FEDRAT/ 100.0

END: It is used to stop the machine at the end of a section of the program.

MACHIN: It is used to specify the machine tool and to call the post-processor for that machine tool.

MACHIN/ MILL, 1

The MILL identifies the machine tool type and 1 identifies the particular machine and postprocessor.

TURRET: It is used to specify the turret position on the turret lathe or drill or to call a specific tool from an automatic tool changer.

TURRET/T30

SPINDL: It is used to specify the spindle speed in a revolution per minute.

SPINDL/3000

REWIND: It is used to rewind the control tape to a known tape mark, which is generally the start of the tape.

15.7 AUXILIARY COMMANDS

These commands are used to prepare the computer for accepting the part program, improve the readability of the part program and control the output of the computer.

CLPRNT: It is used to obtain the computer printout of the cutter location sequence on the CNC tape.

FINI: It is used to indicate the end of the computer program.

PARTNO: It is used at start of program to identify the part program.

15.8 REPETITIVE PROGRAMMING

The sequence of similar statements which need to be referred more often in a part program are best referred to by a MCARO statement. This feature is similar to a sub-routine in FORTRAN and other computer programming languages. The MACRO sub-routine is defined as follows:

Symbol = MACRO/parameter definitions

The symbol must be of six or fewer characters and at least one of the characters must be a letter of the alphabet.

The parameter definitions following slash would identify certain variables in the sub-routines, which might change each time the sub-routine is called into use.

In order to activate the MACRO sub-routine, the call statement must be used as follows:

CALL/symbol, parameter specification

The symbol would be the name of the MACRO that is to be called. The parameter specification identifies the particular values of the parameters that are to be used in the execution of the MACRO sub-routines.

The very last statement is TERMAC.

The syntax of MACRO statement is as follows:

<name>=MACRO/<parameters>

TERMAC

All the statements that are enclosed between the MACRO statement and the TERMAC statement are to be executed whenever this macro is called by

CALL/name, <parameters>

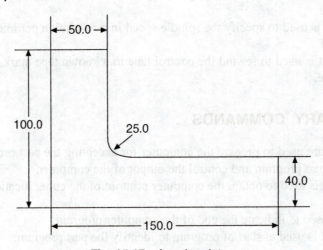

Fig. 15.17 Angular plate.

Example 15.1 Write an APT part programming to cut the profile as shown in Figure 15.17 with the cutter is 6.5 mm dia, cutting speed of 900 rpm and feed rate of 7.5 mm/min.

Solution

The component is labelled to define the geometry as shown in Figure 15.18.

```
PARTNO/01
MACHIN/MILL1
INTOL/0.001
OUTTOL/0.001
CUTTER/6.5
SPINDL/900
FEDRAT/7.5
COOLNT/ON
P0 = POINT/-25.0, -25.0,0.0
P1 = POINT/0.0, 0.0, 0.0
P2 = POINT/150.0, 0.0, 0.0
P3 = POINT/150.0, 40.0, 0.0
P4 = POINT/50.0, 100.0, 0.0
P5 = POINT/0.0, 100.0, 0.0
```

```
P6 = POINT/75.0, 65.0, 0.0
L1 = LINE/P1, P2
L2 = LINE/P2, P3
C1 = CIRCLE/CENTRE, P6, RADIUS, 25.0
L3 = LINE/P3, LEFT, TANTO, C1
L4 = LINE/P3, RIGHT, TANTO, C1
L5 = LINE/P4, P5
L1 = LINE/P5, P1
PL1 = PLANE/P1, P2, P5
FROM/P0
RAPID
GO/TO, L1, TO, PL1, TO, L6
GO/TO P1
GORGT/L1, PAST, L2
GORGT/L2, PAST, L3
GOLFT/L3, TANTO, C1
GOFWD/C1, PAST, L4
GOFWD/L4, PAST, L5
GOLFT/L5, PAST, L6
GOLFT/L6, PAST, L1
GOTO/P0
COOLNT/OFF
SPINDL/OFF
FINI
END
```

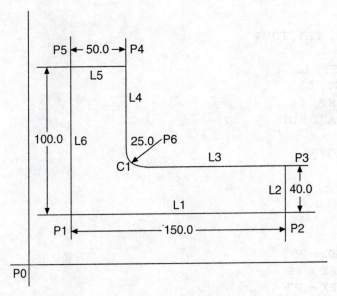

Fig. 15.18 Dimensioning in Cartesian coordinates.

Example 15.2 Write an APT part program for the profile shown in Figure 15.19 with cutting speed and feed rate of 500 rpm and 100 mm/min, respectively. The cutter is of 10 mm dia. Use MACRO statement for drilling operations.

Solution

```
PARTNO/02
MACHIN/MILL 05
CLPRNT
SPINDL/500
FEDRAT/100.0
P0 = POINT/- 25.0, -25.0, 0.0
P1 =POINT/0.0, 0.0, 0.0
P2 = POINT/90.0, 0.0,0.0
P3 = POINT/90.0, 45, 00
P4 = POINT/0.0, 45, 0.0
P5 = POINT/15, 10, 0.0
P6 = POINT/60.0, 20.0, 0.0
P7 = POINT/75.0, 35.0, 0.0  -
P8 = POINT/40.0,35.0, 0.0
P9 = POINT/15.0, 35.0, 0.0
L1 = LINE/PI, P2
L2 = LINE/P2, P3
L3 = LINE/P3, P4
L4 = LINE/P4, PI
PL1 = PLANE/PI, P2, P3
COOLNT/ON
FROM/P0
GO/TO, L1,TO, PL1,TOL4
GO/TO, LI
GORGT/L1, PAST, L2
GOFWD/L2, PAST, L3
GOLFT/L3, PAST, L4
GOBACK/L4, PAST, LI
GOTO/PO
DRILL  = MACRO/PX
GO/TO  PX
GODLTA/0, 0, -10.0
GODLTA/0, 0, 10.0
TERMAC
FROM/PO
CALL/DRILL, PX = P5
CALL/DRILL, PX = P6
CALL/DRILL, PX = P7
CALL/DRILL, PX = P8
CALL/DRILL, PX = P9
RAPID
```

```
GOTO/P0
COOLNT/OFF
SPINDL/OFF
FINI
END
```

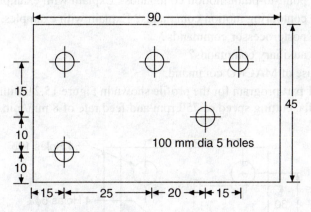

Fig. 15.19 Plate with holes.

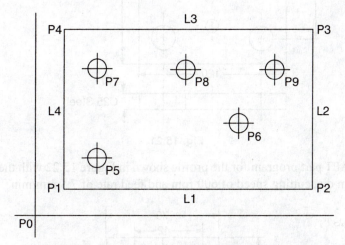

Fig. 15.20 Dimensioning in cartesian coordinates.

QUESTION BANK

A. Descriptive Questions

1. What are the part programming languages? Compare their merits.
2. Describe APT language structure.
3. What are geometry commands? Explain them with examples.
4. Define different methods of expressing a point in APT language.
5. Define different methods of expressing a line in APT language.

6. Define different methods of expressing a circle in APT language.
7. Define different methods of expressing a plane in APT language.
8. What are the motion commands?
9. What are the set-up commands? Explain with examples.
10. What are the point-to-point motion commands? Explain with examples.
11. What are the contouring motion commands? Explain with examples.
12. What are the postprocessor commands?
13. What are the auxiliary commands?
14. Explain the use of MACRO command.
15. Write an APT part program for the profile shown in Figure 15.21 with the cutters is 5 mm and 10 mm dia, cutting speed of 750 rpm and feed rate of 8 mm/min.

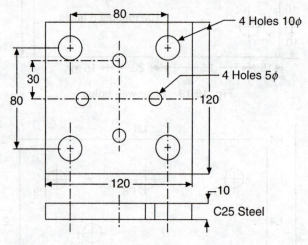

Fig. 15.21

16. Write an APT part program for the profile shown in Figure 15.22 with the cutters is 8 mm and 12 mm dia, cutting speed of 600 rpm and feed rate of 7.5 mm/min.

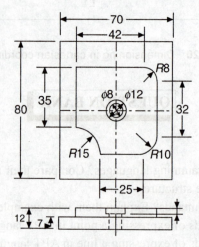

Fig. 15.22

B. Multiple Choice Questions

1. In APT, geometric commands describe:
   (a) Part
   (b) Cutter movement
   (c) Machine control functions
   (d) Post processor

2. Which one of the following is a point-to-point statement:
   (a) GOHOME
   (b) GOTO
   (c) GO/TO
   (d) GODLTA

3. In contouring motion statements, the tool always moves along the:
   (a) Part surface
   (b) Check surface
   (c) Drive surface
   (d) None

4. In contouring motion statements, the tool will change its direction with respect to:
   (a) Part surface
   (b) Check surface
   (c) Drive surface
   (d) All the above

5. Which is the last statement in APT program?
   (a) CLOSE
   (b) END
   (c) FINI
   (d) FINISH

6. MACRO definition in APT is equivalent to:
   (a) Sub-program
   (b) Loop program
   (c) Parametric program
   (d) Main program

Chapter 16

Direct Numerical Control

After reading this chapter, the reader will be able to understand the following concepts:

- ⊃ Components of a DNC system
- ⊃ Functions of DNC systems: NC without punched tape, NC part program storage, data collection, processing, and reporting and communications
- ⊃ Types of DNC systems: BTR system, SMCU system
- ⊃ Relative features of BTR and SMCU
- ⊃ Communication interfaces: EIA RS 232C and IEEE 488 Interface
- ⊃ Networks
- ⊃ Advantages of DNC
- ⊃ What happens if the computer breaks down?

16.1 INTRODUCTION

Direct numerical control can be defined as a manufacturing system in which a number of machines are controlled by a computer through direct connection and in real-time. The fundamental component is the distribution of control information at the appropriate time to several machines whereby the computer monitors the functions of the numerical control.

In principle, one large computer can be used to control more than 100 separate machines. The DNC computer is designed to provide instructions to each machine tool on demand. The tape reader is omitted. The part program is directly transmitted to the machine tool directly from the computer memory. DNC also involves data collection and processing from the machine tool back to the computer.

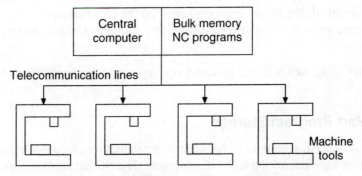

Fig. 16.1   General configuration of a DNC system.

16.2   COMPONENTS OF A DNC SYSTEM

The basic components of a DNC system are:

1. Central computer
2. Bulk memory
3. Telecommunication lines
4. Machine tools

The computer calls the part program instructions from bulk storage and sends them to the individual machines as the need arises. It also receives data back from the machines. This two-way information flow occurs in real-time, which means that each machine's requests for instructions must be satisfied almost instantaneously. Similarly, the computer must always be ready to receive information from the machines and to respond accordingly. The remarkable feature of the DNC system is that the computer is servicing a large number of separate machines tools, all in real-time.

16.3   FUNCTIONS OF DNC SYSTEMS

The principal functions of a DNC system are:

1. NC without punched tape
2. NC part program storage
3. Data collection, processing, and reporting
4. Communications

16.3.1   NC without Punched Tape

The main objective of a DNC system is to eliminate the use of punched tape. The problems associated with the NC tape are:

1. A relatively unreliable tape reader
2. The fragile nature of the paper tape

3. Difficulties in editing the program contained on the punched tape
4. The expense associated with the manufacturing equipment of punched tape and punched tape reader.

The problems associated with the punched tape and costs can be eliminated with the DNC system.

16.3.2   NC Part Program Storage

The management of a large volume of NC data in a production computer offers considerably more scope for storing and working with NC programs. The NC data distribution entails making the NC programs available and transmitting the NC data to the machine. The form of transmission is dependent upon the hardware configuration of the complete system. The DNC program storage system consists of an active storage and a second storage. The active storage is used to store NC programs, which are frequently used. The active storage can be readily accessed by the DNC computer to drive an NC machine in production. A typical mass storage device for this purpose would be a disk. The secondary storage would be used for NC programs, which are not frequently used. Examples of secondary storage include magnetic tape, tape cassettes, floppy disks, and disk packs.

The important functions of the storage system are:

1. The programs must be made available for downloading to the NC machine tools.
2. The storage system must allow for new programs to be entered, old programs to be deleted, and existing programs to be edited as the need arises.
3. The DNC software must accomplish the post-processing function. The part programs are stored as the CLFILE. The CLFILE must be converted into instructions for a particular machine tool. This conversion is performed by the post-processor.
4. The storage system must be structured to perform certain data processing and management functions such as file security, display of programs, manipulation of the data, and so on.

16.3.3   Data Collection, Processing and Reporting

These functions involve the transfer of data from the machine tools back to the central computer. Their basic purpose is to monitor production in the factory. When the machine operator requests a particular NC program, the production computer first tests the compatibility and looks for any barring with respect to the NC machine and the program. The data output buffer is prepared and filled, and its acceptance or rejection is transmitted to the requesting terminal in accordance with the results of the tests. If this is an acceptable signal, the transmission of N data to the machine control unit commences. Data are collected on production piece counts, tool usage, machine utilisation and other factors that measure performance in the factory. These data must be processed by the DNC computer, so that reports can be prepared to provide management with the information necessary for running the factory.

16.3.4   Communications

The important communication links in DNC system are between the following components of the system:

1. Central computer and machine tools
2. Central computer and NC programmer terminals
3. Central computer and bulk memory

Data transmission can be handled by either a loop or a radial data transmission network depending on the DNC configuration and specifications.

16.4 TYPES OF DNC SYSTEMS

There are two types of systems by which the communication link is established between the control computer and the machine tool. They are:

1. Behind the tape reader (BTR) system
2. Special machine control unit (SMCU) system

16.4.1 BTR System

In this arrangement, the computer is linked directly to the regular NC controller unit. The replacement of the tape reader by the telecommunication lines to the DNC computer is what gives the BTR configuration its name. The connection with the computer is made between the tape reader and the controller unit—behind the tape reader.

Except for the source of the command instructions, the operation of the system is very similar to conventional NC. The controller unit uses two temporary storage buffers to receive blocks of instructions from the DNC computer and to convert them into machine actions. While one buffer is receiving a block of data, the other is providing control instructions to the machine tool.

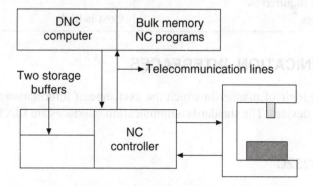

Fig. 16.2 BTR system.

16.4.2 SMCU System

In this arrangement, a special machine control unit completely replaces the regular NC controller. This special MCU is a device that is specially designed to facilitate communication between the machine tool and the computer.

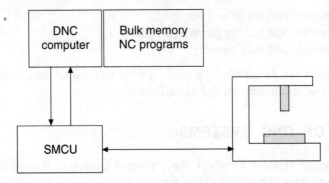

Fig. 16.3   SMCU system.

16.5   RELATIVE FEATURES OF BTR AND SMCU

The relative features are tabulated as follows:

S.No.	BTR System	SMCU System
1.	Inferior balance between accuracy of the interpolation and fast metal removal rate	Superior balance between accuracy of the interpolation and fast metal removal rate
2.	Hard-wired	Soft-wired
3.	It is more difficult to make changes in the regular NC controller because re-writing is required	Control functions can be altered with relative ease to make improvements
4.	Cost is less	Cost is high

16.6   COMMUNICATION INTERFACES

PROTOCOL is the logic of manner in which the exchange of information takes place between the communicating devices. The standard communication interfaces are EIA RS232C and parallel IEEE 488.

16.6.1   EIA RS232C

EIA RS232C is a serial interface for the transfer of data to and from any external device. RS232C terminals have a standardised 25-pin connector on them. The RS232C standard defines the mechanical size and shape of the connector, the voltage levels, and the meaning of each of the signals on the pins.

When the computer and the terminal are far apart, it is frequently seen that the only practical way to connect them is over the telephone system. Unfortunately, the telephone system is not capable of transmitting the signals required by the RS232C standard, so a device called a modem (Modulator-Demodulator) has to be inserted between the computer and the telephone and also between the terminal and the telephone, to perform signal conversion.

Figure 16.4 shows the placement of the computer, modem and terminal when a telephone line is used. When the terminal is close enough to the computer that it can be wired up directly, modems are not used, but the same RS232C connectors and cables are still used, though those pins related to modem control are not needed.

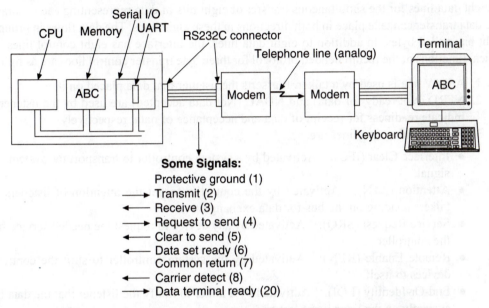

Fig. 16.4 Connection of RS232C terminal to a computer. The numbers in parentheses in the list of signals are the pin numbers.

In order to communicate with each other, the computer and terminal each contain a chip called a UART (Universal Asynchronous Receiver Transmitter), as well as logic to access the memory and present it to the UART, which then shifts it out onto the RS232C cable bit-for-bit. In effect, UART is really a parallel-to-serial converter, since an entire character (I byte) is given to it at once, and it outputs the bits one at a time at a specific rate. The most common rates are 11, 300, 1200, 2400, 9600 and 19,200.

In the terminal, another UART receives the bits and rebuilds the entire character, which is then displayed on the screen. The input from the terminal's keyboard goes through a parallel-to-serial conversion in the terminal, and is then re-assembled by the UART in the computer.

The RS232C standard defines 25 signals, but in practice, only a few are used. Pins 2 and 3 are for transmitting and receiving data, respectively. Each handles a one-way bit stream, in the opposite direction. When the terminal or computer is powered up, it asserts (i.e., sets to 1) the Data Terminal Ready signal to inform the modem that it is on. Similarly, the modem asserts Data Set Ready to signal its presence. When the terminal or computer wants to send data, it asserts Request to Send to ask permission. If the modem is willing to grant that permission, it asserts Clear to Send as a response. Other pins are used for various status, testing, and timing functions.

16.6.2 IEEE 488 Interface

This is a parallel interface laid down by the Institute of Electrical and Electronics Engineers (IEEE) and is also referred to as General Purpose Interface Bus (GPIB). This interface was originally developed by Hewlett-Packard for their programmable instruments. The interface consists of eight data lines for the simultaneous transfer of eight bits of data representing each character. The data transfer can take place in both directions in these eight lines. The data flows in groups of eight bits called bytes. In addition to eight data lines, the interface has eight control lines. The logical functions of the recommended protocol for three byte transfer control lines are as follows:

1. A DAV line is used by a talker. It asserts the listener that data placed on it.
2. NFRD (Not ready for data) and NDAC (Not data accepted) are used by the listeners to indicate readiness for receipt of data and acceptance of data, respectively.
3. The remaining five lines are:

   - Interface Clear (IFC): Activated by a system controller to transport the system reset signal.
   - Attention (ATN): Activated by the controller to get the attention of listeners and talkers residing on the bus for data exchange.
   - Service Request (SRQ): Activated by any device to request the needed service from the controller.
   - Remote Enable (REN): Activated by the system controller to shift the control of devices to itself.
   - End-Or-Identity (EOI): Activated by a talker to notify the listener that the data byte currently on the lines is the last one.

16.7 NETWORKS

Local area network (LAN) is a widely used communication technology for DNC systems. A LAN is a data communication system that allows various types of digital devices to talk to each other over a common transmission medium. Shielded coaxial cables and fibre-optic connections are used for communications. The most popular LAN configurations are:

- Ring LAN
- Bus LAN

Ring LAN is one in which the devices are connected in the form of a ring-like structure as shown in Figure 16.5. The data moves in the ring and when the correct address comes up, it is picked by the device. There is no single system to act as a server and all the nodes can transmit and receive data through the network. The advantages of ring LAN are:

- The databases on one workstation can be shared by others in the network
- If one workstation fails, the rest remain operational.

The bus LAN is an open-loop system, which may take the form of a main bis or branched or tree systems. This network is particularly suitable for use when the devices to be connected are dissimilar. Bus LAN is shown in Figure 16.6.

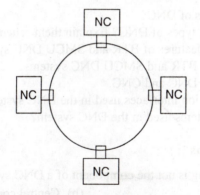

Fig. 16.5 Ring LAN.

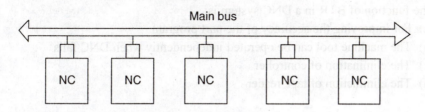

Fig. 16.6 Bus LAN.

16.8 ADVANTAGES OF DNC

The various advantages of DNC are:

1. Elimination of punched tapes and tape readers
2. Greater computational capability for such functions as circular interpolation
3. Time sharing or the control of more than one machine by the computer
4. Programs stored as CLFILE
5. Reporting of shop performance
6. Remote computer location—the computer is located in a computer-type environment

16.9 WHAT HAPPENS IF THE COMPUTER BREAKS DOWN?

If the computer breaks down, this has not turned out to be too much of a problem simply because the central computer is much more reliable than the conventional NC machines.

QUESTION BANK

A. Descriptive Questions

1. What is the need for DNC? Explain.
2. What are the components of DNC?

3. What are the functions of DNC?
4. What are the different types of DNC? Explain them schematically.
5. What are the relative features of BTR and SMCU DNC systems?
6. Differentiate between BTR and SMCU DNC systems.
7. Differentiate between DNC and CNC.
8. What are communication interfaces used in the DNC system?
9. What are network systems used in the DNC system?

B. Multiple Choice Questions

1. Which of the following is not the component of a DNC system:
   (a) Bulk memory   (b) Central computer
   (c) Tape reader   (d) Networking
2. The function of BTR in a DNC system is:
   (a) For improving the accuracy of the part program
   (b) The machine tool can be operated independently when DNC fails
   (c) The elimination of controller
   (d) The elimination of tape reader

17

Adaptive Control Machining Systems

After reading this chapter, the reader will be able to understand the following concepts:

- Adaptive control
- Where to use adaptive control?
- What are the sources of variability in machining?
- Elements of an adaptive control machining system
- Types of adaptive control: Adaptive control optimisation (ACO) and adaptive control constraint (ACC)
- Advantages of adaptive control machining systems

17.1 INTRODUCTION

Adaptive control machining has been developed to optimise machining characteristics. The adaptive control (AC) machining is an evolutionary outgrowth of numerical control. It is a control system that measures certain output process variables and uses these to control speed and/or feed. Some of the process variables that have been used in adaptive control machining systems include spindle deflection or force, torque, cutting temperature, vibration amplitude, metal removable rate cost per volume of metal removed, and horsepower.

17.2 ADAPTIVE CONTROL

The adaptive control feedback provides sensory information on machining process variables such as spindle deflection or force, torque, cutting temperature, workpiece tool air gaps, material property variations, vibration amplitude, metal removable rate cost per volume of metal removed, and horsepower. The data is processed by an adaptive controller that converts the process information into feedback data to be incorporated into the machine control unit (Figure 17.1).

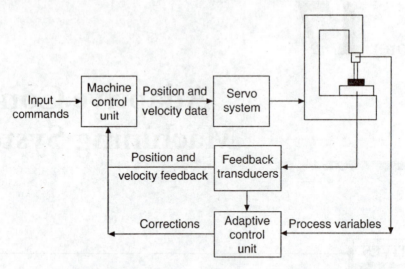

Fig. 17.1 Adaptive control machining system.

17.3 WHERE TO USE ADAPTIVE CONTROL?

The main advantage of NC/CNC is that it reduces the non-productive time in a machining operation. This time saving is achieved by reducing workpiece handling time, set-up of the job, tool changes, and other sources of operator and machine delay. If these non-productive elements are reduced relative to the total production time, a large proportion of the time can be spent in actually machining the workpiece. Although NC/CNC has a significant effect on the reduction of non-productive time, it can do relatively little to decrease the in-process time as compared to a conventional machine tool.

NC/CNC controls the sequence of tool positions or the continuous tool path of the tool during machining. There is every possibility of spindle deflection or increasing of cutting temperature, or workpiece tool air gaps, or material property variations, or machine tool vibration. These process parameters waste productive time. The most promising means of reducing the productive time is the use of adaptive control. Adaptive control determines the proper speeds/feeds during machining as functions of variations in process variables such as work-material hardness, width or depth of cut, air gaps in the part geometry, and so on. Adaptive Control (AC) has the capability to respond to and compensate for these variations during the process.

AC should be utilised in applications where the following characteristics are found:

1. The in-process time consumes a significant portion of the total production time.
2. There are significant sources of variability in the job for which AC can compensate. In essence, AC adapts speed/feed to these variable conditions.
3. The cost of operating the machine tool is high.

17.4 WHAT ARE THE SOURCES OF VARIABILITY IN MACHINING?

The typical sources of variability in machining are as follows:

1. *Variable geometry of cut in the form of changing depth or width of cut:*   In these cases, the feed rate is usually adjusted to compensate for the variability. This type of variability is often encountered in profile milling or contouring operations.
2. *Variable workpiece hardness and variable machinability:*   When hard spots or other areas of difficulty are encountered in the workpiece, either speed or feed is reduced to prevent premature failure of the tool.
3. *Variable workpiece rigidity:*   If the workpiece deflects as a result of insufficient rigidity in the set-up, the feed rate must be reduced to maintain accuracy in the process.
4. *Tools wear:*   It has been observed in research that as the tool begins to dull, the cutting forces increase. AC will typically respond to tool dulling by reducing the feed rate.
5. *Air gaps during cutting*:   The workpiece geometry may contain shaped sections where no machining needs to be performed. If the tool were to continue feeding through these so-called air gaps at the same rate, precious time would be wasted. Accordingly, the typical procedure is to increase the feed rate by a factor 2 or 3, when air gaps are encountered.

These sources of variability present themselves as time-varying and, for the most part, unpredictable changes in the machining process.

17.5 ELEMENTS OF AN ADAPTIVE CONTROL MACHINING SYSTEM

The machining process is affected by many process variables. In addition to cutting forces, and position and velocity feedback, the AC monitors vibrations, cutting temperature and spindle horsepower. In order to fulfil these requirements, AC requires sophisticated transducers and sensors.

Strain gauges are used to sense the cutting force, tool deflection and torque. Typical strain gauges are illustrated in Figure 17.2a. The strain gauges are bonded to the tool holding structure so that both horizontal and vertical forces cause corresponding tool strains, which can be measured as shown in Figure 17.2b.

Motor horsepower input is determined by measuring motor current. The cutting temperature is measured by using the thermocouple principle (Figure 17.3). The e.m.f. in a thermo-electric circuit is ascribed to the following two phenomena:

1. **Peltier effect:**   This governs the e.m.f. resulting solely from the contact of two different metals and magnitude varying with the temperature of this contact.
2. **Thomson effect:**   This is the e.m.f. resulting from the temperature gradient along the single wire and is less predominant.

Tool vibration is determined by mounting an accelerometer on the spindle housing (Figure 17.4).

The air gap can be sensed by a tool force sensor. For an air gap, the tool force sensor indicates zero force reading.

Optimisation logic continuously attempts to increase performance in a selected process parameter until constraint violation occurs. Constraints define the permissible range of operation for the adaptive control unit (ACU). Depending on the process variable that caused the constraint violation, the logic system increments or decrements the value of the ACU output. For example, if the cutting force is exceeded the predetermined value, feed rate or spindle speed may be reduced.

Figure 17.5 represents a typical adaptive control machining system. It operates on the principle of maintaining a constant cutter force during the machining operation. When the force increases due to increased workpiece hardness or the depth or width of cut, the feed rate is reduced to compensate for this. When the force decreases owing to decreases in the forgoing variables or air gaps in the part, the feed rate is increased to maximise the rate of the metal removed.

Figure 17.5 shows the presence of an air gap over-ride feature which monitors the cutter force and determines if the cutter is moving through air or through metal. This is usually sensed by means of a low threshold value of cutter force. If the actual cutter force is below this threshold level, the controller assumes that the cutter is passing through an air gap. When an air gap is sensed, the feed rate is doubled or tripled to minimise the time wasted while travelling across the air gap. When the cutter re-engages metal on the other side of the gap, the feed reverts to the cutter force mode of control. More than one process variable may be measured in an AC machining system.

Originally, attempts were made to employ three measured signals in the Bendix system: temperature, torque, and vibration. The Mactech system has used both cutter load and horsepower generated at the machine motor. The purpose of the power sensor is to protect the motor from the overload when the metal removal rate is constrained by spindle horsepower rather than spindle force.

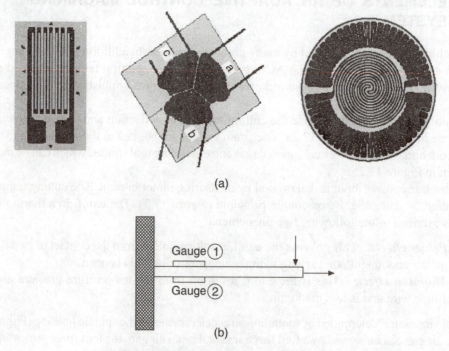

(a)

(b)

Fig. 17.2 Strain gauge configurations.

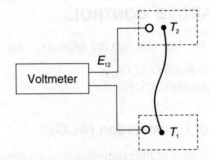

Fig. 17.3 Thermocouple principle.

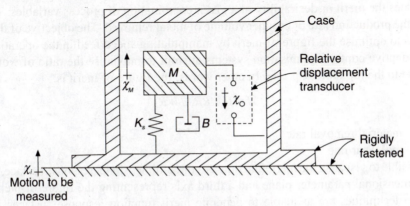

Fig. 17.4 Accelerometer.

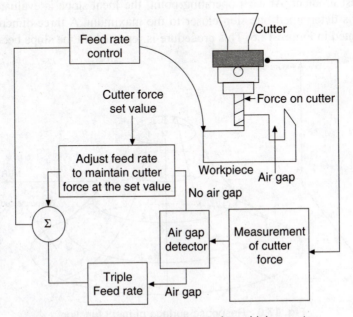

Fig. 17.5 A typical adaptive control machining system.

17.6 TYPES OF ADAPTIVE CONTROL

Adaptive control systems can be classified into the following two categories:

1. Adaptive Control Optimisation (ACO)
2. Adaptive Control Constraint (ACC)

17.6.1 Adaptive Control Optimisation (ACO)

ACO optimises the overall efficiency of the production process or selected process parameters. In this form of adaptive control, a figure-of-merit, M is specified for the system. The figure-of-merit is called merit function, which is a numerical measure of efficiency. The magnitude of figure-of-merit indicates the merit or desirability of a given combination of process variables. The figure-of-merit is the production rate or cost per volume of metal removed. The objective of the adaptive controller is to optimise the figure-of-merit by manipulating speed/feed in the operation.

Most adaptive control optimisation systems attempt to maximise the ratio of work material removal rate to the top tool wear rate. In other words, the figure-of-merit is:

$$M = f(MRR, TWR) \tag{17.1}$$

where

MRR = material removal rate

TWR = tool wear rate

It is possible to visualise the merit function as a three-dimensional response surface, consisting of a two-dimensional parameter plane and a third axis representing the figure-of-merit. Various optimisation techniques are available to generate merit function response surfaces. The merit function can be maximised by using the hill climbing technique. The response surface is ascended along the steepest gradient. At each operating point, the local slope is evaluated and the next operating point is determined one step closer to the maximum. A three-dimensional response surface is illustrated in Figure 17.6. This procedure is repeated till the slope becomes zero.

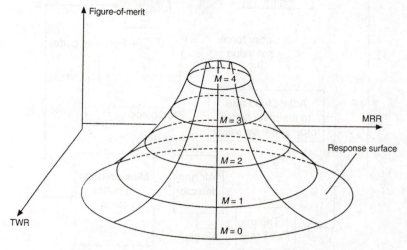

Fig. 17.6 Response surface of merit function.

17.6.2 Adaptive Control Constraint (ACC)

The objective of the adaptive controller is to manipulate speed/feed to maintain the measured variables at or below their constraint limit values. Constraints define the permissible range of operation. The constraint violation detection logic determines whether the process variable exceeded the pre-defined limit or not. If constraint violation has occurred, the ACU logic sub-system increments or decrements the value of the ACU output such that the process variable is within the pre-defined limits.

The flow chart of a constraint violation detection system is shown in Figure 17.7. If dangerous conditions are found, the constraint violation detection system stops the machining operations and shuts down the machine tool.

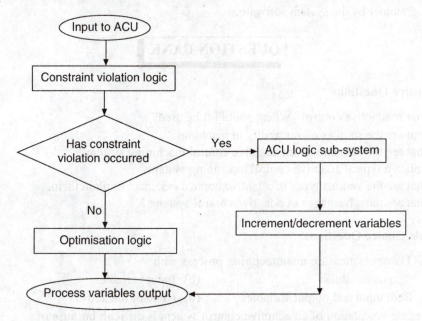

Fig. 17.7   Constraint violation detection system.

17.7   ADVANTAGES OF ADAPTIVE CONTROL MACHINING SYSTEMS

There are several advantages of adaptive control machining systems. These are listed below:

1. *Increased production rates:*   On-line adjustments to allow for variations in work geometry, material, and tool wear, provide the machine tool with the capability to achieve the highest metal removal rates that are consistent with existing conditions. This capability translates into more parts per hour. The right, AC will yield significant gains in production rate as compared to NC or CNC.
2. *Increased tool life:*   AC facilitates a more efficient and uniform use of the cutter throughout its tool life. Since adjustments are made in the feed rate to prevent severe loading of the tool, fewer cutters will be broken.

3. *Greater part protection:* Instead of setting the cutter force limit on the basis of the maximum allowable cutter and spindle deflection, the force limit can be established on the basis of the work size tolerance. In this way, the part is protected against an out-of-tolerance condition and possible damage.

4. *Less operate intervention:* The advent of AC machining has transferred the control of the process even further out of the hands of the operator and into the hands of management via the part programmer.

5. *Easier part programming:* In AC part programming, the selection of the feed is largely left to the controller unit rather than to the part programmer. The constraint limit on force, horsepower, or any other variable must be determined according to the particular job and cutter used. However, this can often be calculated from known parameters for the programmer by the system software.

QUESTION BANK

A. Descriptive Questions

1. What is adaptive control? Where should it be used?
2. What are the sources of variability in machining?
3. What are the elements of an adaptive control machining system?
4. Explain a typical adaptive control machining system.
5. What are the various types of adaptive control systems? Explain them.
6. What are the advantages of adaptive control systems?

B. Multiple Choice Questions

1. ACO controls measure manufacturing process with:
   (a) Output variables   (b) Input variables
   (c) Both input and output variables   (d) None of the above
2. The implementation of an adaptive control system is difficult because of:
   (a) Complexity of the system   (b) Lack of sensor technology
   (c) Identification of the objective function (d) All the above

Chapter 18

Group Technology

18.1 INTRODUCTION

Group Technology (GT) is a manufacturing philosophy in which similar parts are identified and grouped together to facilitate exploitation of their similarities in manufacturing and design. Similar parts are arranged into *part families*. Grouping the production equipment into machine cells where each is specialized in the production of a family of products is known as *Cellular Manufacturing*.

411

In this chapter, formation of parts classification based on part families and coding systems are discussed.

18.2 PART FAMILIES

A part family is a collection of parts, which are similar either because of their geometric shape and size or because similar processing steps are required in their manufacture. The parts within a family are different, but their similarities are close enough to merit their identification as members of the part family.

The part family is illustrated with a simple example as shown in Figure 18.1. P1, P2, . . . , Pn are the *n* number of products manufactured from three components, say a square, circular and rectangle of different sizes. Hence, the parts of *n* products can be grouped into three families namely the square, circular and rectangle families. Parts classification and coding are concerned with identifying the similarities among parts. Part similarities are based on design attributes and manufacturing attributes.

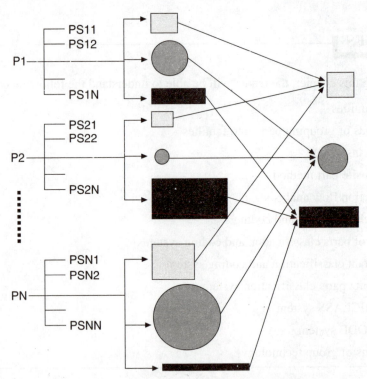

Fig. 18.1 Illustration of simple part families.

One of the important manufacturing advantages of grouping product parts into families can be explained with reference to Figures 18.2 and 18.3. Figure 18.2 shows a process type layout for a batch production in a machine shop. Lathes, milling machines, drilling machines, grinding machines and assembling units are arranged in different departments on the basis of their functions. Thus, there is a lathe department, milling department, drilling department, grinding department and assembling department. The workpiece must be transported among various functional departments as per the sequence of operations, with perhaps the same section being visited several times. This results in a significant amount of material handling, large in-process inventory, many machine set-ups, long manufacturing lead times and high cost. Figure 18.3 shows a group technology layout with machines arranged into cells. Each cell is organised to specialise in the production of a particular part family. The advantages of a GT layout include reduced material handling, small in-process inventory, fewer machine set-ups, shorter manufacturing lead times and low cost. The main disadvantage of a GT layout, however, is the formation of part families.

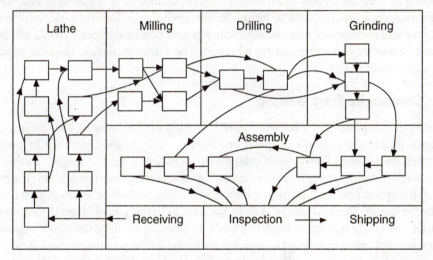

Fig. 18.2   Process layout.

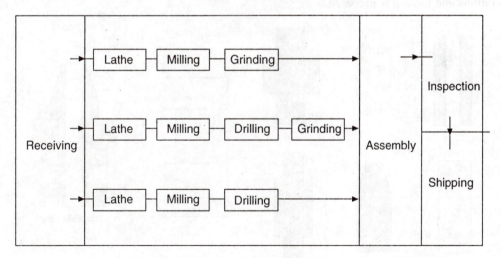

Fig. 18.3   Group technology layout.

18.3 METHODS OF GROUPING PARTS INTO FAMILIES

There are four general methods for grouping parts into families. These methods are:

1. Visual inspection
2. Composite method
3. Production flow analysis
4. Parts classification and coding

18.3.1 Visual Inspection

The grouping of parts into small and medium batch manufacture is not an easy task. One of the ways of forming such groups could be *visual*. In this, grouping is done by looking for similarities in shape, size and methods of manufacture. It is obvious that this practice would not be correct and as such cannot be recommended for adoption. The visual method is the least sophisticated and least expensive method.

18.3.2 Composite Part Method

In this method, a hypothetical *composite part* is formed on the basis of the features of all the components forming the group in question. Figure 18.4 shows a number of components manufactured on a lathe. The various operations include setting the length, facing, turning, grooving, drilling, boring, reaming, counter-boring, chamfering, parting off, etc. Each job may not need all the operations. An imaginary component is composed which involves all the operations needed for the group. The tool setting is done for such a component on a multi-tool set-up, say a turret, which can easily handle up to eleven tools. Depending on the particular component to be worked on, instructions are prepared to indicate the tools and the sequence in which they are to be used. Whenever a new component is to be made, its group is determined and then its sequence of operations and tooling is prepared.

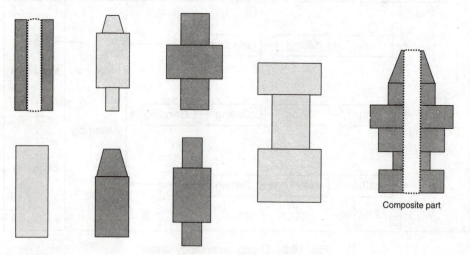

Composite part

Fig. 18.4 Composite part method.

18.3.3 Production Flow Analysis

This method makes use of the information contained on route sheets rather than on part drawings. Work-parts with identical or similar routings are classified into part families. Production flow analysis uses manufacturing data rather than design data to identify part families. The procedure of production flow analysis is as follows:

1. **Data collection:** The data such as part number and operation sequence is collected from the manufacturing data contained in the route sheets.
2. **Sorting:** The parts are segregated and arranged into groups according to similar or identical routings.
3. **Preparation of chart:** The chart is a tabulation of the process or machine code numbers for all the parts of a part family. In this tabulation, the entries are cross-marked (X). The cross-mark (X) indicates ith part requiring jth machine. If $X_{ij} = 0$, there is no processing of the ith part on the jth machine. The chart is given in Table 18.1.

Table 18.1 PFA Chart

Part No.	Machine No.										
	5	2	6	7	9	4	1	3	11	8	10
4	X	X		X	X						
2	X	X	X	X							
6	X		X	X	X						
3						X	X				
8						X	X	X			
1						X		X			
5									X	X	
9									X		X
7									X	X	X

18.3.4 Parts Classification and Coding

In this method, the parts are grouped into families by considering the individual design and/or manufacturing attributes of each part. The attributes of the part are uniquely identified by means of a code number. This classification and coding may be carried on the entire list of parts of a family.

Many systems have been developed throughout the world, but none has been universally adopted. One of the reasons for this is that a classification and coding system should be custom-engineered for a given company or industry. One system may be best for one company while a different system may be more suited to another company.

18.4 TYPES OF PARTS CLASSIFICATION AND CODING SYSTEMS

Classification of parts refers to grouping of parts on the basis of the essential features of parts. Coding is the process of assigning symbols to the parts. The symbols may represent design attributes or manufacturing attributes or both.

18.4.1 Parts Classification Schemes

The following three types of systems are used for the parts classification on the basis of the following attributes:

1. Systems based on part design attributes

   - Basic external shape
   - Basic internal shape
   - Length/diameter ratio
   - Material type
   - Part function
   - Major dimensions
   - Minor dimensions
   - Tolerances
   - Surface finish

2. Systems based on part manufacturing attributes

   - Major process
   - Minor operations
   - Major dimension
   - Length/diameter ratio
   - Surface finish
   - Machine tool
   - Operation sequence
   - Production time
   - Batch size
   - Annual production
   - Fixtures needed
   - Cutting tools

3. Systems based on both design and manufacturing attributes

   - Basic external shape
   - Basic internal shape
   - Length/diameter ratio
   - Material type
   - Part function
   - Major dimensions
   - Minor dimensions
   - Tolerances
   - Surface finish
   - Major process
   - Minor operations
   - Machine tool
   - Operation sequence
   - Production time

- Batch size
- Annual production
- Fixtures needed
- Cutting tools

18.4.2 Coding Schemes

Coding systems use number digits. There are three basic code structures used in GT applications. These are:

1. *Hierarchical structure:* In the hierarchical structure, the interpretation of each succeeding symbol depends on the value of the preceding symbols. The hierarchical structure is also called 'monocode'. This provides a relatively compact structure, which conveys a lot of information about the part in a limited number of digits. The first digits (0 to 9) divides the parts into major groups such as machined parts, cast parts, forged parts, sheet metal parts, etc. The second digits may sub-divide the machine parts into rotational and non-rotational parts. The third and subsequent digits may partition the machine into sub-groups. Therefore, the digits in a hierarchical code cannot be interpreted independently; the interpretation depends on the information contained in the preceding symbol. The hierarchical structure is given in Figure 18.5.

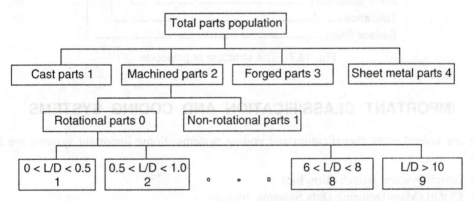

Fig. 18.5 The hierarchical structure.

For example, the three digits code for the machined rotational part shown in Figure 18.6 are coded as 208.

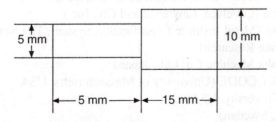

Fig. 18.6 Machined rotational part with L/D ratio of 8.0.

2. *Chain-type structure:* This is also called 'polycode'. In this structure, the interpretation of each symbol in the sequence is fixed and does not depend on the value of the preceding digits. The problem associated with polycode is that it tends to be relatively long. On the other hand, the use of a polycode allows for convenient identification of a specific part attribute. The polycode structure is illustrated in Figure 18.7.

3. *Hybrid structure:* The hybrid structure is an attempt to achieve the best features of monocodes and polycodes. Hybrid codes seem to best serve the needs of both design and production.

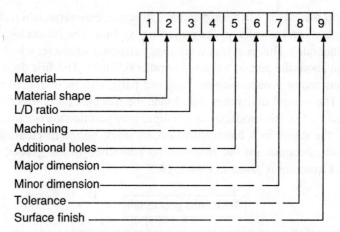

Fig. 18.7   The structure of polycode.

18.5   IMPORTANT CLASSIFICATION AND CODING SYSTEMS

There are several parts classification and coding systems. Some important systems are listed below:

- Brisch System (Brisch-Birn, Inc)
- CODE (Manufacturing Data Systems, Inc)
- CUTPLAN (Metcut Associates)
- DCLASS (Brigham Young university)
- Optiz (H. Optiz of the University of Aachen, West Germany)
- MultiClass (OIR—Organisation for Industrial Research)
- Par Analog System (Lovelace, Lawrence and Co., Inc.)
- MICLASS System (Metal Institute Classification System, The Netherlands Organisation for Applied Science Research)
- TOSHIBA (Toshiba Machine Co. Ltd., Japan)
- ASSEMBLY PART CODE (University of Massachusetts, USA)
- SAGT (Purdue University, USA)
- PGM (PGM Ltd., Swedan)
- PERA (Production Engineering Research Association, UK)
- LITMO (Leningrad Institute for Pre and Optics, USSR)

18.5.1 The Optiz Parts Classification System

This system uses the following digit sequence:

12345 6789 ABCD

The basic structure consists of nine digits divided into two parts, namely form code and supplementary code. The first nine digits are intended to convey both design and manufacturing data. The first five digits, 12345, are called the 'form code' and describe the primary design attributes of the part. The next four digits, 6789, constitute the 'supplementary code' which indicates some of the attributes that would be of use to manufacturing (dimensions, work material, starting raw work piece shape, and accuracy). The extra four digits, ABCD, are referred to as the 'secondary code' and are intended to identify the production operation type and sequence. The secondary code can be designed by the firm to serve its own particular needs. Secondary code normally consists of a polycode stucture.

Example 18.1 Define the form code using Optiz system for the part shown in Figure 18.8.

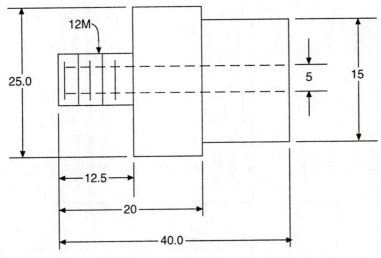

Fig. 18.8 Dimensions are in mm.

Solution

The overall length/diameter ratio = 1.6

So the first digit code = 1

The part is stepped on both ends with a screw thread on one end.

So the second digit code = 5

There is a through hole.

So the third digit = 1

The fourth and fifth digits are both 0, since no surface machining is required and there are no auxiliary holes or gear teeth on the part.

The complete form code = 15100

To add the supplementary code, the sixth through the ninth digits are coded with data on dimensions, material, starting work piece and shape, and accuracy.

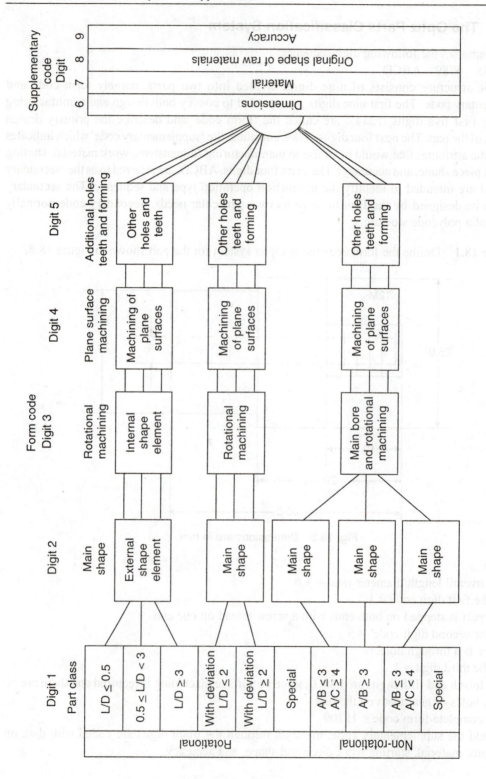

Fig. 18.9 Basic structure of Optiz system.

Code	Digit 1: Part class		Digit 2: External shape, external shape elements		Digit 3: Internal shape, internal shape elements		Digit 4: Plane surface machining	Digit 5: Auxiliary holes and gear teeth	
0	Rotational parts	L/D ≤ 0.5	Stepped to one end or smooth	Smooth, no shape elements	Smooth or stepped to one end	No hole, no break-through	No surface machining	No gear teeth	No auxiliary hole
1	Rotational parts	0.5 < L/D < 3	Stepped to one end or smooth	No shape elements	Smooth or stepped to one end	No shape elements	Surface plane and/or curved in one direction, external	No gear teeth	Axial, not on pitch circle diameter
2	Rotational parts	L/D ≥ 3	Stepped to one end or smooth	Thread	Smooth or stepped to one end	Thread	External plane surface related by graduation around a circle	No gear teeth	Axial on pitch circle diameter
3	Rotational parts		Stepped to one end or smooth	Functional groove	Smooth or stepped to one end	Functional groove	External groove and/or slot	No gear teeth	Radial, not on pitch circle diameter
4	Rotational parts		Stepped to both ends	No shape elements	Stepped to both ends	No shape elements	External spline (polygon)	No gear teeth	Axial and/or radial and/or other direction
5	Rotational parts		Stepped to both ends	Thread	Stepped to both ends	Thread	External plane surface and/or solt, external spline	No gear teeth	Axial and/or radial on PCD and/or other directions
6	Non-rotational parts		Stepped to both ends	Functional groove	Stepped to both ends	Functional groove	Internal plane surface and/or slot	With gear teeth	Spur gear teeth
7	Non-rotational parts			Functional groove		Functional cone	Internal spline (polygon)	With gear teeth	Bevel gear teeth
8	Non-rotational parts			Operating thread		Operating thread	Internal and external polygon, groove and/or slot	With gear teeth	Other gear teeth
9	Non-rotational parts			All others		All others	All others	With gear teeth	All others

Fig. 18.10 Form code of Optiz system.

18.5.2   The MICLASS System

MICLASS stands for Metal Institute Classification System. It was developed in the Netherlands and is maintained in USA by the Organisation for Industrial Research (OIR). This system was developed to help automate and standardise a number of design, production, and management functions. The MICLASS classification number can range from 12 to 30 digits. The first 12 digits constitute a universal code that can be applied to any part. Up to 18 additional digits can be used to code data that are specific to the particular company or industry. For example, lot size, piece time, cost data, and operation sequence might be included in the 18 supplementary digits.

The work part attributes coded in the first 12 digits of the MICLASS number are as follows:

1st digit	Main shape
2nd and 3rd digits	Shape elements (external and internal)
4th digit	Position of shape elements
5th and 6th digits	Main dimensions
7th digit	Dimension ratio
8th digit	Auxiliary dimension
9th and 10th digits	Tolerance codes
11th and 12th digits	Material codes

One of the unique features of the MICLASS system is that in it, parts can be coded by using a computer interactively. In order to classify a given part design, the user responds to a series of questions asked by the computer. The number of questions depends on the complexity of the part.

18.5.3   The CODE System

The CODE system has eight digits. It is based on a chain type structure. Each digit has 16 possible values (0 through 9 and A through F) to describe the design and manufacturing attributes of parts. The first digit indicates the basic geometry of the part. The interpretation of the remaining seven digits depends on the value of the first digit. The second and third digits represent additional information pertaining to the basic geometry and manufacturing process. Digits 4, 5 and 6 indicate secondary manufacturing processes such as grooves, slots, threads, etc. Digits 7 and 8 specify the overall size of the part. Figure 18.11 shows a portion of the CODE system for concentric parts (major division, 1).

The CODE system is a parts classification and coding system developed and marketed by Manufacturing Data Systems, Inc. of Arbor, Michigan.

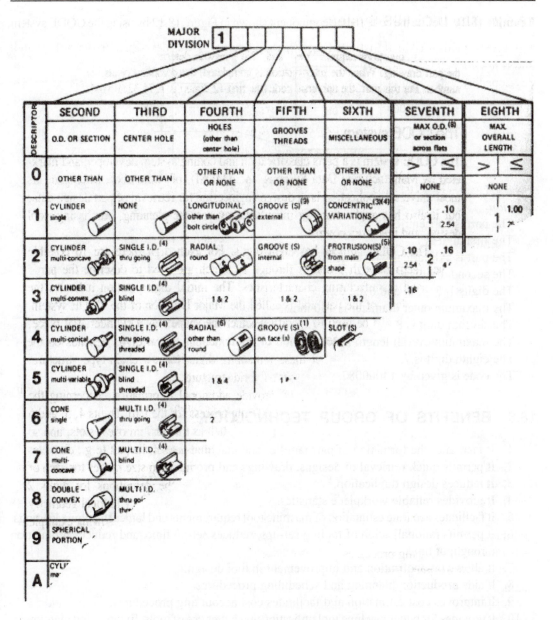

Fig. 18.11 A portion of CODE system.

Example 18.2 Define the code for the component shown in Figure 18.12 by using the CODE system.

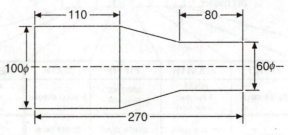

Fig. 18.12

Solution

The part is concentric.
The first digit is 1.
The part is cylindrical with cone.
The second digit is 4.
The digits 1, 3, 4, 5, and 6 are 0s.
The maximum outer diameter is 100 mm.
The seventh digit is 8.
The maximum overall length is 270 mm.
The eighth digit is 7.
The code is given by 14000087.

18.6 BENEFITS OF GROUP TECHNOLOGY

1. It facilitates the formation of part families and machine cells.
2. It permits quick retrieval of designs, drawings and process plans.
3. It reduces design duplication.
4. It provides reliable workpiece statistics.
5. It facilitates accurate estimation of machine tool requirements and logical machine loadings.
6. It permits rationalisation of tooling set-ups, reduces set-up time, and reduces production throughput time.
7. It allows rationalisation and improvement in tool design.
8. It aids production planning and scheduling procedures.
9. It improves cost estimation and facilitates cost accounting procedures.
10. It provides for better machine tool utilisation and better use of tools, fixtures, and manpower.
11. It facilitates NC part programming.

QUESTION BANK

A. Descriptive Questions

1. What is group technology?
2. Why is GT more important in the present manufacturing scenario?

3. What is the basis for forming part families in GT?

4. Classify the methods of grouping parts into families. Explain any two systems.

5. Explain the concept of composite part with an example.

6. What is a production flow analysis PFA? Discuss various steps involved in PFA.

7. What are the various types of parts classification and coding systems?

8. Explain different types of parts classification schemes.

9. Explain different types of coding schemes.

10. Compare the process layout with the GT layout.

11. Explain the Optiz coding system with an example.

12. Explain the MICLASS coding system with an example.

13. Explain the CODE coding system with an example.

14. Differentiate between monocode and polycode.

15. What are the benefits of GT?

16. What are the limitations of GT?

17. Develop form code for the part shown in Figure 18.13.

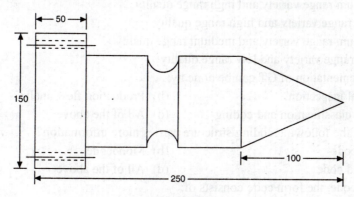

Fig. 18.13

18. Develop form code for the part shown in Figure 18.14.

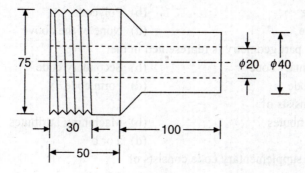

Fig. 18.14

19. Develop form code for the part shown in Figure 18.15.

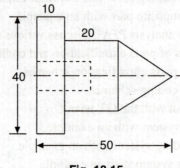

Fig. 18.15

B. Multiple Choice Questions

1. GT is suitable for the production of:
   (a) Medium range variety and high range quality
   (b) High range variety and high range quality
   (c) Medium range variety and medium range quality
   (d) Low range variety and low range quality

2. The implementation of GT can be done by:
   (a) Visual inspection
   (b) Production flow analysis
   (c) Parts classification and coding
   (d) All of the above

3. Which of the following coding structure carries more information?
   (a) Polycode
   (b) Monocode
   (c) Mixed code
   (d) All of the above

4. In Optiz code, the form code consists of:
   (a) 8 digits
   (b) 9 digits
   (c) 16 digits
   (d) 18 digits

5. In Optiz code, the form code is an example of:
   (a) Monocode
   (b) Polycode
   (c) Mixedcode
   (d) None of the above

6. In Optiz code, part geometry is represented in the:
   (a) Supplementary code
   (b) Secondary code
   (c) Primary code
   (d) Form code

7. Optiz code consists of:
   (a) Design attributes
   (b) Machining attributes
   (c) Both
   (d) a or b

8. In Optiz code, supplementary code consists of:
   (a) 8 digits
   (b) 4 Digits
   (c) 5 digits
   (d) 6 digits

9. The secondary code of Optiz code consists of:
   (a) Numerical values   (b) Alphabetic
   (c) Alpha-numeric   (d) Symbols
10. MICLASS coding is based on:
    (a) Hierarchical structure   (b) Chain-type structure
    (c) Polycode structure   (d) Mixed stucture
11. MiClass coding consists of:
    (a) 9 digits   (b) 18 digits
    (c) 16 digits   (d) 8 digits

Chapter 19

Computer-aided Process Planning

After reading this chapter, the reader will be able to understand the following concepts:

- What is process planning?
- Difficulties in traditional process planning
- Computer-aided process planning (CAPP): Retrieval-type CAPP system, generative CAPP system, and hybrid CAPP system
- Process planning systems
- Machinability data systems: Mathematical modelling, and database systems
- Benefits of CAPP

19.1 INTRODUCTION

Process planning is the function within a manufacturing facility that establishes which processes and parameters are to be used to convert a workpiece to its final predetermined form in an engineering drawing. The initial form of the workpiece may be casting, forging, etc. The process planner has to prepare a list of processes after selecting raw workpiece to convert it into a predetermined final shape. Process planning serves as an interface between design and manufacturing.

19.2 WHAT IS PROCESS PLANNING?

Process planning is concerned with determining the sequence of individual manufacturing operations needed to produce a given part or product. The resulting operation sequence is documented on a form referred to as a 'route sheet'. The route sheet is a listing of the production operations and associated machine tools for a work part or assembly.

19.3 DIFFICULTIES IN TRADITIONAL PROCESS PLANNING

There are variations in the level of detail found in route sheets among different companies and industries. In one extreme case, process planning is accomplished by releasing the part print to the production shop with the instructions 'make to drawing'. Most firms provide a more detailed list of steps describing each operation and identifying each work centre.

In any case, it is traditionally the task of the manufacturing engineers in an organisation to write these process plans for new part designs to be produced by the shop. The process planning procedure is highly dependent on the experience and judgment of the planner. It is the manufacturing engineer's responsibility to determine an optimal routing for each new part design.

Accordingly, there are differences among the operation sequences developed by various planners. New machine tools in the factory render old routings less than optimal. Machine breakdowns force shop personnel to use temporary routings, and these become the documented routings even after the machine is repaired.

19.4 COMPUTER-AIDED PROCESS PLANNING (CAPP)

In view of the problems encountered with manual process planning, attempts have been made to capture the logic, judgment, and experience required for this important function and to incorporate them into computer programs. On the basis of the characteristics of a given part, the program automatically generates the manufacturing operation sequence. A computer-aided process planning system offers the potential for reducing the routine clerical work of manufacturing engineers. At the same time, it provides the opportunity to generate production routings which are rational, consistent, and perhaps even optimal.

The following alternative approaches to CAPP have been developed:

1. Retrieval type CAPP (variant) systems
2. Generative CAPP systems
3. Hybrid CAPP systems

19.4.1 Retrieval Type CAPP System

In this approach, the parts produced in the plant are grouped into part families, and distinguished according to their manufacturing characteristics. For each part family, a standard process plan is established. The standard process plan is stored in computer files and then retrieved for new work parts, which belong to that family. The user initiates the procedure by entering the part code number at a computer terminal. The CAPP program then searches the part family matrix file to determine if a match exists. If the file contains an identical code number, the standard machine routing and operation sequence are retrieved from the respective computer files for display for the user. The standard process plan is examined by the user to permit any necessary editing of the plan to make it compatible with the new part design. After editing, the process plan formatter prepares the paper document in the proper form (Figure 19.1).

If an exact match cannot be found between the code numbers in the computer file and the code number for the new part, the user may search the machine routing file and the operation sequence file for similar parts that can be used to develop the plan for the new part. Once the process plan for a new part code number has been entered, it becomes the standard process for future parts of the same classification.

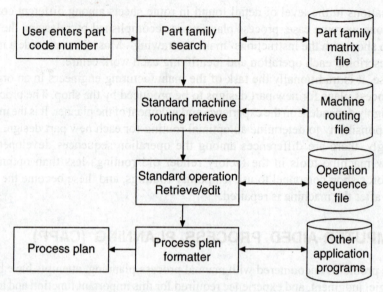

Fig. 19.1   Retrieval type CAPP system.

19.4.2 Generative CAPP System

Generative process planning involves the use of the computer to create an individual process plan from scratch, automatically and without human assistance (Figure 19.2). The computer would employ a set of algorithms to progress through the various technical and logical decisions toward a final plan for manufacturing. Inputs to the system would include geometric and manufacturing data.

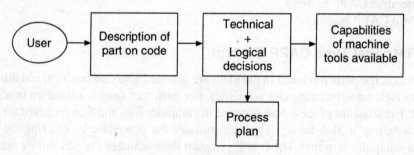

Fig. 19.2   Generative CAPP system.

The generative system is implemented through the development of decision rules appropriate for the parts to be processed. The decision rules are specified by decision tress, if-then, if-then-else or artificial intelligence approaches.

A pure generative system can produce a complete process plan from GT codes with part classification and design data. Two types of planning are available: forward and backward planning.

Using forward planning, we begin with the stock as the initial state and the part features are removed until the final part is obtained.

Using backward planning, we begin with the final part as the initial state and the part features are buildup until the stock is obtained.

19.4.3 Hybrid CAPP System

The hybrid system can be characterised as an advanced application of retrieval type CAPP with additional features of generative type CAPP.

The hybrid system can be implemented in the following three ways:

1. The generative mode can be used to create a process plan from scratch to the maximum extent possible, and then the variant mode can be used to fill in the remaining details.
2. The variant mode can be used to retrieve the general process plan, and then the generative mode can be used to modify it.
3. For complicated part features, the generative mode can be used, while for simple and moderate part features, the variant mode can be used.

19.5 PROCESS PLANNING SYSTEMS

Various CAPP systems are available. Some of them are given in Table 19.1

Table 19.1 CAPP Systems

Type	Software
Variant CAPP	MIPLAN, MITURN, UNIVATION, CINTURN, CAMSS, GLM, and MULTICAPP
Generative CAPP	AUTAP, KAPLAN, IKOOP, PART, TVCAPP, ALPS, CROPS, GFAS, GEOPDE, GLM, MCOES, RATE and TIPPS
Hybrid CAPP	COMPLAN, RDCAPP, SMT, and TAMCAM

19.6 MACHINABILITY DATA SYSTEMS

The machinability data systems are based on two important techniques. These are:

1. Mathematical modelling based on empirically derived equations that fit a range of experimental data.
2. Database systems that enable machinability data acquisition from a large database.

19.6.1 Mathematical Modelling

Mathematical modelling represents machinability variables in terms of machining parameter groups. In general, a machinability variable y (metal removal rate, tool wear rate, part surface finish), can be expressed as:

$$y = f(x_1, x_2, x_3, ..., x_n) \tag{19.1}$$

where $x_1, x_2, x_3, ..., x_n$ are metal cutting parameters.

The most important mathematical model for the metal cutting processes is Taylor's tool life formula:

$$vT^n = C \tag{19.2}$$

where

v is the cutting speed.

T is the tool life in minutes.

n is the empirically derived tool life exponent.

C is a constant of the material.

For known values of n and C, the cutting speed can be computed on the basis of a specified tool life as follows:

$$\log y = \log C - n \log T \tag{19.3}$$

19.6.2 Database Systems

A machinability database system makes use of a large file, which can store all the information pertaining to machinability data. The database system consists of three files. These are:

1. *Material file:* It consists of information belonging to the machinability characteristics of the materials being used for various products. The information includes experimentally derived depth of cut, feed rate and speed pertaining to various tools and operations for a particular workpiece material.
2. *Tool file:* It contains information on tools such as, the tool number, diameter, flute length, number of teeth, single point tool, multi-point tool, rake angles, tool holder-adapter configuration, cutter compensation, tool material, etc.
3. *Machine file:* It describes the range of operations, maximum and minimum spindle speeds, feed rates, horse power, number of axes, number of spindles, turret capacity, rigidity, accuracy, etc.

The machinability database is stored in a high-speed storage device, which can be directly accessible to the processing program. The machinability is updated periodically. The database is illustrated schematically in Figure 19.3.

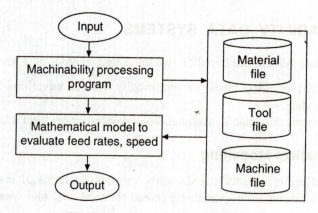

Fig. 19.3 Machinability database.

19.7   BENEFITS OF CAPP

The benefits of implementing and using a CAPP system are as follows:

1. A computer-automated preparation of operation routing is likely to be more consistent, logical, and optimal than its manual counterpart. The process plans will be consistent because the same computer software is being used by all planners.
2. The productivity of process planners increases on account of reduced clerical effort, fewer errors, and immediate access to the process planning database.
3. While working with the CAPP system, the process planner is able to prepare a route sheet for a new part in less time as compared to a manual operation. This leads to an overall reduction in manufacturing lead time.
4. The computer prepared document is neater and easier to read than manually written route sheets. This improves legibility of the document.
5. The process planning system can be designed to operate in conjunction with other software packages to automate many of the time-consuming manufacturing support functions.
6. It facilitates savings of material.
7. It leads to improved production scheduling and capacity utilisation.
8. It facilitates improved cost estimating procedures.
9. It saves list of tooling.

QUESTION BANK

A. Descriptive Questions

1. What do you understand by process planning?
2. What are the difficulties in traditional process planning?
3. Explain the need for computer-aided process planning.
4. Discuss a retrieval type computer-aided process planning system.
5. Discuss a generative type computer-aided process planning system.
6. Differentiate between retrieval type and generative type computer-aided process planning.
7. What are the various types of machinability data systems? Explain.
8. What are the benefits of CAPP?

B. Multiple Choice Questions

1. For the development of a process plan for new parts, the best one is:
   (a) Retrieval process plan   (b) Variant process plan
   (c) Generative process plan   (d) GT planning
2. Generative process plans are generated by means of:
   (a) Geometry-based data   (b) Production-based data
   (c) Decision logics   (d) Technology algorithms
3. Retrieval process planning works on the principle of:
   (a) Database   (b) Networking   (c) Group technology   (d) Knowledge base
4. Machinability database system makes use of:
   (a) Tool file   (b) Material file (c) Machine file   (d) All the above

Chapter 20

Computer-aided Manufacturing Resource Planning

After reading this chapter, the reader will be able to understand the following concepts:

- ➲ Material resource planning (MRP): Independent and dependent demand, lumpy demand, manufacturing lead times, and common use items

- ➲ Inputs to MRP: Master production schedule, bill-of-materials file, and inventory record file

- ➲ MRP output records

- ➲ Manufacturing resource planning (MRP II)

- ➲ Benefits of MRP

- ➲ Capacity requirements planning (CRP)

- ➲ Inputs and outputs of CRP

- ➲ Enterprise resource planning (ERP)

20.1 INTRODUCTION

In recent years, manufacturing has become highly competitive worldwide. It has become essential to control production and inventory to cater to the increased demand of productivity. The use of computers in manufacturing has resulted in the development of material resource planning (MRP). This concept has been extended to manufacturing resource planning (MRP II), capacity resource planning (CRP) and enterprise resource planning (ERP).

20.2 MATERIAL RESOURCE PLANNING (MRP)

Material resource planning is a computational technique that converts the master schedule for end products into a detailed schedule for the raw materials and components used in the end products. It is an inventory control system. The basic MRP concepts are:

1. Independent and dependent demand
2. Lumpy demand
3. Manufacturing lead times
4. Common use items

20.2.1 Independent and Dependent Demand

Independent demand is the demand for a product, which is unrelated to the demand for other items. End products and spare parts are examples of independent demand.

Dependent demand is the demand for the item, which is directly related to the demand for other items. Piston and cylinder of an automobile engine are the examples of dependent demand.

MRP is an appropriate technique for determining the quantities of dependent demand items.

20.2.2 Lumpy Demand

In a manufacturing system, when the demand becomes very large for a certain item, it is referred to as lumpy demand. MRP is an appropriate technique for determining the inventory of lumpy demand items.

20.2.3 Manufacturing Lead Times

Manufacturing lead time is the time required to process the part through the sequence of workstations specified on the route sheet. It includes both productive and non-productive times. In MRP, lead time is used to determine the starting dates for assembling final products and sub-assemblies, for manufacturing component parts and for ordering raw materials.

20.2.4 Common Use Items

In a manufacturing environment, certain components become common items for the assembling of several final products and sub-assemblies. For example, the same type of steel rod stock may be used to produce different types of screws. Each of the screw types may then be used on several different products. MRP collects these common items required for different products for ordering the raw materials and manufacturing the components.

20.3 INPUTS TO MRP

MRP converts the master production schedule into the detailed schedule for raw materials and components. The inputs to MRP are:

1. The master production schedule and service parts
2. The bill-of-materials file
3. The inventory record file

Figure 20.1 illustrates the structure of MRP representing the flow of data into the MRP processor and its conversion into output records.

The MRP processor operates on the data contained in the master production schedule, the bill-of-material file, and the inventory record file. The master schedule specifies the periodical requirement of final products. The bill-of-material defines the materials and components needed for each product. The inventory record file consists of information on the current and future inventory status of each component. An MRP program computes the quantities of each component and raw material that are needed by exploding the end-product requirements into successively lower levels in the product structure.

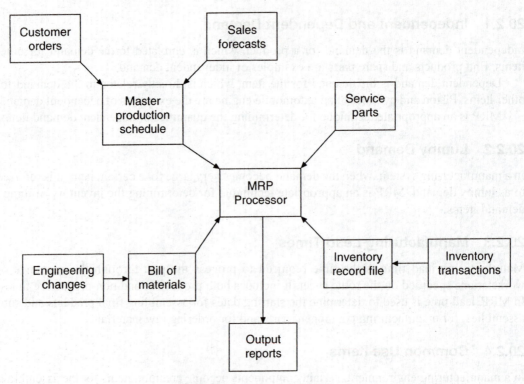

Fig. 20.1   Structure of MRP.

20.3.1 Master Production Schedule

The master production schedule is a list of:

- Types of end products manufactured
- Number of each product produced
- The time when the products would be ready for shipment

The general format of a master production schedule is shown in Figure 20.2.

Work number	1	2	3	4	...	8	9
Product P1		30		45	...	60	
Product P2	20	25	50		...	50	
Product P3		10	20	40	...	50	60
....	...	...	...	...	...	...	...

Fig. 20.2 General format of a master production schedule.

20.3.2 Bill-of-Materials File

It consists of list of component parts and sub-assemblies that make up the end product.

20.3.3 Inventory Record File

Computerised inventory system is used to maintain the inventory record file. A definition of the lead time for the raw materials, components, and assemblies must be established in the inventory record file. The inventory record file is maintained by inputting the inventory transactions to the file.

20.4 MRP OUTPUT RECORDS

The MRP program generates the following outputs:

1. Order release notice
2. Reports showing planned orders
3. Rescheduled notices, indicating changes in due dates for open orders
4. Cancellation notices, indicating cancellation of open orders due to changes in the master schedule
5. Reports on inventory status
6. Performance reports
7. Inventory forecasts indicating projected inventory levels

20.5 MANUFACTURING RESOURCE PLANNING (MRP II)

This is an information system used to plan and control inventories and capacities in manufacturing companies. MRP II coordinates the sales, purchasing, manufacturing, finance and engineering functions. The various modules of MRP II are as follows:

1. Manufacturing applications
2. Engineering applications
3. Financial applications
4. Marketing applications

20.6 BENEFITS OF MRP

The benefits reported by MRP users are listed below:

1. Reduction in inventory
2. Improved customer service
3. Quick response to changes in demand
4. Reduced set-up and product changeover costs
5. Better machine utilisation
6. Higher productivity

20.7 CAPACITY REQUIREMENTS PLANNING (CRP)

CRP is a technique for determining the personnel and equipment capacities that are required to meet the production objectives specified in the master production schedule and material requirement planning.

20.8 INPUTS TO AND OUTPUTS OF CRP

The inputs to the CRP are:

1. Planned orders and released orders from the MRP system
2. Loading information from the cork centre status file
3. Routing information from the shop routing file
4. Changes (i.e., alternative routings, capacity of new equipments, etc.)

The released and planned orders from the MRP system are converted into standard hours of loading by the CRP system. CRP is an iterative process that simulates loads on the work centres and relies upon the planners to suggest changes if the plan cannot be met.

The major outputs of CRP are:

1. Load reports
2. Verification of planned orders for MRP system

20.9 ENTERPRISE RESOURCE PLANNING (ERP)

The activity of ERP is the creation of an integrated data model, covering employees, customers, suppliers, etc. The implementation of ERP system includes the following stages:

1. Definition of the scope of the project
2. Identification of the objectives and goals
3. Identification of the executive responsible for the implementation of ERP
4. Establishment of a project team
5. Development of the work plan
6. Assessment of business
7. Training of employees
8. Investment/profit analysis

QUESTION BANK

A. Descriptive Questions

1. What is MRP?
2. What are the basic concepts of MRP?
3. What are the inputs to MRP?
4. What are the outputs of MRP?
5. What is MRP II?
6. What are the benefits of MRP?
7. What is CRP?
8. What are inputs to and outputs of CRP?
9. What is ERP?

B. Multiple Choice Questions

1. MRP input requires:
   (a) MPS
   (b) BOM
   (c) Inventory file
   (d) All of the above

2. BOM structure is used to calculate:
   (a) Due dates
   (b) Net requirements
   (c) Manpower requirements
   (d) All of the above

3. MRP II is called a closed loop system, because it considers:
   (a) Finance
   (b) Inventory
   (c) Manpower
   (d) Management techniques

4. Capacity planning is concerned with:
   (a) How much labour is required
   (b) How many machines are required
   (c) How much money is required
   (d) Both (a) and (b)

Chapter **21**

Computer-aided
Quality Control

OBJECTIVES

After reading this chapter, the reader will be able to understand the following concepts:

➲ Quality control: Inspection and testing

➲ Statistical quality control (SQC)

➲ Automated inspection: Off-line inspection, on-line inspection, contact inspection, and non-contact inspection

➲ Coordinate measuring machine (CMM)

➲ Scanning laser system

➲ Machine vision: Sensing and digitising, and image processing and analysis

➲ Experimental set-up for machine vision: METAVIS—image analysis system, alloys used for the microstructural analysis, microstructural characteristics, image analysis procedure, and results and interpretation

21.1 INTRODUCTION

Quality is an important criterion for the success of any manufacturing industry. Customers desire an ideal combination of high quality, reliability, and low cost. Significant attention is thus paid to the use of statistical quality control procedures during manufacturing to ensure high quality. Quality control is concerned with the detection of poor quality in the manufactured product and corrective action to eliminate it.

21.2 QUALITY CONTROL

Quality control is achieved by inspection and testing.

21.2.1 Inspection

Inspection is used to assess the quality of the product in relation to the design specifications. The inspection procedure includes:

1. Taking actual measurements of the values of the specified product characteristics: For example, the dimensions are measured by micrometers, calipers, etc. The advantage of measuring the part characteristic is that the actual value of the part characteristic can be recorded and can be used to observe trends in the process of manufacturing the product. The actual value of the part characteristic can also be used for the control of the manufacturing process so that future parts are manufactured with dimensions closer to the nominal design value.
2. Checking whether or not the specified characteristics meet the design standards: For example, the GO/NOGO gauge is used to check the part diameter. The advantage of gauging a part is that the inspection can be carried out quickly and at a lower cost.

21.2.2 Testing

Testing is used to evaluate the quality of the product in relation to the functional aspects of the product. Testing is a procedure in which the part being tested is observed during the actual operation. The testing procedure can be carried out by using destructive testing or non-destructive testing. During the testing procedure, one or more operating variables of the product are measured, and adjustments are made in certain inputs that influence the performance of the operating variables.

21.3 STATISTICAL QUALITY CONTROL (SQC)

In SQC, inferences are made about the quality of a product on the basis of a sample taken from the population of the products. Each product in the sample is inspected for certain quality characteristics of interest. SQC uses control charts. The important control charts are as follows:

$\overline{X}$ *chart:* This control chart is used to plot the average measured value of a certain quality characteristic for each of a series of samples taken from the manufacturing process.

R chart: This control chart is used to plot the range of each sample.

P chart: This chart is used to plot the percentage of defectives in the sample.

C chart: The number or count of defects in the sample is plotted as a function of time.

21.4 AUTOMATED INSPECTION

Manual inspection often leads to errors. The error may be due to two sources: inherent errors of the measurement procedure and mistakes by the operator. The cost of 100 per cent manual inspection is high. Automation of the inspection process thus offers an opportunity to overcome the problems associated with 100 per cent manual inspection. Automated inspection is classified into the following categories:

1. Based on the manufacturing process—This includes:
   - Off-line inspection
   - On-line inspection

2. Based on sensor technology—This includes:
   - Contact inspection
   - Non-contact inspection

21.4.1 Off-line Inspection

Off-line inspection is performed away from the manufacturing process as shown in Figure 21.1. It involves a statistical sampling procedure, and is suitable for high production runs with short cycle times.

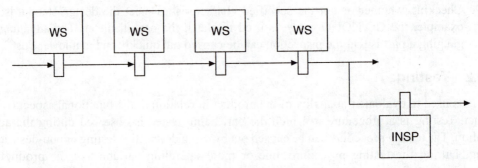

Fig. 21.1 Off-line inspection.

21.4.2 On-line Inspection

On-line inspection is performed during the manufacturing operation as shown in Figure 21.2. As the parts are being made, the measuring or gauging of the parts carried out simultaneously.

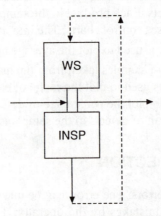

Fig. 21.2 On-line inspection.

21.4.3 Contact Inspection

Contact inspection uses a mechanical probe or other device to contact the workpiece. It can be carried out in the following three different ways:

1. Using coordinate measuring machines
2. By flexible inspection systems
3. Using inspection probes

21.4.4 Non-contact Inspection

In non-contact inspection, the sensor is not in direct contact with the workpiece. The sensor is located at a distance from the workpiece to measure or gauge the desire features. Non-contact inspection is performed by using the following techniques:

1. Optical inspection techniques
2. Electrical field techniques
3. Radiation techniques

21.5 COORDINATE MEASURING MACHINE (CMM)

The coordinate measuring machine is used for the contact inspection of parts. The CMM consists of a machine tool-like structure with precision slide ways and scales and some form of sensor to determine the point of contact and probes (Figure 21.3). When used for computer-integrated manufacturing (CAM), these machines are controlled by CNC. During operation, the probe is

Fig. 21.3 Coordinate measuring machine.

brought into contact with the part surface to be measured and the three coordinate positions (X, Y and Z) are indicated to a high level of accuracy.

The components of CMM are:

1. ***Stationary granite measuring table:*** It acts as a reference plane for locating the parts to be measured.
2. ***Length measuring system:*** Each axis of CMM is provided with a digital incremental length measuring system.
3. ***Air bearings:*** The bridge, cross beam and spindle are supported on air bearings.
4. ***Control unit:*** It is a microprocessor controller.
5. ***Software:*** It includes the measurement of the diameter, centre distances, lengths, etc. The software also provides a generalised method for reverse engineering of complex shaped objects.

Four types of CMM construction are possible as shown in Figure 21.4. They are:

1. Cantilever type CMM
2. Column type CMM
3. Bridge type CMM
4. Gantry type CMM

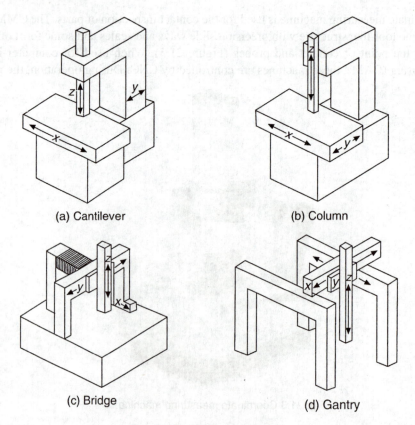

(a) Cantilever   (b) Column

(c) Bridge   (d) Gantry

Fig. 21.4   CMM construction.

21.6 SCANNING LASER SYSTEM

A scanning laser system is used for non-contact inspection. A low energy laser beam is used in the scanning laser device. A schematic diagram of a scanning laser device is shown in Figure 21.5. The laser beam is deflected by a rotating mirror to produce a beam of light which is focused to sweep past an object. The photodetector on the far side of the object senses the light beam except the period during the sweep when it is interrupted by the object. This period can be timed and related to the size of the object in the path of the laser beam. A microprocessor-based system counts the time interruption of the scanning laser beam as it sweeps past the object, and makes the conversion from time to a linear dimension.

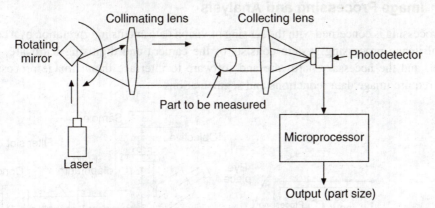

Fig. 21.5 Scanning laser device.

21.7 MACHINE VISION

Machine vision is a system for the acquisition of image data, followed by the processing and interpretation of this data by computer for some useful application. The operation of a machine vision system can be divided into the following three functions:

1. Sensing and digitising image data
2. Image processing and analysis
3. Interpretation

The relationships between the three functions are illustrated in Figure 21.6.

21.7.1 Sensing and Digitising Image Data

Image sensing requires some type of image formation device such as a camera and a digitiser, which stores a video frame in the computer memory. The initial step involves capturing the image of the scene with the vision camera. The image consists of relative light intensities corresponding to the various portions of the scene. These light intensities are continuous analog values, which must be sampled and converted into digital form. The second step, i.e., digitising, is achieved by an analog-to-digital converter.

A variety of commercial imaging devices are available. CCD (charge-coupled devices) cameras, CID (charge injection devices) cameras and SBS (silicon bipolar sensor) cameras are being used for various applications of image capturing.

Good illumination of the scene is important because of its effect on the level of complexity of image processing algorithms rewired. Poor lighting makes the task of interpreting the scene more difficult. Proper lighting techniques, on the other hand, provide high contrast and minimise specular reflections and shadows unless these are specifically designed into the system. Various illumination techniques have been developed. The front lighting technique is being used for microstructural analysis.

21.7.2 Image Processing and Analysis

Image processing is concerned with the sensing of vision data and its interpretation by a computer. A typical image processing system consists of the camera and digitising hardware, a digital computer, and the necessary hardware and software to interface them. Image processing and analysis require image data reductions and segmentations.

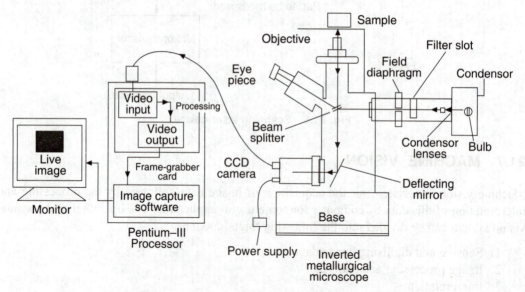

Fig. 21.6 Schematic view of the machine vision system used for microstructural image processing and analysis.

Image data reduction: In image data reduction, the objective is to reduce the volume of data. The following two schemes have found common usage for data reduction:

• Digital conversion
• Windowing

Digital conversion reduces the number of gray levels. Windowing involves the use of only a portion of the total image stored in the frame buffer for image processing and analysis.

Segmentation: In segmentation, the objective is to group areas of an image having similar feature characteristics into distinct entities representing parts of the image. For example, boundaries or regions represent two natural segments of an image. There are many ways to segment an image. These are:

- Thresholding
- Region growing
- Edge detection

Thresholding is a binary conversion technique in which each pixel is converted into a binary value, either black or white. Region growing is a collection of segmentation techniques in which pixels are grouped in regions called grid elements on the basis of attribute similarities. Edge detection considers the intensity change that occurs in the pixels at the boundary.

Object recognition: The next step in image processing is to identify the object that the image represents. Template matching techniques are being used for this purpose.

21.7.3 Interpretation

Image interpretation is the manipulations of images using computer algorithms to enhance, restore and understand the information contained in them.

21.8 EXPERIMENTAL SET-UP FOR MACHINE VISION

An experimental set-up is shown in Figure 21.7. An ideal laboratory set-up consists of an inverted microscope to capture the surface of the specimen. The inverted microscope is equipped with an eyepiece, objectives and a condenser with iris diaphragm/filter holder. The specimen is placed inverted on the mechanical stage of the microscope. Illumination is done through a halogen lamp fixed at the right end of the microscope. The iris diaphragm can be used to induce a contrast to the specimen until the details of the specimen are sharply defined.

The sample is placed inverted on the mechanical stage of the microscope so that the image that will be captured is freed of extra illumination, lighting or shadow effects. The environment is a confined one and the image is made free from noise. The subsequent image obtained is a pure one. One more advantage of such a set-up is the CCD camera attachment provided with the microscope, which directly transmits the captured image to the processor. For microstructural phase analysis, maximum magnification of the image must be undertaken in order to capture more information.

The camera is an industry standard black and white source. It has a manual iris adjustable for high or low light levels. The camera also includes automatic gain control (AGC), which allows the camera to adapt to high or low ambient light levels automatically.

This camera is connected to the frame-grabber card in the PCI slot of the workstation PC. The frame grabber requires the display to be set up with 256 colours. The image is captured through the card in any of the graphic file formats like BMP, GIF, and JPEG as compatible with the frame-grabber card. The frame grabber's main task is to divide the video stream into pixels, quantise each pixel into a byte, and write those bytes into the PC's memory. The PC is standard Windows compatible and has a PENTIUM III processor, with a 19″ VGA monitor and mouse.

The image is captured by using METAVIS software. It grabs images in 8-bit, 16-bit RGB, 24-bit RGB format in various sizes—176 × 144, 352 × 288, 720 × 576. The captured image is saved as a 256 colour bitmap file.

Fig. 21.7 Experimental set-up for machine vision.

21.8.1 METAVIS—Image Analysis System

The METAVIS workstation is a complete image analysis system developed specifically to increase the speed, accuracy and efficiency of measurements for material sciences and metallography. METAVIS uses a high resolution colour CCD camera (mounted on the microscope). A high accuracy image capture card transfers these images to the computer. Once an image is acquired, it is processed and analysed by BIOVIS MATERIALS PLUS image analysis software.

Currently the system can be configured with the following application specific modules:

- z Grain size ASTM E112
- z Phase/volume fraction ASTM E562
- z Inclusion rating ASTM E45/E1122
- z Graphite flake size ASTM A247
- z Nodularity ASTM A247

- Porosity ASTM B276
- Micro-hardness ASTM E384
- De-carburisation depth ASTM E487
- Coating thickness ASTM E487
- Degree of banding ASTM E1268
- Dendrite arm spacing ASTM

21.8.2   Alloys Used for the Microstructural Analysis

Various alloys are used in the present investigation to study different microstructural characteristics, which are commonly employed for an analysis of the behaviour of alloys. The following alloys are used in the present work:

- Al-Si alloy
- Brass
- Nickel-coated steel plate
- Titanium alloy
- Ductile iron
- Gray cast iron

21.8.3   The Microstructural Characteristics

The following microstructural characterisitics are identified for analysing the behaviour of an alloy:

- Volume fraction
- Grain size estimation
- Coating thickness
- Porosity
- Nodularity
- Sizes of graphite flakes

21.8.4   Image Analysis Procedure

The microstructural characteristics like volume fraction, grain size estimation, coating thickness, porosity, nodularity, and sizes of graphite flakes were studied by using an image analysis system for metallography (METAVIS). The microstructural characteristics were computed by using probes, which were geometrical patterns imposed on the image of the sample being studied. These probes produce intersections with the characteristics being studied. The probes are points, lines, parallel lines, line grids, point grids, arcs, cycloids, etc. For example, an unbiased probe for measuring region volume is a point grid, for surface area the probe is a set of lines and arcs.

The volume fraction of each phase contained in the microstructure was measured with the automatic delineation of each phase. The grain size in the microstructure was studied by the intercept method. The coating thickness was measured by the plain metric method. Statistics and distribution of the longest caliper on all detected pores were observed. In addition, the count of pores and the standard deviation of the lengths were also reported. Nodularity of the graphites present in the ductile iron was examined with area probes and the perimeter of the nodules was presented. The graphite flakes in the gray cast iron sample were examined for %graphite area, the graphite flake lengths were classified in eight sizes as per American Society for Testing and Materials (ASTM).

21.8.5 Results and Interpretation

The microstructure of Al-Si alloy is shown in Figure 21.8. The histogram of two phases representing the microstructure is given in Figure 21.9. The statistical report of the microstructure is presented in Table 21.1. The volume fraction of the light area is 47.288 per cent while that of the dark area is 52.712 per cent. The volume fractions of the light and dark areas measured by the optical microscope are 47.474 per cent and 52.526 per cent, respectively. The error in the optical microscope is attributed to the lack of microscope magnification.

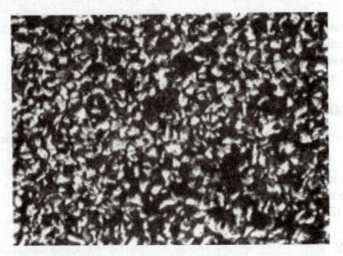

Fig. 21.8 Microstructure of Al-Si alloy.

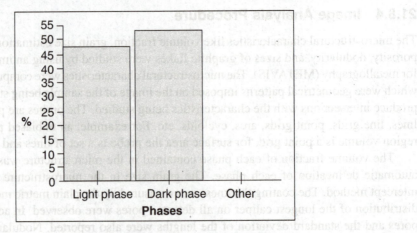

Fig. 21.9 Histogram of Al-Si alloy phases.

The microstructure of brass material is shown in Figure 21.9. The statistical data of the grain size is reported in Table 21.2. The total area of scanning is 0.37223 mm^2 as per ASTM E1382. The number of intercepts is 163 with a mean interception length of 64.32582 μm.

Table 21.1   Statistical report of Al-Si alloy

Measurement	*Light phase*	*Dark phase*
Volume %	47.288	52.712
Estimated volume %	47.474	52.526
SD	3.508	3.508
95% CI	3.682	3.682
%RA	7.787	6.986

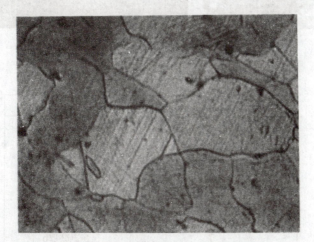

Fig. 21.9 Microstructure of brass metal.

Table 21.2   Statistical data of grain sizes in brass material

Measurement	*Value*
Grain size	4.6
Intercepts	163
Mean intercept length, μm	64.32582
SD	.002
95% CI	.003
%RA	4.96

Nickel coating given on a steel specimen is illustrated in Figure 21.10. The thickness values of the coating are given in Table 21.3. The thickness of the coating was measured at ten different locations across the length of the coating. The average thickness of the coating is 5.093047 mm. The average thickness of the coating is also measured by using conventional Vernier calipers. The average reading of the Vernier calipers is 5.10 mm. The error is due to the least count (0.01mm) of the Vernier calipers.

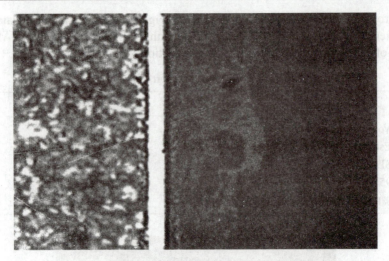

Fig. 21.10 Nickel coating on steel plate.

Table 21.3 Coating thickness data

Measurement	Thickness
1	4.335385
2	6.503078
3	5.121174
4	4.768924
5	5.202462
6	4.335385
7	5.202426
8	5.470843
9	4.768924
10	5.221875
Thickness (AV)	5.093047
Thickness (MIN)	4.335385
Thickness (MAX)	6.503078

The porosity in the cast metal is due to the entrapping of gases released during the solidification process. The microstructure of titanium alloy is revealed in Figure 21.11. The area of the specimen examined is 0.66681 mm². The statistical data of the porosity present in titanium alloy is represented in Table 21.4. The porosity in the titanium alloy casting is 16.2002 per cent. The density was also evaluated theoretically on the basis of the constituents present in the titanium alloy and measured experimentally by using the principle of loss in weight. The theoretical and experimental values of porosity are 15.46 per cent and 15.97 per cent respectively. The error in the theoretical evaluation of porosity is due to the loss of constituents during the melting of titanium alloy. The error in the experimental measurement of porosity is attributed to the sensitivity of the weighing instrument.

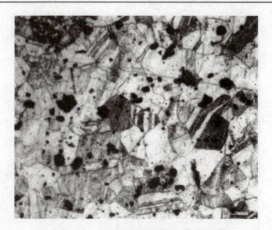

Fig. 21.11 Porosity in Titanium alloy.

Table 21.4 Statistical data of porosity

Measurement	Result	Mean	Min	Max
Porosity %	16.2002			
		19.35663	1.473267	254.8292
Diameter μ m		368.6839	4.341205	158717.18
Area sq. mm		.055291	.000651	2.37207
Area %				

Figure 21.12 shows the microstructure of a ductile iron. The total area scanned to count the number of nodules is 0.88019 mm^2 as per ASTM A-247f. The statistical report of the observation is presented in Table 21.5. The nodule count is 220. But the number of objects detected by the image processing technique is 261. There are 41 objects, which are not spherical. In fact, this is true as per the microstructure of ductile iron. The lines which may be the scratches on the specimen resulted due to poor polishing are also seen in the microstructure. The image processing technique presents also the type of shapes of nodules. There are some nodules of the shape: flake, vermicular and irregular.

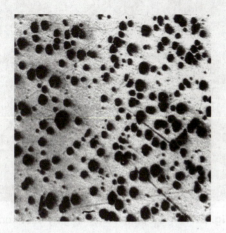

Fig. 21.12 Nodular counts in ductile iron.

Table 21.5   Nodular data of ductile iron

Measurement	Result
Total objects	261
Nodule count	220
% Nodularity	84.29119
Nodule area %	13.97126
Nodules/sq.mm	249.9466
AV size, μm	17.5627
Min size, μm	0
Max size, μm	62.61206
Size 1 %	
Size 2 %	
Size 3 %	
Size 4 %	
Size 5 %	.455
Size 6 %	23.636
Size 7 %	33.182
Size 8 %	42.727
% Flake	1.149
% Vermicular	2.299
% Irregular	12.261

The graphite flakes in the gray cast iron are illustrated in Figure 21.13. The histogram representation of the flake sizes is shown in Figure 21.14. The statistical data of the flakes is given in Table 21.6. The flake area is 22.39659 per cent of the total area examined as per ASTM A-247. As per the standards established by ASTM, the total area of 0.12292 mm^2 was scanned for all eight sizes. The maximum flake length is 1147.729 mm. No flakes of Size 3 are observed.

Fig. 21.13   Graphite flakes in gray cast iron.

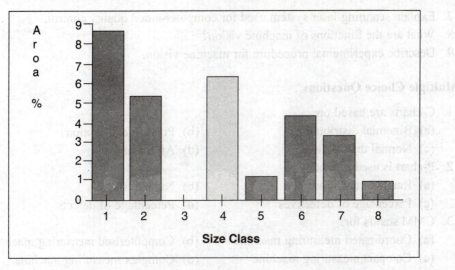

Fig. 21.14 Histogram of graphite sizes in gray cast iron.

Table 21.6 Graphite flake size data

Measurement	Result
Flakes area%	22.39659
Max length, μm	1147.729
Size 1%	8.784
Size 2%	5.302
Size 3%	
Size 4%	6.462
Size 5%	1.282
Size 6%	4.417
Size 7%	3.434
Size 8%	1.081

QUESTION BANK

A. Descriptive Questions

1. Define quality.
2. What are the techniques employed to achieve quality control?
3. Explain SQC.
4. What are the various methods of automated inspection? Explain.
5. What are the components of CMM?
6. What are the various types of CMM?

7. Explain scanning laser system used for computer-aided quality control.
8. What are the functions of machine vision?
9. Describe experimental procedure for machine vision.

B. Multiple Choice Questions

1. C-charts are based on:
   (a) Binomial distribution
   (c) Normal distribution
   (b) Poisson distribution
   (d) All the above

2. P-chart is used to plot:
   (a) Range of each sample
   (c) Percentage of defectives
   (b) Number defects
   (d) Percentage of defects

3. CMM stands for:
   (a) Coordinated measuring machine
   (c) Compact measuring machine
   (b) Computerised measuring machine
   (d) Complex measuring machine

4. Machine vision is an example of:
   (a) On-line inspection
   (c) Contact inspection
   (b) Off-line inspection
   (d) None of the above

Chapter 22

Industrial Robots

OBJECTIVES

After reading this chapter, the reader will be able to understand the following concepts:

- ➲ Mechanical role of a robot manipulator
- ➲ General structure of a robot manipulator
- ➲ Links and joints: Joints and links
- ➲ Degrees of freedom (robot motions)
- ➲ Characteristics of an industrial robot: Work volume, speed of movement, weight-carrying capacity, and precision of movement
- ➲ Configuration of industrial robots: Polar configuration robot, cylindrical configuration robot, cartesian coordinate configuration robot, jointed-arm configuration robot, and SCARA configuration
- ➲ Industrial robot actuators: Hydraulic actuators, electric actuators, and pneumatic actuators
- ➲ Robot control systems: Limited sequence control, playback robot with point-to-point control, playback robot with continuous path control, and intelligent robot control
- ➲ End effectors: Grippers and tools
- ➲ Sensors: Vision sensors, tactile sensors and voice sensors
- ➲ Robot programming: Manual set-up, walkthrough method, leadthrough programming, off-line programming, and robot programming languages
- ➲ Robot cell design: Robot-centred cell, in-line robot cell and mobile robot cell
- ➲ Characteristics of industrial robot applications
- ➲ Industrial robot applications

22.1   INTRODUCTION

An *industrial robot* has been defined as a re-programmable multi-functional manipulator, designed to move materials, parts, tools, or other specialised devices by means of variable programmed motions and to perform a variety of other tasks. In a broader context, the term robot also includes manipulators that are activated directly by an operator. This includes manipulators used in nuclear fields, medical investigation or surgery as well as robots used for underwater exploration or works.

More generally, an industrial robot has been described by the International Organisation for Standardisation (ISO) as follows: **A machine formed by a mechanism including several degrees of freedom, often having the appearance of one or several arms ending in wrist capable of holding a tool, a workpiece, or an inspection device**.

22.2   MECHANICAL ROLE OF A ROBOT MANIPULATOR

Irrespective of the function assigned to it (like handling, painting, assembly, or welding), a robot manipulator is designed to mechanically locate in space a tool often called an end effector. The end effector can simply be a gripper designed to grasp a part, or a painting gun, or may consist of any other tool.

The geometric location of the end effector is generally quite arbitrary in the reachable range, called workspace of the manipulator, and is continuously changing with time: it follows a path or trajectory corresponding to the specified task. At a crude but important level, it is completely described through a sequence of positions of one given point on the effector and its orientation about these points. At a higher level, the trajectory planning might also take into account environmental constraints.

In order to describe the position and orientation of the effector in space, it is necessary to attach to it a coordinate system, or frame, and describe the position and orientation of this frame to some reference system. Frame transformations thus play a fundamental role in the use of a robot manipulator.

22.3   GENERAL STRUCTURE OF A ROBOT MANIPULATOR

The general structure of a robot manipulator consists of five main components (Figure 22.1). These are as follows:

1. *Mechanical structure:*   This is ideally made of rigid members or links articulated together through mechanical joints. It carries at its end the tool or effector.
2. *Actuators:*   These provide the mechanical power in order to act on the mechanical structure against gravity, inertia and other external forces to modify the configuration and thus, the geometric location of the tool. The actuators can be of electric, hydraulic or pneumatic type and have to be controlled in the appropriate manner.
3. *Mechanical transmission devices:*   These devices, such as, gear trains, connect and adapt the actuators to the mechanical structure. Their role is two-fold: to transmit the mechanical efforts from the power sources to the mechanical joints, and to adapt the actuators to their load.

4. *Sensors:* These provide senses to the robot. They can be tactile, optical or electrical devices.

5. *Controller:* This collects and processes the information provided by the sensors; it plans the trajectory motion of the manipulator, and communicates the information with the manipulator and its environment.

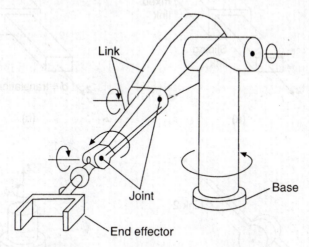

Fig. 22.1 An industrial robot manipulator.

22.4 LINKS AND JOINTS

The joints are the bits that rotate or slide; the links are the bits that separate the joints.

22.4.1 Joints

The joints in a robot are restricted to 1 DOF each. Joints can rotate, *revolute* joints, or translate, *prismatic* joints. The joints are as follows:

1. *Linear (L) joint:* The relative movement between the input link and the output link is a linear sliding motion (Figure 22.2a).

2. *Orthogonal (O) joint:* This also gives a linear sliding motion, but the input and output links are perpendicular to each other (Figure 22.2b).

3. *Rotational (R) joint:* This provides a rotational relative motion of the joints, with the axis of rotation perpendicular to the axes of the input and output links (Figure 22.2c).

4. *Twisting (T) joint:* This joint involves a rotary motion, but the axis of rotation is parallel to the axes of the two links (Figure 22.2d).

5. *Revolving (V) joint:* In this joint, the axis of the input link is parallel to the axis of rotation of the joint and the axis of the output link is perpendicular to the axis of rotation (Figure 22.2e)

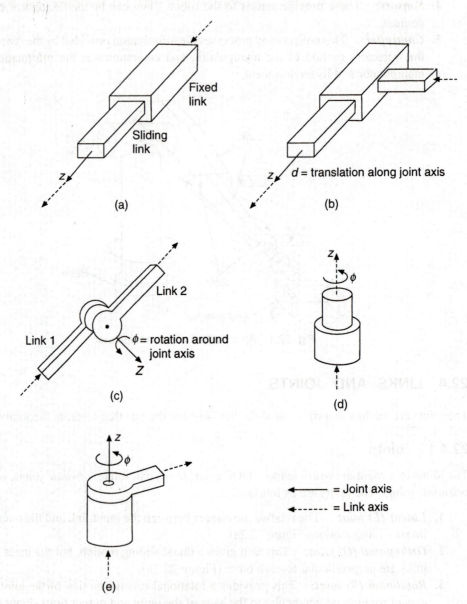

Fig. 22.2   Joints.

22.4.2   Links

Links are the solid structures between joints. Links have a *proximal* end closest to the base and a *distal* end closest to the tool. The proximal end of the link has the lower joint number. Each type of link has four parameters, two-directions of translation and two axes of rotation. These are called the *link parameters*.

The links shown in Figure 22.3 represent eight common link configurations. These are:

Type 1 link: Parallel revolute joints with no twist between joint axes (Figure 22.3a).

Type 2 link: Parallel revolute joints with no 90 degree twist between joint axes (Figure 20.3b).

Type 3 link: Revolute joints with intersecting axes at 90 degree (Figure 22.3c).

Type 4 link: Revolute joints with perpendicular axes wherein the coordinate frame origins coincide (Figure 22.3d).

Type 5 link: Intersecting prismatic joints with 90 degree twist angle (Figure 22.3e).

Type 6 link: Intersecting revolute and prismatic joints with 90 degree twist angle (Figure 22.3f)

Type 7 link: Parallel and revolute and prismatic joints (Figure 22.3g).

Type 8 link: Intersecting prismatic and revolute joints (Figure 22.3h)

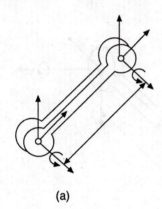

(a)

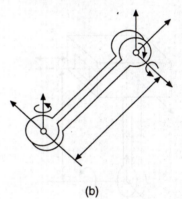

(b)

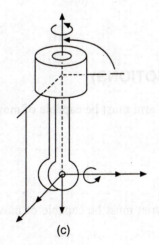

(c)

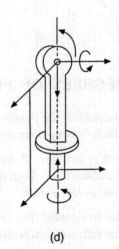

(d)

(*Cont...*)

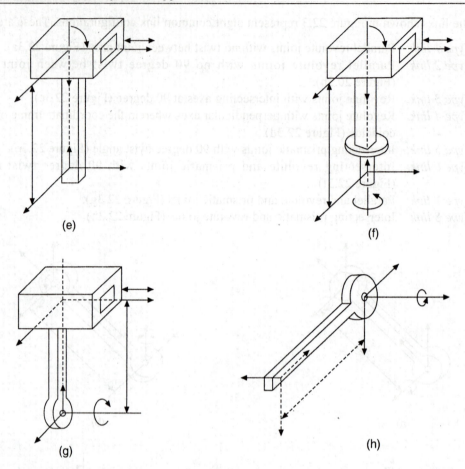

Fig. 22.3 Links.

22.5 DEGREES OF FREEDOM (ROBOT MOTIONS)

In order to establish the position of the object the body and arm must be capable of moving the object in the following three directions (Figure 22.4):

1. *Vertical motion:* Z-axis motion
2. *Radial motion:* In-and-out or Y-axis motion
3. *Right-to-left motion:* X-axis motion

In order to establish the orientation of the object the wrist must be capable of moving the object in the following three directions:

1. *Wrist swivel:* Rotation of the wrist
2. *Wrist bend:* Up or down movement of the wrist
3. *Wrist yaw:* Right or left swivel of the wrist.

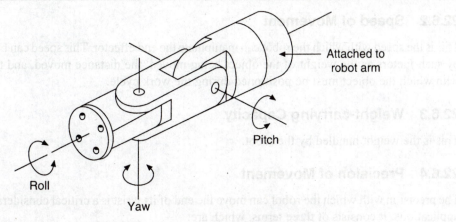

Fig. 22.4 Wrist degrees of freedom.

22.6 CHARACTERISTICS OF AN INDUSTRIAL ROBOT

The important characteristics of an industrial robot are as follows:

1. Work volume
2. Speed of movement
3. Weight-carrying capacity
4. Spatial resolution
5. Accuracy
6. Repeatability

22.6.1 Work Volume

This is the space or envelope within which the robot can rotate (Figure 22.5). Depending on robot configuration and size of the links and wrist joints, robots can reach a collection of points. The shape of the work volume for each robot is uniquely related to its characteristics.

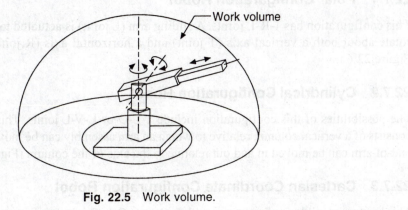

Fig. 22.5 Work volume.

22.6.2   Speed of Movement

This is the speed with which the robot can manipulate the end effector. This speed can be determined by such factors as the weight of the object being moved, the distance moved, and the precision with which the object must be positioned during the work cycle.

22.6.3   Weight-carrying Capacity

This is the weight handled by the robot.

22.6.4   Precision of Movement

The precision with which the robot can move the end of its wrist is a critical consideration in most applications. It consists of three terms, which are:

- *Spatial resolution:*   This is the smallest increment of motion at the wrist end that can be controlled by the robot.
- *Accuracy:*   This is the capability of the robot to position its wrist end at a given target point within its work volume.
- *Repeatability:*   This is the robot's ability to position its wrist end back to a point in space that was previously taught.

22.7   CONFIGURATIONS OF INDUSTRIAL ROBOTS

Five basic configurations of commercial industrial robots are as follows:

1. Polar configuration
2. Cylindrical configuration
3. Cartesian coordinate configuration
4. Jointed arm configuration
5. SCARA configuration

22.7.1   Polar Configuration Robot

This configuration has T-R-L joints. A sliding arm (L joint) is actuated to the body, which can rotate about both a vertical axis (T joint) and a horizontal axis (R joint). This is shown in Figure 22.6a.

22.7.2   Cylindrical Configuration Robot

The possibilities of this configuration include T-L-O or L-V-L joints. This robot configuration consists of a vertical column, relative to which an arm assembly can be moved up and down. The end-of-arm can be moved in and out relative to the axis of the column (Figure 22.6b).

22.7.3   Cartesian Coordinate Configuration Robot

This has two possible configurations with L-O-O or O-L-O joints. It is composed of three sliding joints, two of which are orthogonal. This is shown in Figure 22.6c.

22.7.4 Jointed Arm Configuration Robot

This configuration has T-R-R or V-V-R joints. This robot has the general configuration of a human arm (Figure 22.6d). Its arm has a shoulder joint and an elbow joint, and the arm can be swivelled about the base.

22.7.5 SCARA Configuration

SCARA is an abbreviation for Selective Compliance Assembly Robot Arm. This permits the robot to perform insertion tasks (for assembly) in a vertical direction where some side-to-side adjustment may be needed to mate the two parts properly. SCARA configuration has V-R-O joints. The SCARA is unique in that it typically does not have a separate wrist assembly. The insertion is made from above. Accordingly, the orientation requirements are minimal and the wrist is therefore not needed. This configuration is shown in Figure 22.6e.

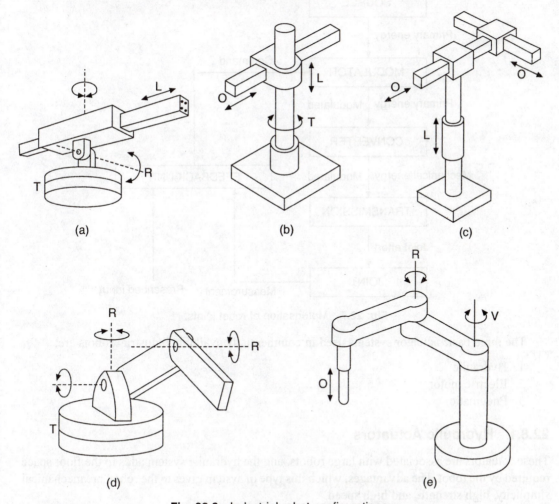

Fig. 22.6 Industrial robot configurations.

22.8 INDUSTRIAL ROBOT ACTUATORS

The arm and wrist architectures together form the mechanical structure of the robot. Let us now examine the way in which this mechanical structure is put into motion. For activating each joint, motorisation implies:

1. Providing a primary energy, most often in pneumatic, hydraulic or electrical form;
2. Modulating the energy brought to the system;
3. Converting the primary energy into mechanical energy;
4. Transmitting the mechanical energy to the joint;
5. Controlling and measuring the motion variables (position, velocity, acceleration, force, etc.)

Figure 22.7 summarises these different functions.

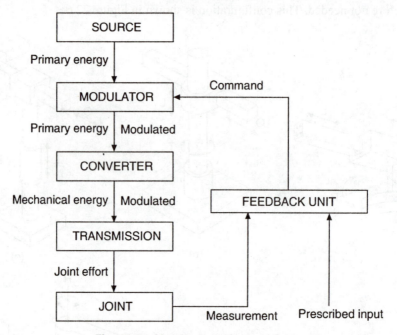

Fig. 22.7 Motorisation of robot joints.

The three basic actuator systems used in commercially available industrial robots are:

1. Hydraulic
2. Electric motor
3. Pneumatic

22.8.1 Hydraulic Actuators

These actuators are associated with large robots, and the hydraulic system adds to the floor space required by the robot. The advantages, which this type of system gives to the robot, are mechanical simplicity, high strength, and high speed.

Pistons are very simple and effective hydraulic systems, which exist in either linear or rotary form. In their linear version, the displacement range is generally of a few centimeters, while in the rotary version, the angular displacement is limited to about 270 degrees. Axial piston motors provide a continuous rotation but their technology is significantly more complicated.

22.8.2 Electric Actuators

Among the electric actuators, the step motors, and direct current (DC) motors with constant inductor flux (generated either by a permanent magnet or through a constant inductor current) and controlled by the armature current are used efficiently. Electric motors do not possess the physical strength or speed of hydraulic units, but their accuracy and repeatability is generally better. Less floor space is required due to the absence of the hydraulic power unit.

22.8.3 Pneumatic Actuators

These are the linear and rotary pistons. The pneumatic actuators are smaller and technologically less sophisticated than the other two types. Pick-and-place tasks and other simple, high-cycle-rate operations are examples of the kinds of applications usually reserved for these robots.

22.9 ROBOT CONTROL SYSTEMS

A microprocessor-based controller is commonly used today in robotics as the control system hardware. The controller is organised in a hierarchical structure so that each joint has its own feedback system, and a supervisory controller coordinates the combined actuations of the joints and sequences the motions according to the sequence of the robot program.

Depending on the level of sophistication of the robot controller, the controllers are classified as:

1. Limited sequence control
2. Playback robot with point-to–point control
3. Playback robot with continuous path control
4. Intelligent robot control

22.9.1 Limited Sequence Control

This is the most elementary control type and can be utilised only for simple motion cycles, such as pick-and-place operations (i.e., picking an object up at one location and placing it at another location). It is usually implemented by setting limits or mechanical stops for each joint and sequencing the actuation of the joints to accomplish the cycle.

22.9.2 Playback Robot with Point-to-Point (PTP) Control

The controller has a memory for recording not only the sequence of the motions in a given work cycle, but also the locations that are associated with each element of the motion cycle. These locations and their sequences are programmed into memory, and subsequently played back during the operation. In PTP control, individual positions of the robot arm are recorded into memory. These positions are not limited to the mechanical stops set for each joint as in the case of limited sequence robots. Feedback control is used during the motion cycle to ascertain that the individual joints have achieved the desired locations defined in the program.

22.9.3 Playback Robot with Continuous Path Control

Servo control is used to maintain continuous control over the position and speed of the manipulator. A playback robot with continuous path control has the inherent capacity for PTP control as well. In a continuous path motion, the movement of the arm and wrist is controlled during the motion.

22.9.4 Intelligent Robot Control

Some of the characteristics that make a robot appear intelligent include its capacity to interact with its environment, to make decisions when things go wrong during the work cycle, to communicate with human beings, to make computations during the motion cycle, and to operate in response to advanced sensor inputs such as machine vision. In addition, these robots possess the playback capability for either PTP or continuous path control. These features require a relatively high level of computer control and an advanced programming language in order to input the decision-making logic and other intelligence into memory.

22.10 END EFFECTORS

The end effector is defined as a device, which is attached to the robot's wrist to perform a specific task. The task may be work part handling, spot welding, spray painting, or any one of a great variety of other operations. The end effectors are classified as:

1. Grippers
2. Tools

22.10.1 Grippers

Grippers are used to hold either work parts or tools. The grippers are:

1. Mechanical grippers (Figure 22.8)
2. Suction grippers
3. Magnetised grippers
4. Hooks
5. Scoops or ladles

22.10.2 Tools

The tool is fastened directly to the robot wrist and becomes the end effector. The tools are:

1. Spot welding gun
2. Arc welding electrode
3. Spray painting gun
4. Drilling spindle
5. Routers, grinders, wire brushes
6. Heating torches

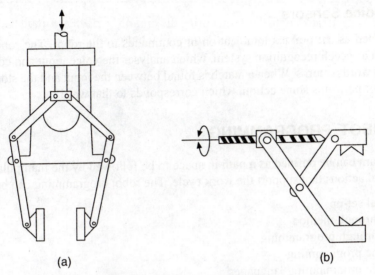

(a)   (b)

Fig. 22.8 Mechanical grippers.

22.11 SENSORS

The robot takes on more human-like senses and capabilities in order to perform the task in a satisfactory way. These senses and capabilities include vision and eye coordination, touch, and hearing. The sensors are classified as follows:

1. Vision sensors
2. Tactile sensors
3. Voice sensors

22.11.1 Vision Sensors

Robot vision is made possible by means of a video camera, a light source, and a computer program to process data. The camera is mounted on the robot or in a fixed position above the robot so that its field of vision includes the robot's work volume. The computer software program enables the vision system to sense the presence of an object, and its position and orientation.

22.11.2 Tactile Sensors

These sensors provide the robot with the capability to respond to contact forces between itself and other objects within its work volume. Tactile sensors are:

- Touch sensors
- Stress sensors

Touch sensors: These sensors are used simply to indicate whether contact has been made with an object. A simple micro-switch can serve the purpose of a touch sensor.

Stress sensors: These are used to measure the magnitude of the contact force. Strain gage devices are employed in force measuring sensors.

22.11.3   Voice Sensors

It can be defined as the oral communication of commands to the robot. The robot controller is equipped with a speech recognition system, which analyses the voice input and compares it with a set of stored word patterns. When a match is found between the input and the stored vocabulary word, the robot performs some action, which corresponds to that word.

22.12   ROBOT PROGRAMMING

A robot program can be defined as a path in space to be followed by the manipulator, combined with peripheral actions that support the work cycle. The robot programming can be classified as:

1. Manual set-up
2. Walkthrough method
3. Leadthrough programming
4. Off-line programming
5. Robotic programming languages

22.12.1   Manual Set-up

This is not really programming in the conventional sense of the word, but is more like setting up a machine. It is the procedure used for the simpler robots and involves the setting up of mechanical stops, cams, switches, or relays in the robot's control unit. This programming is used for pick-and-place operations.

22.12.2   Walkthrough Method

In this method, the programmer manually moves the robot's arm and hand through the motion sequence of the work cycle. Each movement is recorded into memory for subsequent playback during production. The speed with which the movements are performed can be controlled independently so that the programmer does not have to worry about the cycle time during the walkthrough. The main concern is getting the position sequence correct. The walkthrough method would be appropriate for spray painting and arc welding robots.

22.12.3   Leadthrough Programming

The leadthrough programming method makes use of a teach pendant to power drive the robot through its motion sequence. The teach pendant is usually a small hand-held device with switches and dials to control the robot's physical movements. Each motion is recorded into memory for future playback during the work cycle. Leadthrough programming is very popular among robot programming methods because of its ease and convenience.

22.12.4   Off-line Programming

This method involves the preparation of the robot program off-line, in a manner similar to NC part programming. Off-line robot programming is typically accomplished on a computer terminal. After the program has been prepared, it is entered into the robot memory for use during the work cycle. The advantage of off-line robot programming is that the production time of the robot is not lost to delays in teaching the robot a new task. Programming off-line can be done while the robot is still in production on the preceding job. This means higher utilisation of the robot and of the equipment with which it operates. Another benefit associated with off-line programming is the prospect of integrating the robot into the factory CAD/CAM database and information system.

22.12.5 Robotic Programming Languages

With the introduction of computer control for robots came the opportunity and the need to develop a computer-oriented robot programming language. Following are two such languages:

- *The VAL language:* It stands for Victor's assembly language. This was developed by Victor Scheinman for the PUMA robot.
- *The MCL language:* It stands for machine control language and was developed by McDonnell-Douglas Corporation under contract with the U.S. Air Force. This language is based on the APT NC language.

22.13 ROBOT CELL DESIGN

Industrial robots generally work with other equipments. These equipments may be conveyors, fixtures, tools and machining tools. The robot and associated equipment form the work cell. Robot work cells can be organised into various layouts. These layouts are classified as follows:

1. Robot-centred cell
2. In-line robot cell
3. Mobile robot cell

22.13.1 Robot-centred Cell

In this, the robot is positioned at the centre of the cell and the associated equipment is arranged around the robot. Figure 22.9 shows a robot-centred work cell layout. The robot is programmed to serve several machines. Other examples include die casting, arc welding, plastic moulding and similar production operations.

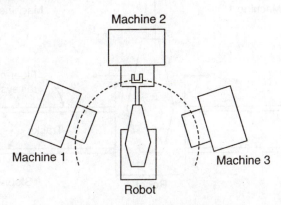

Fig. 22.9 Robot-centred cell.

22.13.2 In-Line Robot Cell

In the In-line robot cell arrangement, the robot is located along a moving conveyor and performs a task on the product as it travels past on the conveyor. The most common example is the car body assembly. Robots are located along the assembly line to spot weld the car body frames and panels. An in-line robot cell is illustrated in Figure 22.10.

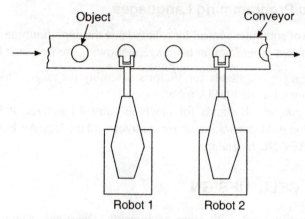

Fig. 22.10 In-line robot cell.

22.13.3 Mobile Robot Cell

In this arrangement, the robot is mounted on a mobile base. The mobile bases used in robot cells are tracks fastened to the floor or overhead rail systems. The robot is moved to various equipment within the workcell. Figure 22.11 illustrates a mobile robot cell in which the robot is mounted on a track.

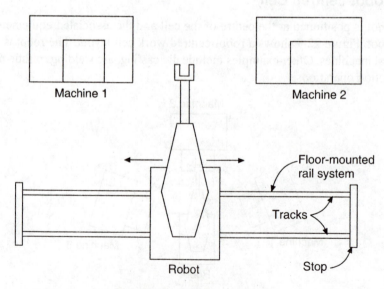

Fig. 22.11 Mobile robot cell.

22.14 CHARACTERISTICS OF INDUSTRIAL ROBOT APPLICATIONS

The general characteristics of industrial robot applications are as follows:

1. *Hazardous or uncomfortable working conditions:* If the working environment is characterised by dangers or health hazards such as heat, radiation, toxicity, etc. for the human operator, the robot can be considered as a substitute.
2. *Repetitive works:* Some industrial operations are repetitive from cycle to cycle. In such situations, the use of a robot is more appropriate than a human worker as it can be programmed to repeat the operations.
3. *Difficult handling:* If the work part is too heavy to be handled by the human operator, industrial robots can be used to lift payloads weighing several tons.

22.15 INDUSTRIAL ROBOT APPLICATIONS

The industrial applications of robots include the following:

1. *Material transfer:* The robot grasps and moves a work part from one location to another. These applications are also called pick-and-place operations because the robot picks the work part from one location and places it in another location.
2. *Machine loading:* The robot loads a raw material into the process and unloads a finished part. Robots have been successfully applied to accomplish the loading/unloading operations in die casting, plastic moulding, machining and forging operations.
3. *Welding:* Robots have been used for spot and arc welding applications.
4. *Spray coating:* The spray coating operations in which robots have been applied include painting of car bodies, engines, spraying paint on appliances, porcelain coating on bathroom fixtures, spray staining of wood products, etc.
5. *Processing operations:* These include drilling, grinding, polishing, deburring, riveting, waterjet cutting, etc.
6. *Assembly:* The assembly process consists of the sequential addition of components to a base part or existing sub-assembly to create a more complete sub-assembly or a complete product. As such, the assembly operations involve handling and orientation of parts to mate them together properly, for which robots can be efficiently used.
7. *Inspection:* This is a quality control operation that involves the checking of parts and assemblies. Robots can be used to accomplish inspection or testing operations for mechanical dimensions and other physical characteristics, and product function and performance.

QUESTION BANK

A. Descriptive Questions

1. What is the mechanical role of a robot manipulator?
2. What is the general structure of a robot manipulator?

3. What are the various types of links used for the construction of a robot manipulator?
4. What are the various types of joints used for the construction of a robot manipulator?
5. What are the degrees of freedom of arm and wrist?
6. What are the various characteristics of an industrial robot?
7. What are the basic configurations of an industrial robot? Explain them schematically.
8. What are the requirements of actuators used for the construction of an industrial robot?
9. What are the basic actuator systems used in commercially available industrial robots?
10. Classify robot control systems. Enumerate their merits and demerits.
11. What are the end effectors?
12. What are the various robotic sensors? Enumerate their limitations.
13. Discuss various robotic programming languages.
14. What are the various types of robot cell layouts? List their advantages.
15. What characteristics need to be satisfied for the application of industrial robots?
16. What are the industrial applications of robots?

B. Multiple Choice Questions

1. Robots are specified by:
    (a) Work volume   (b) Payload
    (c) Degrees of freedom   (d) All the above
2. The work volume is a partial sphere in the case of a:
    (a) Cartesian configuration   (b) Polar configuration
    (c) Cylindrical configuration   (d) Jointed-arm configuration
3. Hydraulic drives are employed for the industrial robots when:
    (a) High power is required   (b) High torque is required
    (c) High speed is required   (d) All the above
4. To find the actual distance of the object the following sensors are used:
    (a) Touch sensors   (b) Range sensors
    (c) Proximity sensors   (d) Tactile sensors
5. No program code is required in the case of:
    (a) Walk through method   (b) Lead through method
    (c) Off-line method   (d) Teach pendent method

Chapter 23

Flexible Manufacturing Systems

OBJECTIVES

After reading this chapter, the reader will be able to understand the following concepts:

➲ FMS equipment: Manufacturing systems, material handling and storage, tool handling and storage, and FMS control system

➲ FMS layouts: In-line FMS layout, loop FMS layout, leader FMS layout, open-field FMS layout, and robot-centred FMS layout

➲ Analysis methods for FMS: Static or deterministic models, queuing models, perturbation analysis, and simulation

➲ Benefits of FMS

23.1 INTRODUCTION

A flexible manufacturing system (FMS) consists of a group of programmable production machines interconnected by means of an automated material handling and storage system, and controlled by an integrated computer system to produce a variety of parts at non-uniform production rates, batch sizes and quantities. A flexible manufacturing system is characterised by the following:

• Variety of products
• Small volume of products
• Less manufacturing lead time
• High quality
• Low cost

23.2 FMS EQUIPMENT

In general, the FMS equipment (Figure 23.1) consists of the following components:

- Manufacturing system
- Tool handling and storage
- Material handling and storage
- Computer control system

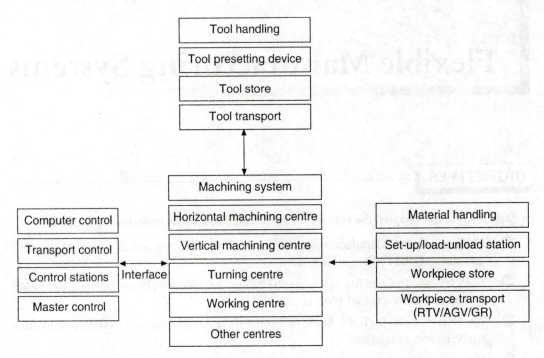

Fig. 23.1 FMS equipment.

23.2.1 Manufacturing System

The machining system consists of CNC machine tools (including horizontal machining centre, vertical machining centre, turning centre, etc.) that perform machining operations on families of parts. However, flexible manufacturing systems also include assembly stations, sheet metal presses, inspection stations, etc. The machining system is capable of performing several of the operations on the workpiece automatically. A typical FMS is shown in Figure 23.2.

Machining centres consist of an automatic tool changing and tool storage, pallet changer, CNC control and DNC control.

Assembly workstations are used for assembling products typically made in batches. Industrial robots are usually considered to be the most appropriate as automated workstations. They can be programmed to perform tasks with variations in the sequence and motion pattern to accommodate the different product styles made on the system.

Inspection stations are incorporated into FMS either by including an inspection operation at a given workstation, or by designating a specific station for inspection. Coordinate measuring machines, special inspection probes that can be used in a machine tool spindle, and machine vision represent three methods of inspecting on FMS.

Sheet metal processing machines consist of pressworking operations such as punching, shearing and bending and forming processes.

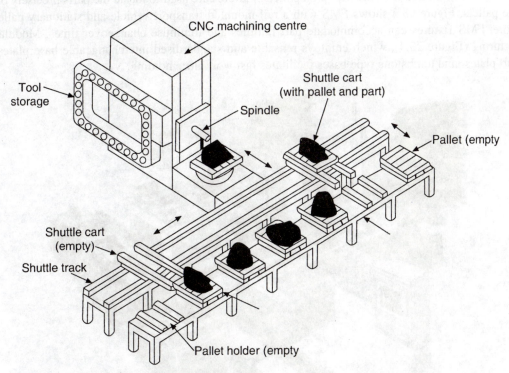

Fig. 23.2 FMS having one machining centre and one part storage unit.

23.2.2 Material Handling and Storage

This system facilitates the timely supply of unmachined workpieces from the storage to the machining centres and transport of the machined parts from the machining centres to the desired locations. The functions of a material handling and storage system are as follows:

- Random, independent movement of workpieces between workstations.
- Accommodation of different part configurations: For prismatic parts, the fixture is located on the top of the pallet and is designed to accommodate different part configurations. For rotational parts, industrial robots are used to load and unload the machine tools and to transfer parts between workstations.
- Compatibility with computer control: The handling system is allowed to control directly by the computer to direct to workstations, load and unload workstations, etc.

The material handling equipment consists of

- Load/unload stations (palletising)
- Robotics
- AGV
- AS/RS

Prismatic components are set up on pallets. Fixtures are used to locate the parts precisely on the pallets. Figure 23.3 shows FMS with a rail-mounted transport vehicle and stationary pallet store. FMS fixtures can accommodate part families and minimise changeover times. Modular fixturing (Figure 23.4), which employs reusable and standardised interchangeable base plates, sub-plates, and tombstone type bases facilitates fast workpiece holding.

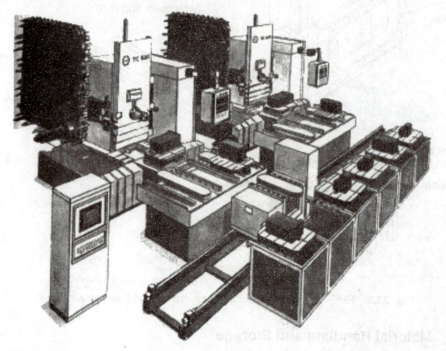

Fig. 23.3   Machining centres with rail mounted transport vehicle and stationary pallet store.

Fig. 23.4   Modular fixturing.

Workpiece storage and retrieval can be automated by using an automatic storage/retrieval system (AS/RS). AS/RS consists of storage racks, a PLC-based or computer-controlled stacker crane. Servomotors used in the cranes can achieve positioning accuracy and reliability. Elevating speeds of the stacker could be as high as 180 m/min. A typical AS/RS is shown in Figure 23.5.

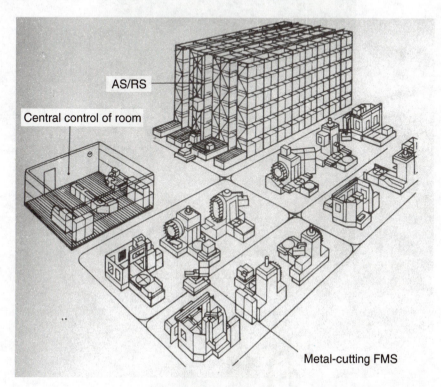

Fig. 23.5 A typical AS/RS.

An automatically guided vehicle (AGV) is a material handling system which uses independently operated, self-propelled vehicles that are guided along defined pathways in the floor. The vehicles are powered by means of on-board batteries. Guidance is achieved by sensors on the vehicles that can follow the guide wires or paint. A typical AGVS unit load carrier is shown in Figure 23.6. It is equipped for automatic loading and unloading by means of powered rollers, moving belts, mechanised lift platforms or other devices.

23.2.3 Tool Handling and Storage

In a flexible manufacturing system, various cutting tools are loaded onto the machines at intervals depending upon their utilisation. The cutting tools are stored in auxiliary tool storage from where the required tools can be transferred to the main tool magazine. Such storage units include drums, chains, discs and other forms. There is a limit to the maximum number of tools available at the machine tool (20–120). Refurbishing of the entire tool magazine is normally done during the start of the shift. A CNC machine tool with tool magazine and automatic tool changer is shown in Figure 23.7.

Fig. 23.6   AGVS unit load carrier.

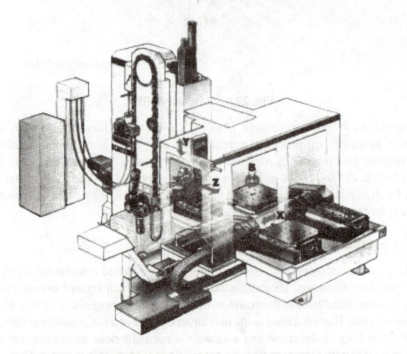

Fig. 23.7   CNC machine with tool magazine and automatic tool changer.

23.2.4 FMS Control System

All the elements in an FMS, machine tools, material handling units, and cutting tools are to be controlled in real-time. A computer is used to control the operations of FMS. The functions performed by the FMS computer control are as follows:

1. *Control of workstations*: It is necessary to continuously monitor various processing or assembly stations. In a fully automated FMS, a centralised computer is used to control and monitor all the processing stations. For a machining system, a CNC is used to control the machine tools.

2. *Production control*: It includes the real-time control of the workstations, load/unload stations, pallets, desired production rate per day for the various parts, volume of raw material available, and tools and material handling units. A data entry unit (DEU) is located in the load/unload area for communication between the operators and the computer.

3. *Traffic control*: This control is for the regulation of the following:
   - Pallet from load area to workstation or buffer
   - Pallet from workstation to buffer or unload area.

   Traffic control is achieved by dividing the transport systems into zones. Each zone is the primary transport system (conveyor, towline chain, etc.). A computer controls each primary transport system.

4. *Shuttle control*: This is used to control the secondary part handling system at each workstation. Each shuttle is coordinated with the primary transport system and is also synchronised with the operations of the workstations.

5. *Tool control*: This control is intended to arrange the availability of the right tool in a good condition at an appropriate place in real-time. There are two aspects of tool control: tool location accounting and tool life monitoring.

   Tool location accounting: In an automated manufacturing system, cutting tools have to be supplied into the system at intervals depending upon their utilisation. The tool magazine of the automatic tool changer is supplied with all tools at each station on the line. If one or more cutting tools required in the processing of a particular workpart are not available at the workstations, the computer control system will not deliver the work part to that workstation.

   Tool life monitoring: The tool has to be continuously monitored while it is cutting. The tool is monitored for tool wear and tool breakage. A file is maintained on the machining time usage of each tool. When the tools are loaded in the tool magazine, the expected tool life is entered in the controller memory along with all other tool-related information such as offsets. As machining proceeds with various work parts, the controller records the actual time for which each tool is used. When the cumulative machining time reaches the life for a given tool, the computer notifies that a replacement is in order.

6. *Scheduling*: This creates the actual sequence of the parts and operations within the specified constraints of the resources.

7. *System performance and monitoring*: The FMS computer is programmed to generate various reports desired by the management on system performance. The computer also monitors the data relating to the architecture of the system in terms of the workstations,

material handling equipment, their relative positioning and other information of the layout. The computer also maintains the resource data in terms of cutting tools, workpiece transport system and fixtures.

23.3 FMS LAYOUTS

The FMS layouts are broadly classified into the following five categories:

1. In-line
2. Loop
3. Ladder
4. Open-field
5. Robot-centred cell

23.3.1 In-Line FMS Layout

The In-line layout configuration is shown in Figure 23.8. It is most appropriate for systems in which the work parts progress from one workstation (WS) to the next in a well-defined sequence with no back flow.

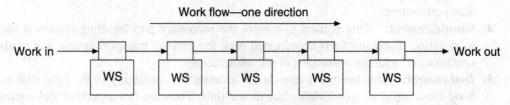

Fig. 23.8 In-line FMS layout.

23.3.2 Loop FMS Layout

The loop layout configuration is shown in Figure 23.9. Work parts usually flow in one direction along the loop with the capability at any workstation. The load/unload stations are located at one end of the loop.

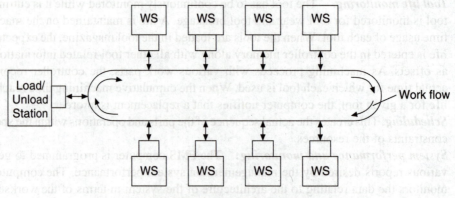

Fig. 23.9 Loop FMS layout.

23.3.3   Ladder FMS Layout

The ladder layout configuration is shown in Figure 23.10. It contains rungs on which workstations are located. This layout reduces the average distance travelled to transfer work parts between stations.

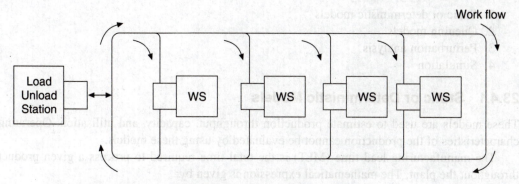

Fig. 23.10   Ladder FMS layout.

23.3.4   Open-field FMS Layout

The open field layout configuration consists of loops, ladders, and sidings organised to achieve the desired processing requirements. This is appropriate for a large family of parts.

23.3.5   Robot-centred FMS Layout

The robot-centred layout configuration is shown in Figure 23.11. The robot is located at the approximate centre of the layout and other workstations are arranged around it. Industrial robot equipped with grippers may be used for the handling of rotational parts. This type of layout is well-suited for the handling of cylindrical or disk-shaped parts.

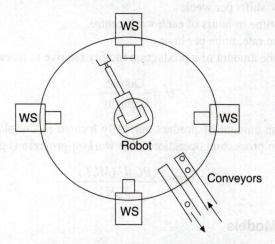

Fig. 23.11   Robot-centred FMS layout.

23.4 ANALYSIS METHODS FOR FMS

FMS is a complex system for study and analysis. The quantitative analysis of FMS can be accomplished by using a number of different mathematical modelling techniques. The basic techniques are as follows:

1. Static or deterministic models
2. Queuing models
3. Perturbation analysis
4. Simulation

23.4.1 Static or Deterministic Models

These models are used to estimate production throughput, capacity, and utilisation. Operating characteristics of the production cannot be evaluated by using these models.

The manufacturing lead time (MLT) is the total time required to process a given product throughout the plant. The mathematical expression is given by:

$$MLT = \sum_{i}^{m} (T_{si} + QT_{oi} + T_{ni})$$

where

T_{si} is the set-up time.
T_{oi} is the time per operation at a given workstation.
T_{ni} is the non-operation time associated with the same workstation.
i is the operation sequence in the processing, $i = 1, 2, 3, ..., m$.

The production capacity (PC) for the group of work centres is given by:

$$PC = WS_w \, HR_p$$

where

W is the number of work centres.
S_w is the number of shifts per week.
H is the operating time in hours of each work centre.
R_p is the production rate, units per hour.

Utilisation (U) is the amount of a production facility relative to its capacity. It is given by:

$$U = \frac{Output}{Capacity}$$

Work-in-progress is the amount of product currently located in the plant that is either being processed or is between processing operations. The work-in-progress is given by:

$$WIP = \frac{(PC)U(MLT)}{S_w H}$$

23.4.2 Queuing Models

These models are based on the mathematics of queues. Queuing models are useful in the preliminary design of manufacturing systems but are not accurate enough at the detailed design/operation stage.

23.4.3 Perturbation Analysis

This model enables parameter sensitivities to be computed in real-time. Perturbation analysis works by observing a nominal experiment, which could be on the actual system or based on the simulation. By performing simple computations, solutions can be obtained questions such as: What will be the performance index if the machines are faster?

23.4.4 Simulation

Discrete event simulation on a computer offers the most flexible approach for modelling the FMS. There are three approaches to simulation modelling of FMS. These are:

1. *Network or graphical models:* In these models, objects are represented by graphical symbols placed in the same physical relationship to each other as the corresponding machines are in the real world. SLAM and SIMAN are two widely used networking tools for FMS.
2. *Data-driven models:* It consists of only numerical data. For example, the numerical data may be:

   - A simple count of machines in a system, or
   - A table of operation times for each process on the route for a given product.
3. *Programming language models:* These provide activity cycles, queues and an optimum cycle. Activity cycle diagram (ACD) is widely used for FMS simulation. It is equivalent to a flow chart of a general purpose computer program. The ACD shows the cycle for every activity in the model.

23.5 BENEFITS OF FMS

The benefits of FMS are as follows:

1. *Greater flexibility:* Capability to cope with changes in production volumes, and in rapid response to market changes.
2. *Higher machine utilisation:* More efficient work handling, off-line set-ups, and better scheduling contribute to FMS machine utilisation of 80 per cent or more.
3. *Reduced work-in-progress:* Since different parts are processed together rather than separately in batches, the number of parts being processed at any moment tends to be less than in a batch production mode.
4. *Lower manufacturing lead times:* Closely correlated with reduced work-in-process is the time spent in process by the parts. This means faster customer deliveries.
5. *Higher labour productivity:* The higher production rate capacity of the FMS and its lower reliance on direct labour means that the productivity per labour is significantly greater than that obtained with conventional production methods. All tool changing and material handling systems are fully automated.

QUESTION BANK

A. Descriptive Questions

1. What are the characteristics of FMS?
2. What do you understand by the term 'flexibility in FMS'?
3. Explain the principal components of FMS.
4. Discuss the various types of material handling systems.
5. What are the functions of FMS control?
6. What are the various types of FMS layouts? Discuss them schematically.
7. What are the different methods of analysis of FMS? Explain.
8. What are the benefits of FMS?

B. Multiple Choice Questions

1. The components of FMS system are:
   (a) Manufacturing system   (b) Material handling system
   (c) Tool handling system   (d) All the above
2. In FMS, the tools are identified by means of:
   (a) Bar code   (b) Colour code
   (c) Digital code   (d) Computer database
3. AGV uses the following guidance technologies:
   (a) Wire-guided system   (b) Infrared guidance system
   (c) Inertial guided system   (d) All the above
4. Gravity principle of material handling system is used for transportation of:
   (a) Fragile items   (b) Explosive items
   (c) Brittle items   (d) Sturdy items
5. In-line FMS layout configuration is best suited for:
   (a) No backflow of parts   (b) Backflow of parts
   (c) Gravity flow of parts   (d) Parts require high process time
6. For heavy payload on large distance the type of AGV employed is:
   (a) Driverless train   (b) AGV pallet trucks
   (c) AGV unit load carriers   (d) Driver train

Chapter **24**

Cellular Manufacturing

OBJECTIVES

After reading this chapter, the reader will be able to understand the following concepts:

○ Objectives of cellular manufacturing

○ Types of machine cell designs: Single machine cell, group machine cell with manual handling, and flow-line cell

○ Cell formation approaches: Direct clustering algorithm, and rank ordering clustering algorithm

24.1 INTRODUCTION

Cellular manufacturing is an application of group technology in which the production equipments are grouped into machine cells where each is specialised in the production of a family of products. When the machines are grouped, the term cellular manufacturing is employed to reduce the process variation. Instead of scheduling parts through a sequence of machines in a process type shop layout, the parts are simply scheduled through the cell. The similarity among parts in the family reduces the complexity of manufacturing scheduling.

24.2 OBJECTIVES OF CELLULAR MANUFACTURING

The typical objectives of cellular manufacturing are:

1. To reduce work in-process inventory
2. To shorten manufacturing lead times
3. To simplify production scheduling

4. To reduce set-up times
5. To provide minimum work part handling
6. To reduce process variation

24.3 TYPES OF MACHINE CELL DESIGNS

Machine cells are classified into the following categories:

1. Single machine cell
2. Group machine cell with manual handling
3. Flow-line cell

24.3.1 Single Machine Cell

The single machine cell consists of one machine with supporting fixtures and tooling organised to produce one or more part families. The conventional turret lathe, CNC milling machine, etc., are examples of single machine cells.

24.3.2 Group Machine Cell with Manual Handling

A group machine cell with manual handling is an arrangement of more than one machine employed to produce one or more part families. The human operator performs the material handling. The machines are organised with proper fixtures, tools and skilled operators to produce the part family. A typical group machine cell with manual handling is shown in Figure 24.1.

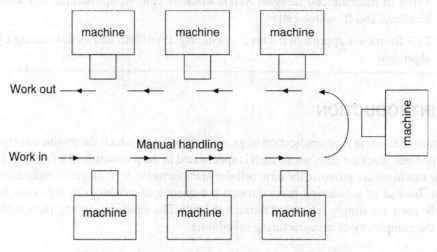

Fig. 24.1   Group machine cell with manual handling.

24.3.3 Flow-line Cell

Flow-line cell (Figure 24.2) uses a mechanised handling system such as conveyor mechanism to move parts between the machines in the cell.

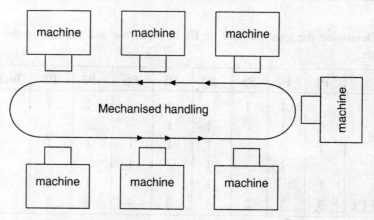

Fig. 24.2 Flow-line cell with mechanized handling.

24.4 CELL FORMATION APPROACHES

Various cell formation approaches are as follows:

1. Direct clustering algorithm
2. Rank ordering clustering algorithm.

24.4.1 Direct Clustering Algorithm

The algorithm is as follows:

Step 1: Determine the total number of 1's in each row and column in the machine part incidence matrix.

Step 2: Sort each row in increasing order corresponding to the total number of 1's.

Step 3: Sort each column in decreasing order corresponding to the total number of 1's.

Step 4: Repeat the preceding steps until the position of each element in each row and column does not change.

Example 24.1 Given the machine part incidence matrix in Figure 24.3, formulate machine cells. Use the direct clustering approach.

P1, P2,..., P8 are parts.

M1, M2, M3, M4 and M5 are machines.

	P1	P2	P3	P4	P5	P6	P7	P8
M1		1	1		1		1	
M2	1	1		1	1			1
M3	1			1	1	1		1
M4		1		1		1	1	1
M5	1		1	1				1

Fig. 24.3 Machine part incidence matrix.

Solution

Step 1:   Determine the total number of 1's in each row and column in the machine part incidence matrix.

	P1	P2	P3	P4	P5	P6	P7	P8	Total of 1's
M1		1	1		1		1	1	5
M2	1	1		1	1			1	5
M3	1			1	1	1	1	1	6
M4		1		1		1			3
M5	1		1	1		1	1	1	6
Total of 1's	3	3	2	4	3	3	3	4	

Step 2:   Sort each row in increasing order corresponding to the total number of 1's.

	P1	P2	P3	P4	P5	P6	P7	P8	Total of 1's
M4		1		1		1			3
M1		1	1		1		1	1	5
M2	1	1		1	1				5
M3	1			1	1	1	1	1	6
M5	1		1	1		1	1	1	6
Total of 1's	3	3	2	4	3	3	3	4	

Step 3:   Sort each column in decreasing order corresponding to the total number of 1's.

	P4	P8	P1	P2	P5	P6	P7	P3	Total of 1's
M4	1			1		1			3
M1		1		1	1		1	1	5
M2	1	1	1	1	1				5
M3	1	1	1		1	1	1		6
M5	1	1	1			1	1	1	6
Total of 1's	4	4	3	3	3	3	3	2	

Step 4:   Stop the procedure, as the position of each element in each row and column does not change.

Machines are formed into single machine cells.

24.4.2   Rank Ordering Clustering Algorithm

Rank ordering clustering (ROC) is a simple algorithm to form machine part groups. The algorithm is based on sorting rows and columns of the machine and part incidence matrix. The algorithm is as follows:

Step 1: Assign binary weight and calculate a decimal weight for each row and column using the following relations

$$\text{Decimal weight for row, } i = \sum_{p=1}^{m} b_{ip} \, 2^{m-p}$$

$$\text{Decimal weight for column, } j = \sum_{p=1}^{n} b_{jp} \, 2^{n-p}$$

Step 2: Rank the rows in order to decrease the decimal weight values.

Step 3: Repeat Steps 1 and 2 for each column.

Step 4: Continue the preceding steps until there is no change in the position of each element in each row and column.

Example 24.2 Given the machine part incidence matrix in Figure 24.3, formulate machine cells. Use the rank ordering clustering approach. Compare the results of Example 24.3.

Solution

Step 1: Calculate the total binary weight of each column *j*.

$$w_j = \sum 2^i m_{ij} \qquad \forall i$$

	P1	P2	P3	P4	P5	P6	P7	P8	2^i	i
M1		1	1		1		1	1	2	1
M2	1	1		1	1			1	4	2
M3	1			1	1	1	1	1	8	3
M4		1		1		1			16	4
M5	1		1	1		1	1	1	32	5
w_j	44	22	34	60	14	56	42	46		
Rank	5	2	3	8	1	7	4	6		

Step 2: Sort the column into rank order.

	P5	P2	P3	P7	P1	P8	P6	P4
M1	1	1	1	1		1		
M2	1	1			1	1		1
M3	1			1	1	1	1	1
M4		1					1	1
M5			1	1	1	1	1	1
w_j	14	22	34	42	44	46	56	60
Rank	1	2	3	4	5	6	7	8

Step 3:   Calculate the total binary weight of each row *i*.

$$w_i = \sum 2^j m_{ij} \qquad \forall j$$

	P5	P2	P3	P7	P1	P8	P6	P4	w_i	i
M1	1	1	1	1		1			94	1
M2	1	1			1	1		1	358	2
M3	1			1	1	1	1	1	498	4
M4		1					1	1	388	3
M5			1	1	1	1	1	1	504	5
2^j	2	4	8	16	32	64	128	256		
j	1	2	3	4	5	6	7	8		

Step 4:   If all rows are in rank order stop the procedure, otherwise, sort the rows into rank order, and then go to Step 1.

	P5	P2	P3	P7	P1	P8	P6	P4	w_i	i
M1	1	1	1	1		1			94	1
M2	1	1			1	1		1	358	2
M4		1					1	1	388	3
M3	1			1	1	1	1	1	498	4
M5			1	1	1	1	1	1	504	5

Step 1:   (Second time)
Calculate the total binary weight of each column *j*.

	P5	P2	P3	P7	P1	P8	P6	P4	2^i	i
M1	1	1	1	1		1			2	1
M2	1	1			1	1		1	4	2
M4		1					1	1	8	3
M3	1			1	1	1	1	1	16	4
M5			1	1	1	1	1	1	32	5
w_j	22	14	34	50	52	54	56	60		
2	1	3	4	5	6	7	8			

Step 2: (Second time)
Sort the column into rank order.

	P2	P5	P3	P7	P1	P8	P6	P4
M1	1	1	1	1		1		
M2	1	1			1	1		1
M4	1						1	1
M3		1		1	1	1	1	1
M5			1	1	1	1	1	1
w_j	14	22	34	50	52	54	56	60
Rank	1	2	3	4	5	6	7	8

Step 3: (Second time)
Calculate the total binary weight of each row i.

	P2	P5	P3	P7	P1	P8	P6	P4	w_i	Rank
M1	1	1	1	1		1			94	1
M2	1	1			1	1		1	358	2
M4	1						1	1	386	3
M3		1		1	1	1	1	1	500	4
M5			1	1	1	1	1	1	504	5
w_j	2	4	8	16	32	64	128	256		
j	1	2	3	4	5	6	7	8		

Step 4: (Second time)
If all rows are in rank order stop the procedure, otherwise, sort the rows into rank order, and then go to Step 1. Yes the rows are in rank order; stop the procedure.

	P2	P5	P3	P7	P1	P8	P6	P4	w_i	Rank
M1	1	1	1	1		1			94	1
M2	1	1			1	1		1	358	2
M4	1						1	1	386	3
M3		1		1	1	1	1	1	500	4
M5			1	1	1	1	1	1	504	5

Machines are formed into single machine cells. There is a difference only in the product flow.

Example 24.3 Given the machine part incidence matrix in Figure 24.4, formulate machine cells and corresponding part family. Use the rank ordering clustering approach.
P1, P2,..., P9 are parts.
M1, M2, ..., M8 are machines.

	P1	P2	P3	P4	P5	P6	P7	P8	P9	P10
M1	1		1	1	1			1	1	
M2				1						
M3	1		1		1			1	1	
M4		1								1
M5		1								
M6						1	1			1
M7	1					1				
M8							1			1

Fig. 24.4   Machine part incidence matrix.

Solution

Step 1:   Calculate the total binary weight of each column *j*.

$$w_j = \sum 2^{i} m_{ij} \qquad \forall i$$

	P1	P2	P3	P4	P5	P6	P7	P8	P9	P10	2^i	i
M1	1		1	1	1			1	1		2	1
M2				1							4	2
M3	1		1		1			1	1		8	3
M4		1								1	16	4
M5		1									32	5
M6						1	1			1	64	6
M7	1					1					128	7
M8							1			1	256	8
w_j	138	48	10	6	10	192	320	10	10	336		
Rank	4	3	2	1	2	5	6	2	2	7		

Step 2:   Sort the column into rank order.

	P4	P3	P5	P8	P9	P2	P1	P6	P7	P10
M1	1	1	1	1	1		1			
M2	1									
M3		1	1	1	1		1			
M4						1				1
M5						1				
M6								1	1	1
M7							1	1		
M8									1	1
w_j	6	10	10	10	10	48	138	192	320	336
Rank	1	2	2	2	2	3	4	5	6	7

Step 3: Calculate the total binary weight of each row i.

$$w_i = \sum 2m_{ij} \qquad \forall j$$

	P4	P3	P5	P8	P9	P2	P1	P6	P7	P10	w_i	Rank
M1	1	1	1	1	1		1				190	4
M2	1										2	1
M3		1	1	1	1		1				188	3
M4						1				1	1088	6
M5						1					64	2
M6								1	1	1	1792	8
M7							1	1			384	5
M8									1	1	1536	7
2^j	2	4	8	16	32	64	128	256	512	1024		
j	1	2	3	4	5	6	7	8	9	10		

Step 4: If all rows are in rank order stop the procedure, otherwise, sort the rows into rank order, and then go to Step 1.

	P4	P3	P5	P8	P9	P2	P1	P6	P7	P10	w_i	Rank
M2	1										2	1
M5						1					64	2
M3		1	1	1	1		1				188	3
M1	1	1	1	1	1		1				190	4
M7							1	1			384	5
M4						1				1	1088	6
M8									1	1	1536	7
M6								1	1	1	1792	8

Step 1: (*Second time*)

Calculate the total binary weight of each column j.

	P4	P3	P5	P8	P9	P2	P1	P6	P7	P10	2^i	i
M2	1										2	1
M5						1					4	2
M3		1	1	1	1		1				8	3
M1	1	1	1	1	1		1				16	4
M7							1	1			32	5
M4						1				1	64	6
M8									1	1	128	7

(Cont...)

											256	8
M6								1	1	1	256	8
w_j	18	24	24	24	24	68	56	272	384	448		
Rank	1	2	2	2	2	4	3	5	6	7		

Step 2:   (*Second time*)
Sort the column into rank order.

	P4	P3	P5	P8	P9	P1	P2	P6	P7	P10
M2	1									
M5							1			
M3		1	1	1	1	1				
M1	1	1	1	1	1	1				
M7						1		1		
M4							1			1
M8									1	1
M6								1	1	1
w_j	18	24	24	24	24	56	68	272	384	448
Rank	1	2	2	2	2	3	4	5	6	7

Step 3:   (*Second time*)
Calculate the total binary weight of each row *I*.

	P4	P3	P5	P8	P9	P1	P2	P6	P7	P10	w_i	Rank
M2	1										2	1
M5							1				68	2
M3		1	1	1	1	1					152	3
M1	1	1	1	1	1	1					170	4
M7						1		1			328	5
M4							1			1	516	6
M8									1	1	832	7
M6								1	1	1	1104	8
w_j	18	24	24	24	24	56	68	272	384	448		
Rank	1	2	2	2	2	3	4	5	6	7		

Step 4:   (*Second time*)
If all rows are in rank order stop the procedure, otherwise, sort the rows into rank order, and then go to Step 1. Yes the rows are in rank order; stop the procedure.

	P4	P3	P5	P8	P9	P1	P2	P6	P7	P10	w_i	Rank
M2	1										2	1
M5							1				68	2
M3		1	1	1	1	1					152	3
M1	1	1	1	1	1	1					170	4
M7						1		1			328	5
M4							1			1	516	6
M8									1	1	832	7
M6								1	1	1	1104	8
	Part family 1						Part family 2					

The machine cells and corresponding part families are as follows:

Machine cell	Part family
M2, M3, M1, M7	P4, P3, P5, P8, P9, P1
M5, M4, M8, M6	P2, P6, P7, P10

QUESTION BANK

A. Descriptive Questions

1. What is cellular manufacturing?
2. What are the objectives of cellular manufacturing?
3. What are the different types of machine cell designs? Explain them schematically.
4. Discuss various cell formation approaches.
5. Given machine-part incidence matrix in Figure 24.5. Formulate machine cells and corresponding part family. Use direct clustering approach.

	1	2	3	4	5	6	7	8
1		1	1		1		1	1
2	1	1		1			1	1
3	1		1		1	1	1	1
4		1		1		1		
5	1			1		1	1	1

Fig. 24.5

6. Given machine-part incidence matrix in Figure 24.6. Formulate machine cells. Use rank ordering clustering approach.

	1	2	3	4	5	6
1		1	1		1	1
2	1			1		1
3	1		1		1	1
4		1		1		1
5	1			1		1

Fig. 24.6

B. Multiple Choice Questions

1. Cellular manufacturing system is designed on the basis of:
   (a) JIT   (b) MRP   (c) CRP   (d) GT

2. Cellular manufacturing uses the information of:
   (a) Part-machine incidence index   (b) Parts classification and coding
   (c) Coding structure   (d) None of the above

Chapter 25

Lean Manufacturing

After reading this chapter, the reader will be able to understand the following concepts:

- ⟳ Lean manufacturing elements
- ⟳ Lean manufacturing terms
- ⟳ Objectives of lean manufacturing
- ⟳ Principles of lean manufacturing
- ⟳ What kinds of companies benefit most from lean?
- ⟳ Lean manufacturing concepts: Value creation and waste, kinds of waste, pull production, different models of pull production, why high levels of inventory increase defects and wastage, impact of pull production on production planning, continuous flow, mixing continuous and discontinuous flow, Kaizen, worker involvement, cellular layout, and administrative lean.
- ⟳ Lean manufacturing tools and methodologies: Standard work, communication of standard work to employees, standard work and flexibility, visual management, quality at the source, value stream mapping, the five s's preventive maintenance, total productive maintenance, changeover set-up time, batch size reduction, production layout and point of use storage, Kanban, production levelling, pacemaker, and overall equipment effectiveness.
- ⟳ Implementing lean: Senior management involvement, start with a partial implementation of lean, start small, use an expert, and develop a plan
- ⟳ Reconciling lean with other systems: Toyota production system, lean six sigma, lean and ERP, and lean with ISO 9001:2000

25.1 INTRODUCTION

A shift is occurring in manufacturing around the world. Manufacturers throughout industries from automotive to aircraft to paint to computers to the furniture industries are moving to a different system of production called 'lean manufacturing'.

Lean manufacturing implies the systematic elimination of waste, and the implementation of continuous flow concepts and customer pull. Lean is the best management system for satisfying customers on delivery, quality and price.

Many companies are turning to lean manufacturing in an effort to become more profitable. Implementing 'lean' can bring about superior financial and operational results. Lean manufacturing comes from the Toyota production system. Practised by Toyota for many years, the ultimate goal of this system is to produce quality products through cost reduction activities and a cultural focus on employee involvement through empowerment. Lean manufacturing uses concepts pioneered by Toyota Motor Company's former Vice President, Taiichi Ohno. This 'new' manufacturing culture is employed in every facet of the value stream, to include instilling of discipline for reducing costs, to generate capital, to increase profits, to bring in more sales, and to remain competitive in a growing global market.

25.2 LEAN MANUFACTURING ELEMENTS

Waste elimination, continuous one-piece workflow, and customer pull are the basic elements of lean manufacturing. Focusing these elements in the areas of cost, quality, and delivery forms the basis of a lean production system.

Lean techniques can also be applied to the service industry. In the service industry, eliminating waste pertains to the process of eliminating anything that does not add value to the customer.

25.3 LEAN MANUFACTURING TERMS

The following terms are relevant to a lean manufacturing system:

1. *Set-up time:* Work required to change over a machine or process from one to the next.
2. *Cycle time:* The normal time required to complete an operation on a product, which should be less than or equal to *takt* time.
3. *Takt time:* Takt is a German term for rhythm. *Takt* time implies the allowable time to produce one product at the rate at which customers are demanding it.
4. *Kanban:* A card or sheet used to authorise production or movement of an item. When fully implemented, Kanban operates according to the following rules:

   - All production and movement of parts and material take place only as required by a downstream operation, i.e., all manufacturing and procurement are ultimately driven by the requirements of final assembly or its equivalent.
   - The specific tool which authorises production or movement is called a 'Kanban'. Kanbans have various formats and content as appropriate for their usage. A Kanban for a vendor is different from a Kanban for an internal machining operation.

- The quantity authorised per individual Kanban is minimal, ideally one. The number of circulating or available Kanbans for an item is determined by the demand rate for the item and the time required to produce or acquire more. Thus inventory is kept under control while production is forced to keep pace with shipment volume.

5. *Heijunka:* A production scheduling/levelling tool, used to distribute Kanban cards in an efficient manner.

6. *Jidoka:* A form of automation in which machinery automatically inspects each item after producing it, ceasing production and notifying humans if a defect is detected.

7. *Just-in-time:* A production scheduling concept that calls for any item needed at a production operation, be it raw material, a finished item, or anything in between, to be produced and available precisely when needed, neither a moment earlier nor a moment later.

8. *Kaizen:* The philosophy of continual improvement whereby every process can and should be continually evaluated and improved in terms of the time required, resources used, resultant quality, and other aspects relevant to the process.

9. *Mixed model production:* The capability to produce a variety of models that differ in labour and material content, on the same production line, thereby allowing for efficient utilisation of resources while providing a rapid response to marketplace demands.

10. *Flexible manufacturing system:* An integrated manufacturing capability to produce small numbers of a great variety of items at low unit cost, characterised by low changeover time and rapid response time.

11. *Nagara:* Smooth production flow, ideally one piece at a time, characterised by the synchronisation of production processes and maximum utilisation of available time, including overlapping of operations where practical.

12. *Pull system:* A manufacturing planning system based on the communication of actual real-time needs from downstream operations, and ultimately final assembly or its equivalent.

13. *SMED:* Single Minute Exchange of Die implies changing of a die on a forming or stamping machine in a minute or less, i.e., the ability to perform any set-up activity in a minute or less of machine or process downtime.

25.4 OBJECTIVES OF LEAN MANUFACTURING

Lean manufacturing, also called 'lean production', is a set of tools and methodologies that aims for the continuous elimination of all waste in the production process. The main benefits of this are lower production costs, increased output and shorter production lead times. More specifically, some of its goals include:

1. *Defects and wastage:* To reduce defects and unnecessary physical wastage, including excess use of raw material inputs, preventable defects, costs associated with reprocessing of defective items, and unnecessary product characteristics which are not required by customers.

2. *Cycle times:* To reduce manufacturing lead times and production cycle times by reducing waiting times between processing stages, as well as process preparation times and product/model conversion times.

3. *Inventory levels:* To minimise inventory levels at all stages of production, particularly works-in-progress between production stages. Lower inventories also mean lower working capital requirements;

4. *Labour productivity:* To improve labour productivity, both by reducing the idle time of workers and by ensuring that when workers are working, they are using their effort as productively as possible (including not doing unnecessary tasks or unnecessary motions);

5. *Utilisation of equipment and space:* To use equipment and manufacturing space more efficiently by eliminating bottlenecks and maximising the rate of production through existing equipment, while minimising machine downtime;

6. *Flexibility:* To have the ability to produce a more flexible range of products with minimum changeover costs and changeover time.

7. *Output:* Insofar as reduced cycle times, increased labour productivity and elimination of bottlenecks and machine downtime can be achieved, companies can generally significantly increase output from their existing facilities.

Most of these benefits lead to lower unit production costs. For example, more effective use of equipment and space leads to lower depreciation costs per unit produced, while more effective use of labour results in lower labour costs per unit produced and lower defects lead to lower cost of goods.

25.5 PRINCIPLES OF LEAN MANUFACTURING

The key principles behind lean manufacturing can be summarised as follows:

1. *Recognition of waste:* The first step is to recognise what does and does not create value from the customer's perspective. Any material, process or feature which is not required for creating value from the customer's perspective is waste and should be eliminated. For example, transporting materials between workstations is a waste because it can potentially be eliminated.

2. *Standard processes:* Lean requires the implementation of very detailed production guidelines, called 'Standard Work', which clearly state the content, sequence, timing and outcome of all actions by workers. This eliminates variation in the manner in which workers perform their tasks.

3. *Continuous flow:* Lean usually aims for the implementation of a continuous production flow free of bottlenecks, interruption, detours, backflows or waiting. When this is successfully implemented, the production cycle time can be reduced by as much as 90 per cent.

4. *Pull-production:* Also called Just-in-Time (JIT), pull production aims to produce only what is needed, when it is needed. Production is pulled by the downstream workstation so that each workstation should only produce what is requested by the next workstation.

5. *Quality at the source:* Lean aims for defects to be eliminated at the source and for quality inspection to be done by the workers as part of the in-line production process.

6. *Continuous improvement:* Lean necessitates striving for perfection by continually removing layers of waste as they are uncovered. This, in turn, requires a high level of worker involvement in the continuous improvement process.

25.6 WHAT KINDS OF COMPANIES BENEFIT MOST FROM LEAN?

Lean is most widely used in industries that are assembly-oriented or have a high amount of repetitive human processes. These are typically industries for which productivity is highly influenced by the efficiency and attention to detail of the people who are working manually with either tools or operating equipment. For these kinds of companies, improved systems can eliminate significant levels of waste or inefficiency. Examples of this include companies engaged in wood-processing, garment manufacturing, automobile assembly, electronics assembly and equipment manufacturing.

Since lean manufacturing eliminates many of the problems associated with poor production scheduling and line balancing, lean manufacturing is particularly appropriate for companies that do not have ERP systems in place or do not have strong material requirements planning (MRP), production scheduling or production allocation systems in place. This is particularly significant in Vietnam where many private Vietnamese manufacturing companies are believed to be operating significantly below their potential capacities, or experiencing a high level of late deliveries due to problems with their current production scheduling and production management systems.

Lean manufacturing is also appropriate in industries for which it is a strategic priority to shorten the production cycle time to the absolute minimum as a source of competitive advantage for the company.

Recently, some companies in Vietnam actively conducted training programmes and implemented lean methods to eliminate process inefficiencies. This resulted in an improvement in their production and service lead times. For example, Toyota Ben Thanh, a service centre of Toyota in Vietnam, has implemented lean methods to significantly reduce the process time for its automobile maintenance service from 240 minutes to 45–50 minutes per car, and as a result, increased the total number of cars processed at each service centre from 4–6 cars up to 16 cars per day. Toyota Ben Thanh achieved significant reductions in the process lead time by successfully eliminating unnecessary waiting time, inefficiencies of physical motions and process flow.

25.7 LEAN MANUFACTURING CONCEPTS

25.7.1 Value Creation and Waste

In lean manufacturing, the **value** of a product is defined solely on the basis of what the customer actually requires and is willing to pay for. Production operations can be grouped into the following three types of activities:

- *Value-added activities:* These are activities, which transform the materials into the exact product that the customer requires.
- *Non value-added activities:* These are activities which are not required for transforming the materials into the product that the customer wants. Anything, which is non value-added, may be defined as waste. Anything that adds unnecessary time, effort or cost is considered non value-added. Another way of looking at waste is that it is any material or activity for which the customer is not willing to pay. Testing or inspecting materials is also considered waste since this can be eliminated insofar as the production process can be improved to eliminate defects from occurring. For more on the kinds of waste, please see Section 25.7.2.

- *Necessary non value-added activities:* These are activities that do not add value from the perspective of the customer but are necessary for producing the product unless the existing supply or production process is radically changed. This kind of waste may be eliminated in the long run but is unlikely to be eliminated in the near term. For example, high levels of inventory may be required as buffer stock, though this could be gradually reduced as production becomes more stable.

Research at the Lean Enterprise Research Centre (LERC) in the United Kingdom indicated that for a typical manufacturing company the ratio of activities could be broken down as follows:

Value-added activity	5%
Non value-added activity	60%
Necessary non value-added activity	35%
Total activities	100%

This implies that up to 60 per cent of the activities at a typical manufacturing company can potentially be eliminated.

25.7.2   Kinds of Waste

Originally, the main types of waste were identified as part of the Toyota production system. However, this list has been modified and expanded by various practitioners of lean manufacturing and generally includes the areas specified below.

1. *Over-production:* Over-production implies unnecessarily producing more than demanded or producing it too early before it is needed. This increases the risk of obsolescence, and of producing the wrong products, besides increasing the possibility of having to sell those items at a discount or discard them as scrap. However, there are some cases when an extra supply of semi-finished or finished products is intentionally maintained, even by lean manufacturers.

2. *Defects:* In addition to physical defects which directly add to the costs of the goods sold, this may include errors in paperwork, provision of incorrect information about the product, late delivery, production to incorrect specifications, use of too much raw materials or the generation of unnecessary scrap.

3. *Inventory:* Inventory waste means having unnecessarily high levels of raw materials, works-in-progress and finished products. Extra inventory leads to higher inventory financing costs, higher storage costs and higher defect rates. For more on this, please see Section 25.7.5.

4. *Transportation:* Transportation includes any movement of materials that does not add any value to the product, such as moving materials between workstations. The idea is that transportation of materials between production stages should aim for the ideal situation wherein the output of one process is immediately used as the input for the next process. Transportation between processing stages results in prolonging production cycle times and the inefficient use of labour and space and can also be a source of minor production stoppages.

5. *Waiting:*   Waiting implies idle time for workers or machines due to bottlenecks or inefficient production flow on the factory floor. Waiting also includes small delays between processing of units. Waiting results in a significant cost insofar as it increases labour costs and depreciation costs per unit of output.

6. *Motion:*   Motion includes any unnecessary physical motions or walking by workers which diverts them from the actual processing work. For example, this might include walking around the factory floor to look for a tool, or even unnecessary or difficult physical movements, due to poorly designed ergonomics, which slow down the workers.

7. *Correction:*   Correction, or re-processing, takes place when something has to be re-done because it was not done correctly the first time. This not only results in the inefficient use of labour and equipment but the act of re-processing often causes disruptions in the smooth flow of production and therefore generates bottlenecks and stoppages. Also, issues associated with re-working typically consume a significant amount of management time and, therefore, add to factory overhead costs.

8. *Over-processing:*   Over-processing implies unintentionally doing more processing work than the customer requires in terms of product quality or features, such as polishing or applying finishing on some areas of a product that will not be seen by the customer.

9. *Knowledge disconnection:*   This is when information or knowledge isn't available where or when it is needed. This might include information on correct procedures, specifications, ways to solve problems, etc. Lack of correct information often leads to defects and bottlenecks. For example, the unavailability of a mixing formula may potentially suspend the entire process or create defective items due to time-consuming trial and error tests.

25.7.3 Pull Production

A core concept of lean manufacturing is pull production in which the flow on the factory floor is driven by demand from downstream pulling production upstream as opposed to traditional batch-based production in which production is pushed from upstream to downstream on the basis of a production schedule. This means that no materials will be processed until there is a need (signal) from downstream. For example, in pull production, a customer order creates a demand for the finished product, which, in turn, creates a demand for final assembly, which, in turn, creates a demand for sub-assemblies, and so on up the supply chain. The specific implications of this are detailed below:

1. *Orders start at the most downstream stage:*   When an order is received from the customer and communicated to the factory floor, the production order is initially placed with the most downstream workstation (such as packaging or final assembly) as opposed to the most upstream workstations (such as initial processing of raw materials). This practice requires a very effective communication system which ensures that upstream suppliers are continuously aware of what is needed by their downstream customers. Please also see Section 25.8.13 on Kanban for more information on this.

2. ***The product is pulled through production on the basis of demand from the downstream process:***   Each production stage or workstation is seen as a customer of the production stage or workstation immediately upstream of it. Nothing is produced by the upstream supplier until demanded by the downstream customer.

3. *The rate of production is driven by downstream consumption rates:* The rate of production at each production stage or workstation is equal to the rate of demand/consumption from its downstream customer. Pull production is the same as Just-in-Time (JIT) which means that raw materials or works-in-progress are delivered with the exact amount and 'just in time' when the downstream workstation needs it.

The ideal of pull production is that the materials will be available from the supplier (upstream stage) exactly when the customer (downstream stage) needs them. This means that all inventory in the factory is being processed, as opposed to waiting to be processed, and that the customer usually must plan ahead by anticipating what will be required on the basis of the turnaround time for the supplier. For example, if it takes the supplier two hours to deliver materials when ordered by the customer, the customer will have to order ahead by two hours so that the materials will be ready when the customer needs them.

25.7.4 Different Models of Pull Production

Many lean manufacturers intentionally maintain certain inventories of raw materials, semi-finished products and finished products in order to:

- Protect their companies against variations in customer demand.
- Protect them against unexpected late shipments from suppliers or production slow downs.
- Ensure smooth production flow by producing some items on a continuous basis even if they are not required by the customer.
- Realise the fact that raw materials must be delivered in batches and that finished products must be shipped in batches.
- Understand that some processing must be done in batches due to the nature of the equipment or the process.

Generally speaking, the less predicable customer orders, the more unstable production (such as unintentional slowdowns and bottlenecks), or the less reliable the raw materials suppliers, the greater the inventory that will be required to create a buffer against sudden changes in customer demand, production instability or raw material shortages. In such cases, lean manufacturers intentionally maintain inventories of raw materials, semi-finished products or finished products to create a buffer against such events.

In order to accommodate these situations, the following different models for implementing pull-based production, are used:

1. *Replenishment pull system:* In a replenishment pull system, the company intentionally maintains inventories of each type of finished product and only when the inventory of a certain finished product falls below a certain level, a replenishment order is issued to produce larger quantities of the product. Replenishment pull is more common when a company has a large number of small volume customers who order standardised products. In a replenishment pull system, since production schedules are more predicable, low inventories of raw materials are required.

2. *Sequential pull system:* In a sequential pull system, orders are placed on the factory floor only when the product is demanded by an outside customer. All products are made on a made-to-order basis. Sequential pull is more common when a company has a small

number of large volume customers who order customised products. Although companies using this system should have lower inventories of finished products, they will typically require larger inventories of raw materials or semi-finished materials due to less predictability in the production schedule (due to difficulty in predicting exactly what customer orders will be placed and when).

3. *Mixed pull system:*   In a mixed pull system, certain elements of replenishment and sequential pull systems are used in conjunction with each other. For example, a company may produce some products on a replenishment pull basis while producing other products on a sequential pull basis. Alternatively, a company may use replenishment pull for part of the production process and sequential pull for a different part of the production process. An example of this would be a company that maintains a managed level of inventory of certain semi-finished items but only produces a finished product when it is ordered by the customer. In such a case, the company applies a replenishment pull system for producing the semi-finished items and applies a sequential pull process for the remainder of the production process. In the Toyota production system, production is triggered to re-stock semi-finished items so that whenever an item is needed, it is available.

25.7.5   Why High Levels of Inventory Increase Defects and Wastage

Pull production results in the elimination of unnecessary inventory between processing stages. High levels of inventory between processing stages result in higher defect rates for the following reasons:

1. *Non-detection of defects in batch processing:*   In batch processing, more defective units will be produced before being detected at the next processing stage. For example, if the batch size of a bag printing process is 3000 pieces at a time before going to the next workstation and the quality controller does not identify the defect, it is likely that many defective bags will have been produced before the errors are discovered by the next workstation.

2. *Defects and wastage from storage and transportation:*   Some defects occur during transportation and storage. For example, in the furniture industry, exposure to humidity during storage can contribute to high moisture content which may be considered a defect. Meanwhile, the act of storing inventory requires extra labour, energy and space.

3. *Direct accountability:*   When there is an inventory queue between two production stages, there is no direct connection between the two production stages. The downstream stage may not even know which worker or team has produced particular items. When there is less accountability by the upstream worker/team, it is more likely to make a defective product or not produce exactly to customer specifications. Conversely, a direct handoff and immediate usage by the downstream worker/team will help ensure that the upstream worker/team takes full responsibility to produce only those items which will be accepted by the downstream worker/team.

However, as mentioned in the previous section, there are some cases wherein inventory is essential for ensuring smooth production and, therefore, certain kinds of inventory should be maintained at a managed level to ensure that no disruption occurs.

25.7.6 Impact of Pull Production on Production Planning

Most private manufacturing companies in Vietnam are using a centrally planned system whereby the Production Planning Manager develops a production schedule and allocates orders to workstations in batches. This is a push-based system, meaning that inventory gets pushed though the production process on the basis of the production schedule. The Materials Requirements Planning (MRP) module of most Enterprise Resource Planning (ERP) systems operates on this basis.

In a push-based system, if the production forecasting systems are not accurate (which is often the case for Vietnamese manufacturing companies) or the Production Planning Manager does not have accurate information about the production status and demand at each stage of the production process or does not have effective tools for analysing this (which is also often the case at Vietnamese manufacturing companies), he/she may allocate too much or too little work to different teams and workstations, thereby resulting in bottlenecks, excess inventory, low likelihood of being able to produce on a continuous flow basis, and inefficient use of resources in general.

In contrast, a key element of the pull-based system is that, with the exception of production levelling, the allocation and flow of work on the factory floor is determined on the basis of demand on the factory floor and not on a production schedule or centrally planned production allocation system.

Although lean manufacturing companies still have a production plan, the plan is primarily used for the following:

- Planning capacity requirements, including changes in the configuration of production lines or cells.
- Planning labour requirements.
- Smoothening the flow of orders to the factory floor (see Section 25.8.14 on production levelling); and
- Planning raw material requirements.

25.7.7 Continuous Flow

Continuous flow is the linking of manual and machine operations into a perfectly smooth flow in which works-in-progress are continuously undergoing some form of processing and never become stagnant waiting to be processed. Continuous flow eliminates waiting time for works-in-progress, equipment or workers.

In continuous flow, the ideal is one-piece flow or small batches, which can be processed with virtually no waiting time between production stages.

Continuous flow may necessitate a re-design of the production layout away from groups of similar workstations located near each other and towards highly integrated production lines in which semi-finished products can move as quickly and easily as possible from one production stage to the next.

Continuous flow can result in very substantial reductions in total cycle time. For example:

- When Simms Fishing Products, a U.S.-based manufacturer of garments used by fishermen, implemented lean manufacturing, their production throughout (i.e. the total time from the start to the finish of the production process) fell from 17 days to 2–3 days.
- When Woodland Furniture Company, a U.S.-based manufacturer of high-end wood furniture, implemented lean manufacturing, lead times were reduced from twelve weeks to one week.

25.7.8 Mixing Continuous and Discontinuous Flow

Sometimes continuous flow is not possible for some stages of the production process. In these cases, continuous flow can be implemented in some but not all the production stages. Some examples of cases in which continuous flow is not appropriate for some stages of the process include:

- There may be cycle time mismatches wherein some processes occur at very fast cycle times and must change over to serve multiple product types.
- Distance between processes may be unavoidable in some cases and may mean that transportation of materials must be done in relatively large batches.
- Some processes are too unreliable and therefore have unpredictable yields which can be disruptive to a continuous flow operation.
- Some processes must be done in large batches. For example, kiln drying of wood is done in batches which means that when wood comes out of that process, it may need to be stored as inventory for a least some time because all of it cannot be processed at once.
- Sometimes the use of scrap should be maintained as inventory for future use in order to maximise yields. For example, some scrap which is generated in wood-cutting stages can be re-used at a later time when there is a requirement for a piece of wood with the dimensions of the scrap. This means that some works-in-progress inventory might be intentionally generated at stages where re-usable scrap is produced. In a case like this, a truly continuous flow would result in a higher level of waste than a yield-maximising approach in which some scrap is intentionally created for later use.
- In some cases, the company may intentionally maintain inventories of semi-finished products at some stages of the production process.

25.7.9 Kaizen

A company can never be perfectly efficient. Lean manufacturing requires a commitment to continuous improvement, and preferably a systematic process for ensuring continuous improvement, whereby the company constantly searches for non value-added activities and ways to eliminate those. The focus of continuous improvement should be on identifying the root causes of non value-added activities and eliminating those by improving the production process.

Kaizen is a Japanese term for 'continuous improvement', with an emphasis on small incremental improvements. The main theme of Kaizen is to create a culture of continuous improvement, largely by assigning responsibility to workers, and encouraging them, to identify opportunities for improvement, as described in Section 25.7.10.

25.7.10 Worker Involvement

In lean manufacturing, workers are assigned clear responsibilities to identify sources of non value-added activities and to propose solutions to those. Lean manufacturers typically believe that the majority of useful ideas for eliminating non value-added activities typically originate with the workers involved in those processes. A significant body of research also substantiates this assertion.

In order to ensure that ideas for eliminating non value-added activities are acted upon, the power to decide on changes to the production processes are pushed down to the lowest level possible (i.e., normal workers) but it is necessary for any such changes to meet certain requirements. For example, at Toyota, workers are encouraged to implement improvements in the production processes but the improvement must have a clear logic which is in accordance with the scientific method, the improvement must be implemented under the supervision of an authorised manager and the new process must be documented in a high level of detail covering content, sequence, timing and outcome. Toyota initially implements the proposed changes on a small scale on a trial basis and if the improvement is effective, Toyota decides to implement the change across its manufacturing operations.

Two common ways to encourage worker involvement in the continuous improvement process are:

1. *Kaizen circles:* One way of increasing the levels of worker involvement is to implement Kaizen Circles in which groups of 6-8 workers are formed to generate ideas for solving particular problems. Typically a Kaizen Circle will meet for around one hour per week for 6–8 weeks, and at the end of that period will present some proposals to their managers on how to solve particular problems. Active involvement/support by managers is critical to the success of Kaizen Circles.

2. *Suggestion programs:* Another way of increasing worker involvement is having an active suggestion program wherein people are strongly encouraged to make suggestions and rewarded for suggestions that are successfully implemented. Often the cost of the reward is quite small relative to the value that is created for the company by implementing the improvement.

Some experts in lean manufacturing maintain that high levels of worker involvement in continuously suggesting improvements is a critical success factor in the implementation of lean and is the key factor which differentiates Toyota from other companies in terms of its success in implementing lean manufacturing principles.

25.7.11 Cellular Layout

In cellular production layouts, equipment and workstations are arranged into a large number of small tightly connected cells so that many stages or all stages of a production process can occur within a single cell or a series of cells. Cellular layouts are characterised by the following characteristics:

1. *Continuous flow:* There is a smooth flow of materials and components through the cell with virtually no transport or waiting time between production stages.

2. *One-piece flow:* Cellular manufacturing utilises a one piece flow so that one product moves through the manufacturing process, one piece at a time.

3. *Multi-purpose workers:* There is only one or several workers in each cell and unlike batch processing where workers are responsible for a single process, in cell manufacturing the cell workers are responsible for handling each of the different processes that occur in the cell. Therefore, each worker is trained to handle each process which occurs within the cell.

4. *U-shape:* Cells are usually U-shaped, with the product moving from one end of the U to the other end of the U as it is processed by the worker(s). The purpose of this is to minimise the walking distance and movement of materials within a cell.

A cellular layout helps to achieve many of the objectives of lean manufacturing due to its ability to help eliminate many non value-added activities from the production process such as waiting times, bottlenecks, transport and works-in-progress. Another benefit of cellular manufacturing is that the responsibility for quality is clearly assigned to the worker in a particular cell and he/she, therefore, cannot blame workers at upstream stages for quality problems.

Many companies implement a cellular layout for certain parts of the production process but not for the entire production process. For example, processing stages involving lengthy heating or drying processes would not be appropriate for a cellular layout since it is difficult to connect those to a continuous flow which happens in a cell. Furniture companies typically implement a cellular layout for some cutting, assembly and finishing stages but not for any kiln drying or paint drying stages.

Cellular layouts are not appropriate for all companies and many companies successfully implement lean manufacturing without implementing cellular layouts. For example, some industries require large batch processing due to the nature of the equipment or significant waiting times between production stages and, therefore, these would not be suitable for cellular layouts.

25.7.12 Administrative Lean

Administrative lean implies the application of lean manufacturing concepts and tools to improve administrative processes other than factory floor production. This is particularly relevant for administrative processes which are repetitive and involve a high volume of transactions such as order entry, purchasing, accounting or various kinds of back office processing. However, the application of lean to administrative processes is less common than the application of lean to production processes.

25.8 LEAN MANUFACTURING TOOLS AND METHODOLOGIES

25.8.1 Standard Work

Standard work (also called 'standardised work' or 'standard process') means that production processes and guidelines are very clearly defined and communicated, in a high level of detail, so as to eliminate variation and incorrect assumptions in the way that the work is performed. The goal is that production operations should be performed in the same way every time, except insofar as the production process is intentionally modified. When production procedures are not highly standardised, workers may have different ideas of what the correct operating procedures are and easily make incorrect assumptions. A high level of process standardisation also makes it easier for the company to expand capacity without disruption.

The standard work guidelines used in lean manufacturing are typically defined in significantly greater detail than the minimum required for conformity with 7.5.1. of ISO9001:2000 on 'Control of Production and Service Provision', particularly in terms of standardising the movements and work sequences of particular workers.

In lean manufacturing, standard work has several main elements. These are:

1. *Standard work sequence:* This is the order in which a worker must perform tasks, including motions and processes. This is clearly specified to ensure that all workers perform the tasks in the most similar ways possible so as to minimise variation and the consequent defects. Ideally, this is so detailed as to clearly describe every single hand movement by a worker. For example, in wood cutting, the standard work sequence would describe every specific cut and operating step from the machine set-up to material handling, cutter adjustment, manual movements and processing time. In an assembly process, it would describe the exact sequential step-by step motions by which the item is assembled.

2. *Standard timing: Takt* time is the frequency with which a single piece is produced. *Takt* time is used to clearly specify and monitor the rate at which a process should be occurring at various production stages. For lean manufacturers, the *Takt* time of each production process is actively managed and monitored so that a continuous flow can occur.

3. *Standard in-process inventory:* This refers to the minimum unit of materials, consisting primarily of units undergoing processing, which are required to keep a cell or process moving at the desired rate. This should be clearly determined since it is necessary to maintain this minimum amount of in-process inventory in order to prevent unnecessary downtime. This is used to calculate the volume and frequency of orders, or Kanban, to upstream suppliers.

25.8.2　Communication of Standard Work to Employees

Standard work guidelines should not only be textual manuals but should also include pictures, visual displays and even samples. Employees are unlikely to read boring textual production manuals so visual displays and actual samples, including pictures, should be used as much as possible. The guidelines should be clear and detailed, but at the same time should be presented in such a way that is as easy as possible for employees to understand and relevant to what they need to know. This is particularly true in Vietnam since many of the workers may have low education levels and would find visual displays easier to understand than written materials. Some companies even apply video training for tasks which are more complicated or safety-related.

25.8.3　Standard Work and Flexibility

Some companies in Vietnam have expressed concern that having highly standardised/defined production procedures could lead to inflexibility. Although standard work requires a high level of detail, in lean manufacturing, the standard work guidelines should be updated as frequently as necessary to incorporate ongoing process improvements. In fact, companies are encouraged to maximise the rate of process improvement which means that the standard work guidelines are likely to change frequently. Also, standard work typically includes clear guidelines for workers to handle unusual situations, thereby empowering them to respond in flexible ways to unusual situations.

In order to implement this successfully, responsibility should be clearly delegated for preparing and distributing the necessary documentation and visual aids, as well as ensuring that any changes are clearly communicated to employees by their supervisors. As long as this responsibility is clearly delegated, the standard work procedures can be modified frequently. In fact, lean manufacturing companies such as Toyota are known for their flexibility, both in terms of the product mix and their ability to make rapid improvements to their production processes, which also leads to quicker responses to the customers' changing demands.

25.8.4   Visual Management

Visual management systems ensure that factory workers are well-informed about production procedures, status and other important information to enable them to do their jobs as effectively as possible. Large visual displays are generally much more effective means of communication for workers on the factory floor than written reports and guidelines and should therefore be used as much as possible. When it comes to improving compliance with a process, visual presentation helps the team better understand a complicated process including the correct sequence of events, the correct way to perform each action, internal and external relationships between actions, and other factors. These visual tools may include the following:

1. *Visual displays:*   These include charts, metrics, procedures and process documentation which are reference information for production workers, for example, trend chart of yield performance, percentage variation of defect rate, month-to-date shipping volume status, etc.
2. *Visual controls:*   These include indicators intended to control or signal actions to group members. Such as production status information, quality tracking information, etc. Examples include colour-coded panel for temperature or speed setting control limits that help an operator quickly identify if the process is out of the control range. Kanban cards constitute another example of visual controls.
3. *Visual process indicators:*   These communicate the correct production processes or flow of materials. For example, this would include the use of painted floor areas for non-defective stock and scrap or indicators for the correct flow of materials on the factory floor.

25.8.5   Quality at the Source

Quality at the source, also called 'Do It Right the First Time', means that quality should be built into the production process in such a way that defects are unlikely to occur in the first place, or insofar as they do occur, they will be immediately detected. Lean manufacturing systems often refer to the Japanese word 'Jidoka', which means that problems should be identified and eliminated at the source.

Some of the key implications of this are:

1. *In-line inspection:*   The main responsibility for quality inspection is done in-line by workers, not by separate quality inspectors who inspect sample lots. Although some independent QC inspectors are often still used in lean companies, their role is minimised (ideally there are no QC inspectors because they are also considered a waste in lean manufacturing).
2. *Source inspections:*   In source inspections, the quality inspectors do not inspect for defects themselves, but inspect for the causes of defects. For example, they may inspect if standard

processes are being done correctly by workers, or in a case where defects have occurred, they may be responsible for identifying the source of those defects. From this perspective, the primary job of a quality control team is to troubleshoot the root cause of defects, implement preventive measures and provide training to workers to ensure that defects do not recur.

3. *Clear accountability among workers:* In lean manufacturing, unless there is an intentional inventory of semi-finished products, there is a direct handoff between each upstream stage and downstream stage, meaning that the workers at each upstream stage are fully responsible for the quality of the materials they deliver to the downstream stage and would be held personally accountable for any defects. On the other hand, if there is a large buffer of inventory between two production stages, the workers at the upstream process are less likely to feel personally accountable for any defects.

4. *Poka Yoke:* Simple methods for in-line quality testing (not just visual inspection), sometimes referred to as 'Poka Yoke', are implemented so that defective materials do not get passed through the production process. In Poka Yoke, 100 per cent of the units are tested as part of the production process. These measures are performed in-line by the production workers (not the quality control team).

5. *Intentional shutdowns:* When defects are generated, production is shut down until the source of the defect can be solved. This helps ensure a culture of zero tolerance for defects and also prevents defective items from working their way downstream and causing bigger problems downstream. For example, at Toyota, any worker can shut down the production line. This also helps ensure accountability by upstream workers.

25.8.6 Value Stream Mapping

Value stream mapping comprises a set of methods used to visually display the flow of materials and information through the production process. The objective of value stream mapping is to identify value-added activities and non value-added activities. Value stream maps should reflect what actually happens rather than what is supposed to happen so that opportunities for improvement can be identified.

Value stream mapping is often used in process cycle-time improvement projects since it demonstrates exactly how a process operates with detailed timing of step-by-step activities. It is also used for process analysis and improvement by identifying and eliminating the time spent on non value-added activities.

25.8.7 The Five S's

The Five S's are some rules for workplace organisation which aim to organise each worker's work area for maximum efficiency. These rules are delineated below:

1. *Sort:* Sort what is needed and what is not needed so that the things that are frequently needed are available nearby and as easy to find as possible. Things which are less often used or not needed should be re-located or discarded.

2. *Straighten (or 'Set in order'):* Arrange essential things in order to ensure easy access. The objective is to minimise the amount of motion required to enable workers to do their jobs. For example, a tool box can be used by an operator or a maintenance staff member

who must use various tools. In the tool box, every tool is placed at a fixed spot do that the user can quickly pick it up without spending time looking for it. This arrangement can also help the user to immediately become aware of any missing tools.

3. *Scrub (or 'Shine'):* Keep machines and work areas clean so as to eliminate problems associated with un-cleanliness. In some industries, airborne dust is among the causes of poor product surface or colour contamination. In order to be more aware of dust, some companies paint their working places in light colours and use a high level of lighting.

4. *Stabilise (or 'Standardise'):* Make the first three S's a routine practice by implementing clear procedures for sorting, straightening and scrubbing.

5. *Sustain:* Promote, communicate and train in the five S's to ensure these rules become part of the company's corporate culture. This might include assigning a team to be responsible for supervising compliance with the five S's.

25.8.8 Preventive Maintenance

Preventive maintenance constitutes a series of routines, procedures and steps that are taken in order to try to identify and resolve potential problems before they happen. In lean manufacturing, there is a strong emphasis on preventive maintenance, which is essential for minimising machine downtime due to breakdowns and unavailability of spare parts.

When equipment reliability is low, manufacturers are forced to maintain high inventories of works-in-progress as a buffer. However, high inventories are considered as a major source of waste and defects in lean manufacturing.

25.8.9 Total Productive Maintenance

Total Productive Maintenance (TPM) assigns basic preventive maintenance work including inspection, cleaning, lubricating, tightening and calibration to the production workers who operate the equipment. TPM clearly assigns responsibility to workers to proactively identify, monitor and correct the causes of problems leading to unnecessary machine downtime. With the allocation of this responsibility to the machine operators, maintenance problems are less likely to occur and therefore machine downtime can be reduced. This also requires the operators to give frequent updates to the maintenance team about the machine condition so that potential technical problems can be discovered on a timely basis and prevented.

In TPM, the maintenance team is responsible for the higher value-added maintenance activities such as improving the equipment, performing overhauls and improvements, fixing problems and providing training.

25.8.10 Changeover/Set-up Time

Lean manufacturing aims to reduce unnecessary downtime due to machine set-up or product changeovers since machine downtime is a significant source of unnecessary waste. This necessitates a culture of continuous improvement in which the company is continuously trying to find ways to reduce changeover and set-up times.

Often quicker changeover times can be achieved to some degree by having very standardised (and well-documented) configuration settings for the production of particular products so that there is no uncertainty about how to re-configure the equipment during a changeover. Companies with a wide range of product mix, colour and specifications often under-estimate the conversion cost every time the production process is halted to replace moulds, clean leftover materials with a different colour or specification, adjust machine settings, etc.

Other ways to minimise the changeover/set-up time include changing the physical layout of a process, ensuring the availability of all materials and tools needed, and using dual/spare storage bins to eliminate cleaning downtime.

25.8.11   Batch Size Reduction

Lean manufacturing aims for materials to flow on the factory floor in the smallest batch sizes possible, with the ideal being one piece flow, so that works-in-progress between various processing stages can be minimised. The smaller the batch size, the more likely it is that each upstream workstation will produce exactly what its customer needs, exactly when its customer needs it.

Therefore, instead of a few large production lines with large batch sizes, lean manufacturing usually favours a larger number of small production lines with small batch sizes, with the cellular layout being one version of this. The main benefits of smaller production lines are as follows:

- Smaller batch sizes mean less works-in-progress between processing stages and brings the company closer to the ideal of continuous flow.
- A larger number of production lines with smaller batch sizes allow for a bigger range of products to be made concurrently, therefore reducing downtime and disruptions due to changeovers.
- Smaller production lines have fewer workers and, therefore, lead to greater accountability among the workers at each line.

25.8.12   Production Layout and Point of Use Storage

Lean manufacturing aims to minimise the amount of transportation and handling between any two processing stages. Likewise, works-in-progress should be stored as close as physically possible to the place where they will be used next. This is intended to reduce material handling requirements, misplaced or inaccessible inventory, and damage to materials in transit, and to ensure the discipline of adhering to a pull-based production system.

25.8.13   Kanban

'Kanban' is a pull-based material replenishment system that uses visual signals, such as colour-coded cards, to signal to upstream workstations when inputs are required at a downstream workstation. In effect, Kanban is a communication tool for pull-based production. A Kanban could be an empty bin, a card, an electronic display or any suitable visual prompt.

Typically there are two main kinds of Kanbans. They are:

1. *Production Kanban:*   This is a signal from the internal customer to the internal supplier that something is required from the internal supplier.
2. *Withdrawal Kanban:*   This is a signal from the internal supplier to the internal customer that the supplier has produced something which is available to be withdrawn by the internal customer. In such a case, the internal supplier does not produce more until the withdrawal is made by the internal customer.

There are many variations of the Kanban system and in fact there are many books dedicated to the topic of how to best apply Kanban.

25.8.14 Production Levelling

Production levelling, also called production smoothing, aims to distribute production volumes and the product mix evenly over time so as to minimise peaks and valleys in the workload. Any changes to volumes should be smoothened so that they occur gradually and, therefore, in the most non-disruptive way possible. This will also allow the company to operate at higher average capacity utilisation while simultaneously minimising changeovers.

A key element of production levelling is that the person(s) responsible for placing orders to the factory floor should have a system for automatically smoothening out the orders so that any increases or decreases are gradual and not disruptive. This makes it easier to correctly allocate the necessary equipment and people. In order to apply this methodology, a company needs to know its true capacity as well as the rate of production at each production stage.

25.8.15 Pacemaker

In order to ensure the smooth functioning of continuous flow production in lean manufacturing, each workstation has to produce its product at the correct rate which is not too much or too little compared to what downstream workstations require. In order to achieve this, one workstation is often designated as the 'pacemaker'. The pacemaker sets the pace of production for the entire production line and the production rates at other workstations are increased or decreased so as to match the rate of the pacemaker.

In a replenishment pull system, the pacemaker is usually the final workstation such as final assembly. In a sequential pull system, the pacemaker is often a workstation near the beginning of the value stream.

25.8.16 Overall Equipment Effectiveness

Overall Equipment Effectiveness (OEE) is a measure of the overall capacity utilisation of particular pieces of equipment. OEE can be broken down into:

- *Availability:* This signifies the extent of the time for which the equipment can be potentially operational after considering downtime.
- *Performance efficiency:* This refers to the machine's actual throughput when it is operating as compared to its designed maximum capacity or the maximum it can produce on the basis of continuous processing.

If, for example, availability is 80 per cent and performance efficiency is 75 per cent, then the OEE would be:

Availability × Performance Efficiency = OEE

80% × 75% = 60%

When analysing OEE, many companies may be surprised to find that there is significant room to increase the output of certain pieces of equipment. For example, they may be able to minimise:

- Unnecessary equipment breakdowns;
- Downtime due to set-up and adjustment;
- Idling and minor stoppages due to lack of raw materials to process due to bottlenecks or poor production planning;
- Operation below maximum designed speed due to poor operator efficiency, maintenance constraints or other factors; and
- Defects that require re-processing.

Tracking OEE is helpful for identifying the sources of bottlenecks, for making capital spending decisions and for monitoring the effectiveness of programs to increase machine productivity.

However, lean manufacturing typically prioritises the maximum utilisation of people instead of the maximum utilisation of machines. One reason for this is that factories which produce multiple products will not be able to use all machines at all times since the requirements may differ depending on the product being produced.

25.9   IMPLEMENTING LEAN

25.9.1   Senior Management Involvement

As for any significant process improvement project, the total commitment and support of the most senior management is essential. Problems will almost certainly arise during the implementation of lean production systems and those problems are likely to be solved only if the senior management is fully committed to the successful implementation of lean.

25.9.2   Start with a Partial Implementation of Lean

Some companies may initially implement only some of lean manufacturing and gradually shift towards a more complete implementation. In a 2004 survey of manufacturing companies in the U.S. by *Industry Week Magazine*, among companies which had commenced lean manufacturing programs, 39.1 per cent reported implementing some aspects of lean, 55.0 per cent reported implementing most aspects of lean and only 5.9 per cent reported complete implementation of lean.

Some simple first steps may include:

- Measuring and monitoring machine capacity and output;
- Creating more clearly defined production procedures;
- Implementing the five S's system for shop floor housekeeping; and
- Streamlining the production layout.

25.9.3   Start Small

It is recommended that companies should try to implement lean as a test case in a small part of their operations before applying it through their entire operations, especially for the shift from a push-based to a pull-based system since this can be potentially disruptive. For example, the test case may be a single production line or a small series of processes. This will help minimise the risk of disruption, and educate the staff on the principles of lean while also serving to convince others of the benefits of lean.

25.9.4 Use an Expert

It is also recommended that for most private Vietnamese companies, it would be best to use the services of a lean manufacturing expert to help them implement lean manufacturing systems. In particular, the shift from a push-based to a pull-based production system can be potentially quite disruptive which is why it is best to be guided by someone who has significant experience in this.

25.9.5 Develop a Plan

The company should develop a detailed and clear implementation plan before proceeding with the conversion to lean manufacturing. A list of issues to be covered in the implementation plan can be downloaded from the article 'Building the Lean Machine' from the September 2000 issue of *Advanced Manufacturing* Magazine.

25.10 RECONCILING LEAN WITH OTHER SYSTEMS

25.10.1 Toyota Production System

Although lean manufacturing originated with the Toyota Production System (TPS), it has been adopted by many companies and has, therefore, become broader than what TPS encompasses. TPS can be seen as the manner in which one particular company has implemented lean in a very pure form.

In TPS, several key themes are emphasised. They are listed below.

1. *Standard work:* All production processes are highly specified in terms of work content, sequence of events, timing and outcome. The objective is to eliminate any variation in the way that workers perform their responsibilities.
2. *Direct handoffs:* Every customer/supplier connection must be direct, and there must always be an unambiguous yes-or-no way to communicate production requests between suppliers and customers. This ensures maximum accountability by suppliers and ensures optimal communication flow.
3. *Production flow:* The pathway for every product and service must be simple and direct, with a pre-determined flow. This means that goods do not flow to the next available person or machine but to a specific person or machine and that this person or machine is as close as possible to its supplier.
4. *Worker empowerment for process improvement:* All improvements must be made in accordance with the scientific method, under the supervision of an expert, but should originate at the lowest possible level in the organisation. Toyota encourages workers to propose improvements to the production process which can be implemented on a trial basis, but any changes in the production process must be defined in detail in accordance with Toyota's standards for Standard Work, as described above.

25.10.2 Lean Six Sigma

Six Sigma is a systematic methodology for breakthrough improvement of business processes by identifying the causes of variation in the production process which lead to defects and then eliminating that variation to minimise defects. Since a key objective of lean manufacturing is also to eliminate defects, statistical and problem-solving tools of Six Sigma can be used in the implementation of lean manufacturing. Often, they are implemented concurrently in what is referred to as 'Lean Six Sigma'.

25.10.3 Lean and ERP

Enterprise Resource Planning (ERP) has its roots in Material Requirement Planning (MRP) systems for which production is typically scheduled on the basis of a push-based production plan. The schedules are updated on the basis of information on the production status which is fed from the factory floor on the back into the MRP system. A frequent problem that emerges with MRP systems is that the data from the factory floor on the production status and inventory levels may be inaccurate or not entered on a timely basis, causing the MRP system's production plan to use some incorrect assumptions which cause bottlenecks and/or cause the MRP system to intentionally produce more buffer inventory as a precaution. Most ERP packages are designed for push-based, centrally-planned production.

More recently, some ERP systems have been optimised to support lean manufacturing. Companies should consider this carefully when selecting an ERP system. For more information on evaluating the suitability of ERP systems for lean manufacturing, please see Brian Nakashima's article 'Can Lean and ERP Work Together?' from *Advanced Manufacturing Magazine*.

It should also be noted that ERP systems typically include a number of modules that do not specifically relate to production planning, such as accounting, financial analysis, human resource management, sales management, etc. These can often be very beneficial for the company and have no direct impact on the company's ability to implement lean manufacturing.

25.10.4 Lean with ISO9001:2000

ISO9001:2000 is a quality management system which aims to ensure that the company has basic systems in place to consistently meet the customer's quality requirements. Relative to ISO9001:2000, lean manufacturing may be seen as an efficiency management system which aims to reduce all waste and inefficiency from the production process. Although these goals are overlapping in some ways, particularly insofar as they both should result in minimising the level of defective products delivered to customers, there are substantial differences. For example, a company could have 100 per cent conformity with ISO9001:2000 but still have very high levels of waste and inefficiency. An important distinction is that ISO9001:2000 requires that the company's processes meet certain minimum criteria, whereas lean aims for continuous improvement in the company's processes, and provides a set of methodologies to achieve that. In general, it is considered that ISO9001 provides a good foundation for lean and that the two are complementary to each other.

QUESTION BANK

A. Descriptive Questions

1. What is lean manufacturing?
2. What are the elements of lean manufacturing?

3. What are the objectives of lean manufacturing?

4. What are the principles of lean manufacturing?

5. What kinds of companies benefit most from lean?

6. What are the concepts of lean manufacturing?

7. What are the different kinds of waste in manufacturing?

8. What is pull production?

9. What are the different models of pull production?

10. Why do high levels of inventory increase defects and wastage?

11. What is the impact of pull production on production planning?

12. How can continuous flow reduce the total cycle time? Explain with examples.

13. List examples wherein continuous flow is not appropriate in the process.

14. Explain the Kaizen model in lean manufacturing.

15. What is meant by worker involvement in lean manufacturing?

16. What are the lean manufacturing tools and methodologies?

17. Explain 'standard work'.

18. Discuss the different approaches of achieving quality at the source.

19. What are the five S's in lean manufacturing?

20. What is the importance of preventive maintenance in lean manufacturing?

21. What is the importance of total productive maintenance in lean manufacturing?

22. What are the benefits of smaller production lines?

23. What are the various types of Kanban in lean manufacturing?

24. What is meant by overall equipment effectiveness?

25. What are the various methods of implementing lean?

26. What are the themes used for reconciling lean with other systems?

B. Multiple Choice Questions

1. Lean manufacturing is the systematic elimination of:
   (a) Labour
   (b) Waste
   (c) Management role
   (d) Inventory

2. The core concept of lean manufacturing is:
   (a) Pull production
   (b) Push production
   (c) Both (a) and (b)
   (d) Batch-based production

3. The main theme of Kaizen is to create a culture of continuous improvement of:
   (a) Workers
   (b) Profit to the management
   (c) Quality of products
   (d) All the above

4. Kanban is a pull-based material replenishment system that uses:
   (a) Audio signals
   (b) Punched card
   (c) Visual signals
   (d) All the above

Chapter 26

Computer-integrated Manufacturing

OBJECTIVES

After reading this chapter, the reader will be able to understand the following concepts:

➲ Computer-integrated manufacturing

➲ Benefits of computer-integrated manufacturing

26.1 INTRODUCTION

CIM is the integration of CAD and CAM techniques into one complete process. The factory of the future is the CIM. In the new economic situation, the customer demands variety. With a large variety of products, both the life of the product as well as its volume become limited. For this reason, there is need for flexibility of products and flow manufacturing with the integration of computer-aided design (CAD) and computer-aided and manufacturing (CAM).

The Society of Manufacturing Engineers (SME) defines CIM as follows: *CIM is the integration of the total manufacturing enterprise through the use of integrated systems and data communications coupled with new managerial philosophies that improve organisational and personal efficiency.*

26.2 COMPUTER-INTEGRATED MANUFACTURING (CIM)

Figure 26.1 shows a flowchart of CAD/CAM integration applied to a typical production cycle. The product begins with a need, which is identified on the basis of the demands of customers and markets. The product goes through two main processes from idea conceptualisation to the finished product: the design process and the manufacturing process. Synthesis and analysis are the main sub-processes that constitute the design process.

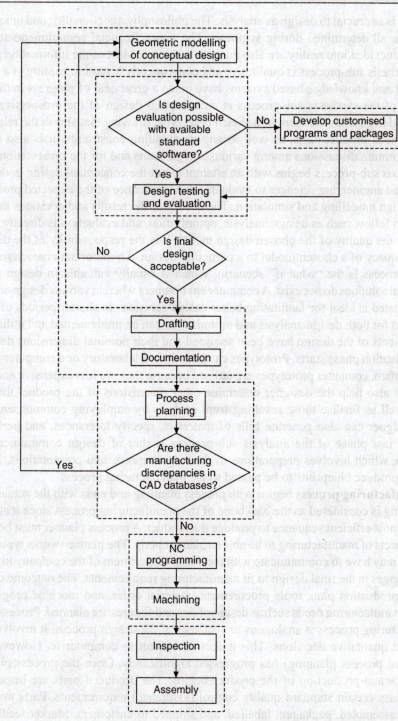

Fig. 26.1 Integration of CAD/CAM.

Synthesis is as crucial to design as analysis. The philosophy, functionality, and uniqueness of the product are all determined during synthesis. The major financial commitments to turn the conceived product idea into reality are also made at this stage. Most of the information generated during the synthesis sub-process is qualitative and consequently is hard to capture in a computer system. Expert and knowledge-based systems have made a great deal of progress in this regard. The end goal of the synthesis sub-process is a conceptual design of the prospective product. Typically, this design takes the form of a sketch or a layout drawing that shows the relationships among the various product parts, as well as any surrounding constraints. It is also employed during brainstorming discussions among various design teams and for the presentation process.

The **analysis** sub-process begins with an attempt to put the conceptual design in the context of the abstracted engineering sciences to evaluate the performance of the expected product. This constitutes design modelling and simulation. The quality of the results and decisions involved in the activities to follow such as design analysis, optimisation, and evaluation is directly related to and limited by the quality of the chosen design model. It is the responsibility of the designer to ensure the adequacy of a chosen model to a particular design. An important characteristic of the analysis sub-process is the "what if" scenario, which is usually valuable in design situations where analytical solutions do not exist. A computer environment wherein various design alternatives can be investigated is ideal for facilitating better design decisions in shorter periods of time.

Algorithms for both design analysis and optimisation can be implemented and utilised. Once the major elements of the design have been analysed and their nominal dimensions determined, the design evaluation phase starts. Prototypes can be built in a laboratory or a computer to test the design. More often, computer prototypes are utilised because they are less expensive and faster to generate. They also help the designer determine other dimensions of the product that are not analysed, as well as finalise those resulting from analysis by employing commonsense design rules. The designer can also generate bills of materials, specify tolerances, and perform cost analyses. The last phase of the analysis sub-process is that of design communication and documentation, which involves preparations of drawings, reports, and presentations. Drawings are utilised to produce blueprints to be passed to the manufacturing process.

The **manufacturing process** begins with process planning and ends with the actual product. Process planning is considered as the backbone of the manufacturing process since it attempts to determine the most efficient sequence to produce the product. A process planner must be aware of the various aspects of manufacturing to be able to plan properly. The planner works typically with blueprints and may have to communicate with the design department of the company to clarify or request for changes in the final design to fit manufacturing requirements. The outcome of process planning is a production plan, tools procurement, material order, and machine programming. Other special manufacturing needs such as design of jigs and fixtures are planned. Process planning to the manufacturing process is analogous to synthesis of the design process; it involves human experience and qualitative decisions. This makes it difficult to computerise. However, CAPP (computer-aided process planning) has progressed significantly. Once the process planning is complete, the actual production of the product begins. The produced parts are inspected and must usually pass certain standard quality control (assurance) requirements. Parts that survive inspection are assembled, packaged, labelled, and shipped to customers. Market feedbacks are usually valuable in enhancing the products. With the market feedback, a closed-loop product cycle results.

The computerised components in an industrial manufacturing are shown in Figure 26.2.

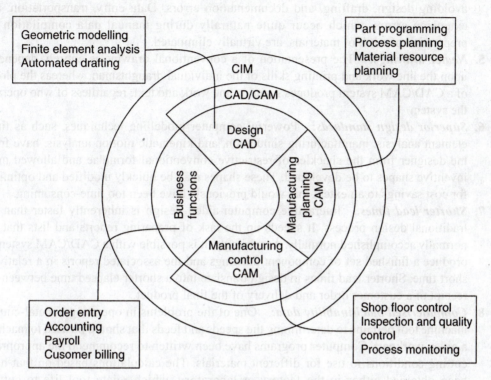

Fig. 26.2   Computerised components in CIM.

26.3   BENEFITS OF CIM

1. *Faster rate of producing drawings:*   On an average, a draughtsman using a CAD/CAM system can produce drawings about three times as fast as could be done on a drawing board. This speeds up the entire design and manufacturing processes and gets the product into the market more quickly.

2. *Greater accuracy of drawings:*   There is also a high level of dimensional control, far beyond the levels of accuracy attainable manually. In some CAD/CAM systems, a change entered on a single item can appear throughout the entire documentation package, effecting the change on all drawings, which utilise that part. The accuracy also shows up in the form of more accurate material and cost estimates, and tighter procurement scheduling.

3. *Easier customer modifications:*   Once a drawing is completed, it may be stored in the computer memory for future use. This is particularly useful when one is drawing a range of components with a similar shape. A stored drawing can also be recalled to design fixtures and analyse tool paths. By conventional means, a separate drawing is required for each of these tasks. Interactive CAD/CAM is equally adept at creating and maintaining isometric, orthographic and oblique drawings. All drawings can be generated and updated with equal ease. Thus an up-to-date version of any drawing can always be made available.

4. *Fewer design errors:* Interactive CAD/CAM systems have an intrinsic capability for avoiding design, drafting, and documentation errors. Data entry, transportation, and extension errors, which occur quite naturally during manual data compilation for preparation of a bill of materials, are virtually eliminated.

5. *Neater drawings:* The presentation of a conventional drawing is entirely dependent upon the line work and printing skills of the individual draughtsman, whereas the plotter of a CAD/CAM system produces superior line work and text, regardless of who operates the system.

6. *Superior design standards:* Powerful computer modelling techniques, such as finite element analysis, manufacturing simulation, and kinematic motion analysis, have freed the designer from the shackles of restrictive conventional formulae and allowed more inventive shapes to be developed. These shapes may be quickly modified and optimised for cost savings to an extent that would previously have been too time-consuming.

7. *Shorter lead times:* Interactive computer-aided design is inherently faster than the traditional design process. It speeds up the task of preparing reports and lists that are normally accomplished normally. Accordingly, it is possible with a CAD/CAM system to produce a finished set of component drawings and the associated reports in a relatively short time. Shorter lead times in design translate into a shorter elapsed time between the receipt of a customer order and delivery of the final product.

8. *Computerised machinability data:* One of the problems in operating a metal-cutting machine tool pertains to determining the speeds and feeds that should be used to machine a given workpart. Computer programs have been written to recommend the appropriate cutting conditions to use for different materials. The calculations based on that have been obtained either in the factory or laboratory, which relate tool life to cutting conditions.

9. *Computer-assisted numerical part programming:* For complex part geometries, computer-assisted part programming represents a much more efficient method of generating the control instructions for the machine tool than manual part programming.

10. *Computer-aided process planning:* Process planning is concerned with the preparation of route sheets which list the sequence of operations and work centres required to produce the product and its components. CAPP systems are available today to prepare these route sheets.

11. *Cost estimating:* The task of estimating the cost of a new product has been simplified in most industries by computerising several of the key steps required to prepare the estimate. The computer is programmed to apply the appropriate labour and overhead rates to the sequence of planned operations for the components of new products. The program then sums the individual component costs from the engineering bill of materials to determine the overall product cost.

12. *Improved work standards:* Establishing standards by direct time study can be a tedious and time-consuming task. There are several commercially available computer packages for setting work standards. These computer programs use standard time data that have been developed for basic work elements that comprise any manual task. By summing the times for the individual elements required to perform a new job, the program calculates the standard time for the job.

13. ***Production and inventory planning:*** The computer has found widespread use for the functions including maintenance of inventory records, automatic re-ordering of stock items when inventory is depleted, production scheduling, maintaining current priorities for the different production orders, material requirements planning, and capacity planning.

14. ***Computer-aided inspection and quality control:*** Savings in inspection by using coordinate measuring machines are significant. Typically, between 5 and 10 per cent of the time is required on a CMM compared to traditional manual inspection methods. Its other advantages include consistency in the inspection process from one part to the next that cannot be matched by manual inspection, and reductions in production delays to get approval of the first workpiece in a batch.

QUESTION BANK

A. Descriptive Questions

1. What is computer-integrated manufacturing?
2. What are the benefits of computer-integrated manufacturing?
3. What are the computerised components in computer-integrated manufacturing?

B. Multiple Choice Questions

1. Computer-integrated manufacturing consists of the components:
   (a) CAD and CAM
   (b) Business functions
   (c) Both (a) and (b)
   (d) None of the above
2. The benefits of CIM are:
   (a) Greater accuracy of drawings
   (b) Superior design standards
   (c) Cost estimating
   (d) All the above

References

Alavala, Chennakesava R. (1991). *Finite Element Methods: Basic Concepts and Applications,* Prentice-Hall of India, New Delhi.

Amirouche, F.M.L. (1993). *Computer-aided Design and Manufacturing,* Prentice-Hall, New Jersey.

Barsky, B.A. (1988). *Computer Graphics and Geometric Modelling Using Beta-splines,* Springer–Verlag, Berlin.

Bedworth, D.D., M.R. Henderson, and P.M. Wolfe (1991). *Computer-integrated Design and Manufacturing,* McGraw-Hill, New York.

Chang, C.H. and M.A. Mekanoff (1989). *NC Machine Programming and Software Design,* Prentice-Hall, New Jersey.

Chang, T.C (1990). *Expert Process Planning for Manufacturing,* Addison-Wesley, Reading.

Chang, T.C., R.A. Wysk, and H.P. Wang (1998). *Computer-aided Manufacturing,* Second edition, Prentice-Hall, New Jersey.

Chasen, S.H. (1978). *Geometric Principles and Procedures for Computer Graphic Applications,* Prentice-Hall, New Jersey.

Deb, S.R. (1994). *Robotics Technology and Flexible Automation,* Tata McGraw-Hill, New Delhi.

Enderle, G., K. Kansy, and G. Pfaff (1987). *Computer Graphics Programming: GKS—The Graphics Standard,* Second edition, Springer–Verlag, Berlin.

Faux, I.D. and M.J. Pratt (1979). *Computational Geometry for Design and Manufacture,* Ellis Harwood, Wiley, London.

Gibbs, D. and T.M. Crandell (1991). *An Introduction to CNC Machining and Programming,* Industrial Press, New York.

Groover, M.P. and E.W. Zimmers, Jr. (1984). *CAD/CAM: Computer-aided Design and Computer-aided Manufacturing,* Second edition, Prentice-Hall, New Jersey.

Groover, M.P. (2001). *Automation, Production Systems and Computer-integrated Manufacturing,* Second edition, Prentice-Hall, New Jersey.

Groover, M.P., M. Weiss, R.N. Nagel, and N.G. Odrey (1986). *Industrial Robotics,* McGraw-Hill, New York.

Hannam, R. (1997). *Computer-integrated Manufacturing from Concepts to Realisation,* Addison-Wesley, England.

Harrington, J. (1973). *Computer-integrated Manufacturing,* Huntington, New York.

Held, M. (1991). *On the Computational Geometry of Pocket Machining,* Springer–Verlag, Berlin.

Hodges, B. (1992). *Industrial Robotics,* Butterworth Heinemann, Oxford.

Horath, L. (1993). *Computer Numerical Control Programming of Machines,* Macmillan, New York.

Hsu, T. and D.K. Sinha (1992). *Computer-aided Design: An Integrated Approach,* St. Paul West Publishers.

Jha, N.K. (1991). *Handbook of Flexible Manufacturing Systems,* Academic Press, San Diego.

Johnson, R.H. (1987). *Solid Modelling,* North Holland, Amsterdam.

Jordan, J.A. Jr. and F.J. Michel (2001). *Valuing Lean Manufacturing Initiatives,* SME Paper No. MS01-104, Society of Manufacturing Engineers.

Kief, H.B. and T.F. Waters (1992). *Computer Numerical Control: A CNC Reference Guide,* Glencoe, Illinois.

Luggen, W.W. (1991). *Flexible Manufacturing Cells and Systems,* Prentice-Hall, New Jersey.

Lynch, M. (1994). *Computer Numerical Control Accessory Devices,* McGraw-Hill, New York.

Madison, James (1996). *CNC Machining Handbook,* Industrial Press, New York.

Mahadevan, B. (1999). *The New Manufacturing Architecture,* Tata McGraw-Hill, New Delhi.

Maleki, R.A. (1991). *Flexible Manufacturing Systems: The Technology and Management,* Prentice-Hall, Englewood Cliffs.

Marciniak, K., *Geometric Modelling for Numerically Controlled Machining,* Oxford University Press.

Miller, R.K. (1987). *Automated Guided Vehicles and Automated Manufacturing,* Society of Manufacturing Engineers.

Mortenson, M.E. (1985). *Geometric Modelling,* John Wiley & Sons, New York.

Newman, W.M. and R.F. Sproull (1979). *Principles of Interactive Computer Graphics,* McGraw-Hill, New York.

Parrish, D. (1990). *Flexible Manufacturing,* Butterworth Heinemann, Oxford.

Pimentel, J.R. (1990). *Communication Networks in Manufacturing,* Prentice-Hall, New Jersey.

Potts, J.F. and J.W. Oler (1989). *Finite Element Applications with Microcomputers,* Prentice-Hall, Englewood Cliffs.

Ranky, P.G. (1990). *Flexible Manufacturing Cells and Systems in CIM,* CIM Ware Ltd.

Rehg, J.A. (2003). *Introduction to Robotics in CIM Systems,* Fifth edition, Prentice-Hall, New Jersey.

Rehg, J.A. and H.W. Kraebber (2001). *Computer-integrated Manufacturing,* Second edition, Prentice-Hall, New Jersey.

Reiter, S. (1992). *CIM—Interfaces: Concepts, Standards and Problems of Interfaces in CIM,* Chapman & Hall, London.

Rembold, U., B.O. Nanji, and A. Storr (1993). *Computer-integrated Manufacturing and Engineering,* Addison-Wesley, England.

Requicha, A.A.G. and H.B. Voelker (1981). *An Introduction to Geometric Modelling and Its Application in Mechanical Design, Advances in Information Systems,* Vol. 8, Plenum Press, New York.

Rogers, D.F. (1985). *Procedural Elements for Computer Graphics,* McGraw-Hill, New York.

Salomon, D. (1999). *Computer Graphics and Geometric Modelling,* Springer, New York.

Scheer, A.W. (1991). *Computer-integrated Manufacturing Towards the Factory of the Future,* Springer–Verlag, Berlin.

Schlechtendahl, E.G. (1989). *CAD Data Transfer for Solid Models,* Springer–Verlag, Berlin.

Seames, W.S. (1990). *Computer Numerical Control: Concepts and Programming,* Second edition, Delmar, New York.

Singh, N. (1996). *Systems Approach to Computer-integrated Design and Manufacturing,* John Wiley, New York.

Smith, G.T. (1993). *CNC Machining Technology,* Vols. 1, 2 and 3, Springer–Verlag, London.

Strasser, W. (1989). *Theory and Practice of Geometric Modelling,* Springer–Verlag, London.

Talavage, J. and R.G. Hannam (1988). *Flexible Manufacturing Systems: Applications, Design and Simulations,* Marcel Dekker, New York.

Teicholz, E., W. Stawood and J. Tchijov (1992). *Computer-integrated Manufacturing,* Edited by R.U. Ayres, Chapman & Hall, London.

Thyer, G.E. (1988). *Computer Numerical Control of Machine Tools,* Heinemann, Oxford.

Valliere (1990). *Computer-aided Design in Manufacturing,* Prentice-Hall, New Jersey.

Vickers, G.W., M.H. Ly, and R.G. Getter (1990). *Numerically Controlled Machine Tools,* Ellis Horwood.

Wakil, E.L. (1989). *Processes and Design for Manufacturing,* Prentice-Hall, New Jersey.

Warnecke, H.J. and R.D. Schraft (1982). *Industrial Robots: Application Experience,* I.F.S. Publications, Bedford.

Womack, J.P. and D.T. Jones (2003). *Lean Thinking: Banish Waste and Create Wealth in Your Corporation,* Revised edition, Free Press, New York.

Womack, J.P., D.T. Jones, and D. Roos (1991). *The Machine that Changed the World: The Story of Lean Production,* Harper Perennial, New York.

Zeid, I. (1991). *CAD/CAM: Theory and Practice,* McGraw-Hill, New York.

Index